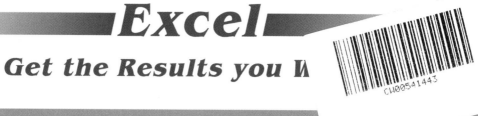

# YEAR 11 MATHEMATICS ADVANCED

## Lyn Baker

PASCAL
PRESS

# CONTENTS

# TOPIC 3: CALCULUS

## CHAPTER 3: INTRODUCTION TO DIFFERENTIATION ............ 96

# TOPIC 4: EXPONENTIAL AND LOGARITHMIC FUNCTIONS

## CHAPTER 4: LOGARITHMS AND EXPONENTIALS ............... 132

# TOPIC 5: STATISTICAL ANALYSIS

## CHAPTER 5: PROBABILITY AND DISCRETE PROBABILITY DISTRIBUTIONS ............... 156

## SAMPLE YEAR 11 EXAMINATION PAPERS .. 185

## Algebraic techniques

### 1 Revision—basic algebra

→ **Like terms** have exactly the same pronumeral part. Only like terms can be added together or subtracted from each other and unlike terms cannot be simplified.

→ When **multiplying**, we multiply any numbers and also multiply any pronumerals. When **dividing**, we divide any numbers and also divide any pronumerals. When **expanding grouping symbols**, every term inside the brackets must be multiplied by the term outside.

→ A **binomial** is an algebraic expression involving the sum, or difference, of two terms. In a **binomial product** both parts of the second expression must be multiplied by both parts of the first: $(a + b)(x + y) = ax + ay + bx + by$.

→ The **square of a binomial** is a special binomial product:
$(a + b)^2 = a^2 + 2ab + b^2$         $(a - b)^2 = a^2 - 2ab + b^2$.

→ Whenever the sum of two terms is multiplied by the difference of the same two terms the result is the **difference of two squares**:     $(a + b)(a - b) = a^2 - b^2$.

### EXAMPLE 1

**Simplify $8pq - 7p + q - 3q + 2p$.**

$8pq - 7p + q - 3q + 2p = 8pq - 5p - 2q$

Collect the like terms:
$-7p + 2p = -5p$; $q - 3q = -2q$.

### EXAMPLE 2

**Expand and simplify $3k(2k - 5) - 4(k^2 - 2k + 3)$.**

$3k(2k - 5) - 4(k^2 - 2k + 3)$
$= 6k^2 - 15k - 4k^2 + 8k - 12$
$= 2k^2 - 7k - 12$

To expand means to remove the brackets by multiplying the terms in the brackets by the number or term outside.

### EXAMPLE 3

**Find $(3m + 4p)^2$.**

$(3m + 4p)^2 = (3m)^2 + 2 \times 3m \times 4p + (4p)^2$
$= 9m^2 + 24mp + 16p^2$

'Square the first, square the last and twice the product of the two.'

### EXAMPLE 4

**Expand and simplify $(7n - 2)(2n - 7) + (5n + 1)(n + 2)$.**

$(7n - 2)(2n - 7) + (5n + 1)(n + 2)$
$= 14n^2 - 49n - 4n + 14 + 5n^2 + 10n + n + 2$
$= 19n^2 - 42n + 16$

Expand both binomial products and then collect like terms.

### EXAMPLE 5

**Expand and simplify $(x - 2)^2 - (x + 1)(x - 1)$.**

$(x - 2)^2 - (x + 1)(x - 1) = x^2 - 4x + 4 - (x^2 - 1)$
$= x^2 - 4x + 4 - x^2 + 1$
$= -4x + 5$

Be very careful with the signs. Here the whole of the second expansion needs to be subtracted.

### → PRACTICE

1   Simplify $9mn - 4m + n - 6n + 7m$.
..................................................
2   Expand and simplify $6p(4p - 1) - 5(3p^2 + 5p - 2)$.
..................................................
3   Find $(5a + 2b)^2$.
..................................................
4   Expand and simplify
    $(3x + 2)(2x - 5) + (5x - 1)(x + 4)$.
..................................................
5   Expand and simplify $(n + 3)(n - 3) - (n - 2)^2$.
..................................................
6*  Subtract $4mn - 2$ from the product of $3m + 5n$ and $m^2 - n$.

Answers ⊃ p. 38

## 2 Review of factorisation

→ When factorising, we rewrite an expression as a **product of its factors**. If each term of an expression has the same factor then the expression has a **common factor**:

$ab + ac = a(b + c)$.

→ An expression involving four or more terms might not have a common factor but some of the terms, grouped together, may have a common factor. This is called **factorising by grouping**:

$ax + ay + bx + by = a(x + y) + b(x + y) = (x + y)(a + b)$.

→ We factorise **trinomials** by looking for two numbers (or terms) whose sum is the coefficient of the middle term and whose product is the end term:
$x^2 + (a + b)x + ab = (x + a)(x + b)$.

- If, in a trinomial, the coefficient of the first term is not 1 the trinomial may still be able to be factorised. We can use **inspection**, the **cross method** or a **grouping method** to find the correct factorisation.
- **Perfect squares** $x^2 + 2ax + a^2 = (x + a)^2$ and $x^2 - 2ax + a^2 = (x - a)^2$ are special cases of trinomials.
- Not all trinomials can be **factorised**.

→ An expression which is the difference of two squares or either the sum or difference of two cubes can also be factorised.

- **Difference of two squares**: $x^2 - y^2 = (x + y)(x - y)$
- **Sum of two cubes**: $x^3 + y^3 = (x + y)(x^2 - xy + y^2)$
- **Difference of two cubes**: $x^3 - y^3 = (x - y)(x^2 + xy + y^2)$

→ We should always **factorise as fully as possible**. This might require a combination of different types of factorisation. When deciding how to factorise an expression, first consider whether there is a common factor. The **number of terms** might help you to find the correct factorisation. If there are two terms, is the expression a difference of two squares or the sum or difference of two cubes? If there are three terms, is it a trinomial that can be factorised? If there are four or more terms, can the expression be factorised by grouping?

### EXAMPLE 1

Factorise $x^2 - xy + x - y$.

$$\begin{aligned} x^2 - xy + x - y &= x(x - y) + 1(x - y) \\ &= (x - y)(x + 1) \end{aligned}$$

Take care when there is a factor of 1. It could be left out in the first line but not in the last.

### EXAMPLE 2

Factorise $a^3 - 10a^2 + 25a$.

$$\begin{aligned} a^3 - 10a^2 + 25a &= a(a^2 - 10a + 25) \\ &= a(a - 5)^2 \end{aligned}$$

Always look for a common factor first.

### EXAMPLE 3

Factorise $8a^3 + 27b^3$.

$$\begin{aligned} 8a^3 + 27b^3 &= (2a)^3 + (3b)^3 \\ &= (2a + 3b)((2a)^2 - 2a \times 3b + (3b)^2) \\ &= (2a + 3b)(4a^2 - 6ab + 9b^2) \end{aligned}$$

Take care with the signs. Check by expanding that the answer is correct.

### EXAMPLE 4

Factorise $8m^2 - 26m + 15$.

$$\begin{aligned} 8m^2 - 26m + 15 &= 8m^2 - 6m - 20m + 15 \\ &= 2m(4m - 3) - 5(4m - 3) \\ &= (4m - 3)(2m - 5) \end{aligned}$$

We replace the middle term with two terms that multiply to the product of the first and last terms ($120m^2$) and add to $-26m$. Then factorise by grouping.

### EXAMPLE 5

Factorise $x^2 - 49 + xy + 7y$.

$$\begin{aligned} x^2 - 49 + xy + 7y &= (x + 7)(x - 7) + y(x + 7) \\ &= (x + 7)(x + y - 7) \end{aligned}$$

When factorising by grouping, there might be a mixture of different types of factorisations.

### → PRACTICE

1 Factorise $p^2 + pq - p - q$.

2 Factorise $x^3 + 12x^2 + 36x$.

3 Factorise $1000x^3 - y^3$.

4 Factorise $3x^2 + 23x - 8$.

5 Factorise $k^2 - 9 + 7km - 21m$.

6* Factorise $14x(2x + 3)^3 + 35x^2(2x + 3)^2$.

Answers ⊃ p. 38

## 3 Index laws

- In the expression $a^m$, $a$ is the **base** and $m$ the **index**, power, or exponent.
- The index tells us how many **factors** of the base are **multiplied together**; for example, $a^5 = a \times a \times a \times a \times a$.
- These **index laws** should all be known:
  - $a^m \times a^n = a^{m+n}$
  - $a^m \div a^n = a^{m-n}$
  - $(a^m)^n = a^{mn}$
  - $a^1 = a$
  - $a^0 = 1$
  - $a^{-m} = \dfrac{1}{a^m}$
  - $a^{\frac{m}{n}} = \sqrt[n]{a^m} = \left(\sqrt[n]{a}\right)^m$.

### EXAMPLE 1

Simplify $(3x^2)^3 \times 4(x^4)^2$.

$$(3x^2)^3 \times 4(x^4)^2 = 27x^6 \times 4x^8 = 108x^{14}$$

When raising to a power, multiply the indices. When multiplying, add the indices.

### EXAMPLE 2

Simplify $\dfrac{18a^4b^7 \div 3ab^6}{4ab \times 3a}$.

$$\frac{18a^4b^7 \div 3ab^6}{4ab \times 3a} = \frac{6a^3b}{12a^2b} = \frac{a}{2}$$

When dividing, subtract the indices.

### EXAMPLE 3

Factorise $p^4q^6 - pq^8$.

$$p^4q^6 - pq^8 = pq^6(p^3 - q^2)$$

A factorisation can always be checked by expanding the answer.

### EXAMPLE 4

Express $\dfrac{1}{x^2\sqrt{x}}$ in index form.

$$\frac{1}{x^2\sqrt{x}} = \frac{1}{x^{\frac{5}{2}}} = x^{-\frac{5}{2}}$$

Indices are usually written as improper fractions where necessary, not mixed numerals.

### EXAMPLE 5

Solve $4^x \times 8^x = \dfrac{1}{2}$.

$$4^x \times 8^x = \frac{1}{2}$$
$$(2^2)^x \times (2^3)^x = 2^{-1}$$
$$2^{2x} \times 2^{3x} = 2^{-1}$$
$$2^{5x} = 2^{-1}$$
$$\therefore 5x = -1$$
$$x = -\frac{1}{5}$$

Express all the terms as powers of 2.

### → PRACTICE

1 Simplify $(2a^3)^2 \times 5(a^2)^7$.

2 Simplify $\dfrac{35x^3y^8 \div 7x^2y^6}{5x \times 2xy}$.

3 Factorise $a^3b^7 - a^4b^6$.

4 Express $\dfrac{1}{x\sqrt{x}}$ in index form.

5 Solve $27^x \times 3^x = \dfrac{1}{9}$.

6* Find $k$ if $8^{k-5} \times 4^{3-k} = 1$.

Answers ➲ p. 38

## 4 Surds

- Numbers such as $\sqrt{2}$, $\sqrt{5}$ and $7\sqrt{3}$ are called **surds**. Surds are **irrational** numbers (i.e. they cannot be expressed in the form $\frac{p}{q}$, where $p$ and $q$ are integers). Square roots of perfect squares are not surds (e.g. $\sqrt{4}$ is not a surd because $\sqrt{4} = 2$.)
- Only **like surds** can be added together or subtracted:
  $a\sqrt{c} + b\sqrt{c} = (a+b)\sqrt{c}$.
- To **multiply and divide** surds we use these rules:
  $a\sqrt{b} \times c\sqrt{d} = ac\sqrt{bd}$ $\quad a\sqrt{b} \div c\sqrt{d} = \dfrac{a\sqrt{b}}{c\sqrt{d}} = \dfrac{a}{c}\sqrt{\dfrac{b}{d}}$.
- Surds can be simplified if they have a **perfect square** as a **factor**:
  $\sqrt{a^2b} = \sqrt{a^2} \times \sqrt{b} = a\sqrt{b}$.
- Always **simplify surds** before adding or subtracting. (Surds that may not seem to be like surds may in fact be like when simplified.)

## EXAMPLE 1

Simplify $9\sqrt{7} - \sqrt{7}$.

$9\sqrt{7} - \sqrt{7} = 8\sqrt{7}$

> Nine lots of $\sqrt{7}$ minus 1 lot of $\sqrt{7}$ leaves 8 lots of $\sqrt{7}$.

## EXAMPLE 2

Simplify $8\sqrt{6} + 4 - 2\sqrt{3} + 7 + 5\sqrt{6}$.

$8\sqrt{6} + 4 - 2\sqrt{3} + 7 + 5\sqrt{6} = 13\sqrt{6} - 2\sqrt{3} + 11$

> $2\sqrt{3}$ cannot be subtracted from $13\sqrt{6}$ because they are not like surds.

## EXAMPLE 3

Find $5\sqrt{2} \times 3\sqrt{2}$.

$$5\sqrt{2} \times 3\sqrt{2} = 15\sqrt{4}$$
$$= 15 \times 2$$
$$= 30$$

> Or simply use the rule $\left(\sqrt{a}\right)^2 = \sqrt{a^2} = a$; so $\left(\sqrt{2}\right)^2 = 2$.

## EXAMPLE 4

Simplify $2\sqrt{18}$.

$$2\sqrt{18} = 2 \times \sqrt{9} \times \sqrt{2}$$
$$= 2 \times 3 \times \sqrt{2}$$
$$= 6\sqrt{2}$$

> Look for a perfect square that divides evenly into 18.

## EXAMPLE 5

Simplify $\sqrt{50} + \sqrt{32}$.

$$\sqrt{50} + \sqrt{32} = \sqrt{25} \times \sqrt{2} + \sqrt{16} \times \sqrt{2}$$
$$= 5\sqrt{2} + 4\sqrt{2}$$
$$= 9\sqrt{2}$$

> Always look for the largest possible perfect square. For example, $\sqrt{32}$ is also equal to $\sqrt{4} \times \sqrt{8}$ but the result, $2\sqrt{8}$, still needs to be simplified. You should eventually get the right answer if you don't start with the largest perfect square, but it will take longer and be more work.

## → PRACTICE

1   Simplify $4\sqrt{6} + \sqrt{6}$.

2   Simplify $8 - 3\sqrt{7} + 7\sqrt{2} - 2 + \sqrt{7}$.

3   Find $3\sqrt{6} \times 7\sqrt{6}$.

4   Simplify $3\sqrt{40}$.

5   Simplify $\sqrt{98} + \sqrt{72}$.

6*   Simplify $2\sqrt{6} \times 3\sqrt{2}$.

Answers ⊃ p. 38

## 5 Rationalising the denominator

→ **Binomial products involving surds** are expanded in exactly the same way as any other binomial product: $(a + b)(c + d) = ac + ad + bc + bd$. The result of expanding a binomial product with surds should always be simplified as much as possible.

→ **Conjugate surds** are binomial surds where we have the sum and difference of the same two surds. The conjugate of $\sqrt{a} + \sqrt{b}$ is $\sqrt{a} - \sqrt{b}$.

→ By multiplying by an appropriate term, any surd can be expressed with a **rational denominator**. Multiplying a binomial surd by its conjugate always gives a rational number.

## EXAMPLE 1

Expand and simplify $\left(2 - 3\sqrt{5}\right)\left(\sqrt{5} - 2\right)$.

$$\left(2 - 3\sqrt{5}\right)\left(\sqrt{5} - 2\right) = 2\sqrt{5} - 4 - 15 + 6\sqrt{5}$$
$$= 8\sqrt{5} - 19$$

> $3\sqrt{5} \times \sqrt{5} = 3 \times 5 = 15$

## EXAMPLE 2

Find $\left(5\sqrt{2} + 3\right)\left(5\sqrt{2} - 3\right)$.

$$\left(5\sqrt{2} + 3\right)\left(5\sqrt{2} - 3\right) = \left(5\sqrt{2}\right)^2 - 3^2$$
$$= 50 - 9$$
$$= 41$$

> Whenever the sum of two terms is multiplied by their difference the result is the difference of two squares.

## EXAMPLE 3

Rationalise the denominator of $\dfrac{3}{\sqrt{3}}$.

$$\frac{3}{\sqrt{3}} = \frac{3}{\sqrt{3}} \times \frac{\sqrt{3}}{\sqrt{3}}$$
$$= \frac{3\sqrt{3}}{3}$$
$$= \sqrt{3}$$

> We are only multiplying by one, so the surd is not changed in value.

## EXAMPLE 4

Express $\dfrac{2}{5-\sqrt{3}}$ with a rational denominator.

$$\dfrac{2}{5-\sqrt{3}} = \dfrac{2}{5-\sqrt{3}} \times \dfrac{5+\sqrt{3}}{5+\sqrt{3}}$$

$$= \dfrac{2\left(5+\sqrt{3}\right)}{25-3}$$

Multiply both the numerator and denominator by the conjugate of the denominator.

$$= \dfrac{2\left(5+\sqrt{3}\right)}{22}$$

$$= \dfrac{5+\sqrt{3}}{11}$$

## EXAMPLE 5

Rationalise the denominator of $\dfrac{\sqrt{5}+\sqrt{6}}{\sqrt{5}-\sqrt{6}}$.

$$\dfrac{\sqrt{5}+\sqrt{6}}{\sqrt{5}-\sqrt{6}} = \dfrac{\sqrt{5}+\sqrt{6}}{\sqrt{5}-\sqrt{6}} \times \dfrac{\sqrt{5}+\sqrt{6}}{\sqrt{5}+\sqrt{6}}$$

$$= \dfrac{5+2\sqrt{30}+6}{5-6}$$

$$= \dfrac{11+2\sqrt{30}}{-1}$$

There is a perfect square in the numerator.

$$= -11-2\sqrt{30}$$

## → PRACTICE

1. Expand and simplify $\left(5-\sqrt{3}\right)\left(2\sqrt{3}-4\right)$.

2. Find $\left(2\sqrt{7}+1\right)\left(2\sqrt{7}-1\right)$.

3. Rationalise the denominator of $\dfrac{10}{\sqrt{5}}$.

4. Express $\dfrac{3}{4+\sqrt{7}}$ with a rational denominator.

5. Rationalise the denominator of $\dfrac{\sqrt{2}-\sqrt{3}}{\sqrt{2}+\sqrt{3}}$.

6* Find the values of the integers $a$ and $b$ such that $\dfrac{7}{5-3\sqrt{2}} = a+\sqrt{b}$.

Answers ➲ pp. 38–39

→ Algebraic fractions are fractions that contain algebraic expressions. They can be **simplified** by first **factorising**, if possible, and **cancelling** any common factors.

→ **Addition or subtraction** of algebraic fractions requires a **common denominator**.

→ We multiply algebraic fractions by **multiplying the numerators** together and **multiplying the denominators** together.

→ To **divide** by any fraction, **multiply by the reciprocal**.

## EXAMPLE 1

Simplify $\dfrac{n^2-4n-5}{n-5}$.

$$\dfrac{n^2-4n-5}{n-5} = \dfrac{(n-5)(n+1)}{n-5}$$

$(n-5)$ divides into the numerator $(n+1)$ times and into the denominator once.

$$= n+1$$

## EXAMPLE 2

Find $\dfrac{2m+3}{12} - \dfrac{3m-7}{8}$.

$$\dfrac{2m+3}{12} - \dfrac{3m-7}{8} = \dfrac{2(2m+3)}{24} - \dfrac{3(3m-7)}{24}$$

$$= \dfrac{4m+6-9m+21}{24}$$

When subtracting, we must take care with the signs. The vinculum (fraction line) works like brackets.

$$= \dfrac{27-5m}{24}$$

## EXAMPLE 3

Find $\dfrac{x+2}{x^2-x} + \dfrac{x+3}{x^2+x}$.

$$\dfrac{x+2}{x^2-x} + \dfrac{x+3}{x^2+x} = \dfrac{x+2}{x(x-1)} + \dfrac{x+3}{x(x+1)}$$

$$= \dfrac{(x+2)(x+1)}{x(x-1)(x+1)} + \dfrac{(x+3)(x-1)}{x(x+1)(x-1)}$$

$$= \dfrac{x^2+3x+2+x^2+2x-3}{x(x+1)(x-1)}$$

$$= \dfrac{2x^2+5x-1}{x(x+1)(x-1)}$$

Factorising the denominator helps us find the lowest common denominator.

## EXAMPLE 4

Simplify $\dfrac{x^2-5x}{x+3} \times \dfrac{x^2+3x}{x^2-3x-10}$.

$$\frac{x^2-5x}{x+3} \times \frac{x^2+3x}{x^2-3x-10} = \frac{x(x-5)}{x+3} \times \frac{x(x+3)}{(x-5)(x+2)}$$

$$= \frac{x^2}{x+2}$$

Only cancel a factor in the numerator with one in the denominator. In this case $(x-5)$ and $(x+3)$ have been cancelled.

## EXAMPLE 5

Simplify $\dfrac{x+4}{x^2+5x} \div \dfrac{x+3}{x^2+4x-5}$.

$$\frac{x+4}{x^2+5x} \div \frac{x+3}{x^2+4x-5} = \frac{x+4}{x^2+5x} \times \frac{x^2+4x-5}{x+3}$$

$$= \frac{x+4}{x(x+5)} \times \frac{(x+5)(x-1)}{x+3}$$

$$= \frac{(x+4)(x-1)}{x(x+3)}$$

Both the numerator and denominator can be left in factorised form.

### → PRACTICE

1  Simplify $\dfrac{x^2+4x+3}{x^2-4x-21}$.

2  Find $\dfrac{8m-7}{15} - \dfrac{3m+7}{10}$.

3  Find $\dfrac{2a+3}{a^2+a} + \dfrac{a-4}{a^2-1}$.

4  Simplify $\dfrac{x^2+4x}{3x+7} \times \dfrac{5x+10}{x^2+6x+8}$.

5  Simplify $\dfrac{x^2+6x}{x^2+5x-6} \div \dfrac{x^2+9x+8}{x^2-1}$.

6*  Simplify $\dfrac{x^2+5x-14}{x^2+2x-8} \times \dfrac{x^2-x-20}{x^2+2x-35}$.

Answers ⊃ p. 39

## 7 Quadratic equations

→ A **quadratic equation** is an equation of the form $ax^2 + bx + c = 0$ ($a \neq 0$). Some quadratic equations cannot be solved. If a quadratic equation can be solved, it might be by factorising, completing the square or using the quadratic formula.

→ To solve by **factorising**, first factorise the trinomial and then use the result that if two numbers multiply to zero at least one must be zero.

→ To solve by **completing the square** we write the equation as a perfect square and then take the square root of both sides, remembering to consider both positive and negative values.

→ Using the **quadratic formula**, the solution of $ax^2 + bx + c = 0$ is given by $x = \dfrac{-b \pm \sqrt{b^2-4ac}}{2a}$.

### EXAMPLE 1

**Solve $x^2 - 6x - 27 = 0$.**

$$x^2 - 6x - 27 = 0$$
$$(x+3)(x-9) = 0$$
$$x+3 = 0 \quad \text{or} \quad x-9 = 0$$
$$x = -3 \quad \text{or} \quad x = 9$$

If we can see that the trinomial factorises, then that is usually the easiest way to solve the equation.

### EXAMPLE 2

**Solve $(x+8)(x+2) = 16$.**

$$(x+8)(x+2) = 16$$
$$x^2 + 2x + 8x + 16 = 16$$
$$x^2 + 10x = 0$$
$$x(x+10) = 0$$
$$x = 0 \quad \text{or} \quad x+10 = 0$$
$$x = 0 \quad \text{or} \quad x = -10$$

If a quadratic expression is equal to a non-zero number we first rearrange it so that the equation is equal to zero.

### EXAMPLE 3

**Solve $9x^2 + 6x = 4$ by completing the square.**

$$9x^2 + 6x = 4$$
$$9x^2 + 6x + 1 = 4 + 1$$
$$(3x+1)^2 = 5$$
$$3x+1 = \pm\sqrt{5}$$
$$3x = -1 \pm \sqrt{5}$$
$$x = \frac{-1 \pm \sqrt{5}}{3}$$

$9x^2 = (3x)^2$; $6x = 2 \times 3x \times 1$; so the number that must be added to make a perfect square is $1^2$ or $1$.

## EXAMPLE 4

Solve $3x^2 - 9x + 4 = 0$, giving the solution correct to three decimal places.

$3x^2 - 9x + 4 = 0$

$a = 3, \quad b = -9, \quad c = 4$

$x = \dfrac{-b \pm \sqrt{b^2 - 4ac}}{2a}$

$= \dfrac{-(-9) \pm \sqrt{(-9)^2 - 4 \times 3 \times 4}}{2 \times 3}$

$= \dfrac{9 \pm \sqrt{33}}{6}$

$x = \dfrac{9 + \sqrt{33}}{6}$ or $x = \dfrac{9 - \sqrt{33}}{6}$

$x = 2.457\,427\,10\ldots$ or $x = 0.542\,572\,89\ldots$

$x = 2.457$ or $x = 0.543$ correct to three decimal places

> Because the answer is to be given to three decimal places, we immediately know that the equation cannot be factorised and it is best to use the quadratic formula.

## EXAMPLE 5

Solve $x^2 - 8x + 13 = 0$, leaving the answer in simplest surd form.

$x^2 - 8x + 13 = 0$

$a = 1, \quad b = -8, \quad c = 13$

$x = \dfrac{-b \pm \sqrt{b^2 - 4ac}}{2a}$

$= \dfrac{-(-8) \pm \sqrt{(-8)^2 - 4 \times 1 \times 13}}{2 \times 1}$

$= \dfrac{8 \pm \sqrt{12}}{2}$

$= \dfrac{8 \pm 2\sqrt{3}}{2}$

$= \dfrac{2(4 \pm \sqrt{3})}{2}$

$= 4 \pm \sqrt{3}$

> $\sqrt{12} = \sqrt{4} \times \sqrt{3} = 2\sqrt{3}$

### → PRACTICE

1   Solve $x^2 - 10x + 16 = 0$.

2   Solve $(x + 3)(x - 4) = 18$.

3   Solve $4x^2 + 28x = -47$ by completing the square.

4   Solve $x^2 - 9x + 11 = 0$, giving each answer correct to three decimal places.

---

5   Solve $2x^2 - 8x - 3 = 0$, leaving the answer in simplest surd form.

6*   Solve $7x^2 = 25x + 12$.

Answers ⊃ pp. 39–40

## Introduction to functions

### 1 Relations and functions

→ In mathematics, a **relation** is a type of connection between different sets of numbers. A rule defines the second set of numbers in terms of the first.

→ A relation **maps** elements of one set (**input**) to another set (**output**).

→ A **function** is a special relation where for every input there is exactly one output.

→ Any **set of ordered pairs** of real numbers $(x, y)$ is a relation.

→ Any set of ordered pairs of real numbers $(x, y)$ where **no two ordered pairs have the same $x$-value** is a **function**.

### EXAMPLE 1

Find the rule for the points in this table of values.

| $x$ | 0 | 1 | 2 | 3 | 4 |
|---|---|---|---|---|---|
| $y$ | 12 | 7 | 2 | -3 | -8 |

The rule is $y = 12 - 5x$.

> Look at the differences between successive values. While the $x$-values increase by 1 each time, the $y$-values decrease by 5 each time so the coefficient of $x$ is –5.

### EXAMPLE 2

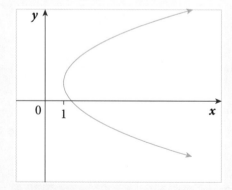

Connie looked at this graph and said: 'When $x = 1$, there is only one value of $y$ so it is a function'. Briefly explain why Connie is wrong.

It is not enough to have one value of $x$ that has only one value of $y$. To be a function there must be, at most, one value of $y$ for every value of $x$.

The function does not have to exist for every possible value of $x$. But for those values of $x$ for which it does exist there must be one, and only one, value of $y$.

→ **PRACTICE**

1 **Find the rule for the points in this table of values.**

| $x$ | 0 | 1 | 2 | 3 | 4 |
|---|---|---|---|---|---|
| $y$ | 7 | 15 | 23 | 31 | 39 |

2

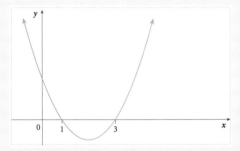

Connor looked at this graph and said:
'When $y = 0$, $x = 1$ or 3, so there are two values of $x$ for a value of $y$ and so it is not a function'. Briefly explain why Connor is wrong.

3* A relation consists of the points (1, 1), (4, 2), (9, 3), (1, –1), (9, –3) and (4, –2). Is this relation a function? Justify your answer.

Answers ⊃ p. 40

## 2 Function notation

→ The **notation** $f(x)$ means the value of the function $f$, at $x$. A function may be referred to as $y = f(x)$, the function $f(x)$, or the function $f$.

→ A function may have a **different definition** for different values of $x$.

→ Some questions with functions may involve the **substitution** of an **algebraic expression**.

→ Although many functions use the notation $y = f(x)$, functions can use **any variables**.

### EXAMPLE 1

If $f(x) = 3x^2 - x + 1$, find:

a $f(4)$

b $f(-1)$

c $f\left(\dfrac{1}{2}\right)$

$$f(x) = 3x^2 - x + 1$$

a $f(4) = 3 \times 4^2 - 4 + 1$
   $= 45$

*x must be replaced every time that it appears.*

b $f(-1) = 3 \times (-1)^2 - (-1) + 1$
   $= 5$

c $f\left(\dfrac{1}{2}\right) = 3 \times \left(\dfrac{1}{2}\right)^2 - \dfrac{1}{2} + 1$

   $= 1\dfrac{1}{4}$

### EXAMPLE 2

If $f(x) = \begin{cases} 5 - x^2, & x \geq 1 \\ (x-3)^2, & x < 1 \end{cases}$, find:

a $f(3)$

b $f(-6)$

a $f(x) = \begin{cases} 5 - x^2, & x \geq 1 \\ (x-3)^2, & x < 1 \end{cases}$

*Because 3 > 1 we use the top part of the definition.*

$f(3) = 5 - 3^2$
   $= -4$

b $f(x) = \begin{cases} 5 - x^2, & x \geq 1 \\ (x-3)^2, & x < 1 \end{cases}$

*Because –6 < 1 we use the bottom part of the definition.*

$f(-6) = (-6 - 3)^2$
   $= 81$

### EXAMPLE 3

Find the value of $\dfrac{f(x+h) - f(x)}{h}$ when $f(x) = x^2 - 2x$.

$$f(x) = x^2 - 2x$$

$$\frac{f(x+h) - f(x)}{h} = \frac{\left((x+h)^2 - 2(x+h)\right) - \left(x^2 - 2x\right)}{h}$$

$$= \frac{x^2 + 2xh + h^2 - 2x - 2h - x^2 + 2x}{h}$$

$$= \frac{2xh + h^2 - 2h}{h}$$

$$= \frac{h(2x + h - 2)}{h}$$

$$= 2x + h - 2$$

*To find $f(x + h)$ every $x$ in $f(x)$ must be replaced by $(x + h)$.*

## EXAMPLE 4

If $h(t) = 1 - 2t^2$, find $h(-2)$.

$$h(t) = 1 - 2t^2$$
$$h(-2) = 1 - 2(-2)^2$$
$$= -7$$

This is a function of $t$ not of $x$.

---

### → PRACTICE

1. If $f(x) = 2x^2 + x - 4$, find:
   a. $f(2)$
   b. $f(-3)$
   c. $f\left(\dfrac{1}{2}\right)$

2. If $f(x) = \begin{cases} 3x-4 & \text{for } x<2 \\ x & \text{for } 2\leq x\leq 3, \\ x^2-6 & \text{for } x>3 \end{cases}$ find:
   a. $f(5)$
   b. $f(-1)$
   c. $f(2.5)$

3. Find the value of $\dfrac{f(x+h)-f(x)}{h}$ when $f(x) = x^2 + 4x$.

4. If $p(n) = 3n^2 - 5n$ find $p(-1)$.

5*. If $f(u) = \dfrac{u-1}{u+1}$, show that $f\left(\dfrac{1}{u}\right) = -f(u)$.

Answers ⊃ p. 40

---

## 3 Domain and range

→ In the function $y = f(x)$ the value of $y$ will vary, depending on the value of $x$, and so $y$ is called the **dependent** variable. $x$ can take any value (for which the function is defined) and so is called the **independent** variable.

→ If $y = f(x)$, the **domain** is the set of all possible values of $x$, and the **range** is the set of all possible values of $y$.

→ In many cases the domain of a particular function is specified in the **definition** of the function (for example, $y = 2x^2 - 3$, for $-1 \leq x \leq 5$). At other times no domain will be specified. The domain in these cases is the set of real numbers for which $f(x)$ is a real number, and is called the **natural domain**.

→ The domain or range could be expressed in **interval notation**. The endpoints of the interval are given in grouping symbols, parentheses when the endpoint is not included and brackets when the endpoint is included; for example, the domain (2, 5] means $2 < x \leq 5$.

---

## EXAMPLE 1

Find the natural domain for $y = \dfrac{1}{2-x}$.

$$y = \dfrac{1}{2-x}$$

Now $2 - x \neq 0$

$x \neq 2$

Division by zero does not produce a real number so the denominator cannot be zero.

The domain is all real numbers except $x = 2$.

---

## EXAMPLE 2

Find the range of the function $5x - y + 1 = 0$, $-2 \leq x \leq 4$.

$$5x - y + 1 = 0$$
$$y = 5x + 1$$

When $x = -2$,
$$y = 5 \times -2 + 1$$
$$= -9$$

When $x = 4$,
$$y = 5 \times 4 + 1$$
$$= 21$$

range: $-9 \leq y \leq 21$

$5x - y + 1 = 0$ is a straight line, so we only need to consider the values at the ends of the domain.

---

## EXAMPLE 3

Find the natural domain and range for the function $y = 4 - x^2$.

$$y = 4 - x^2$$
domain: all real $x$

Now $x^2 \geq 0$ for all real $x$.
$$\therefore -x^2 \leq 0$$
$$4 - x^2 \leq 4$$
range: $y \leq 4$

There is no value of $x$ that cannot be squared and subtracted from 4.

---

## EXAMPLE 4

$f(x) = 7 - x$, $[-2, 6)$. What is the range?

$$f(-2) = 7 - (-2)$$
$$= 9$$
$$f(6) = 7 - 6$$
$$= 1$$

Range is (1, 9].

$f(-2)$ is included in the range. $f(6)$ forms the boundary of the range but is not included.

## → PRACTICE

1. Find the natural domain for $y = \dfrac{1}{x+3}$.

2. Find the range of the function $2x - y + 3 = 0$, $-1 \leq x \leq 5$.

3. Find the natural domain and range for the function $y = x^2 - 7$.

4. $f(x) = 1 - 2x$, $(-4, 4]$. What is the range?

5* Find the natural domain and range for the function $y = \sqrt{1 - x^2}$.

Answers ⊃ pp. 40–41

## 4 Types of relations and functions

→ The **graph of a function** is the result when all of the ordered pairs are shown on a number plane. In many cases the graph is a smooth continuous curve.

→ The **vertical line test** can be used to determine whether a relation is a function. If any vertical line cuts the graph in more than one place, then the graph is not that of a function.

→ A **one-to-one function** is a function where for each element in the output there is exactly one input. If there is more than one input for each output the function is one-to-many. If there is more than one output for each input, it is a relation not a function. A relation may be many-to-one or many-to-many (or one-to-one or one-to-many if it is a function as well as a relation).

→ The **horizontal line test** can be used to determine whether a function is one-to-one. If any horizontal line cuts the graph in more than one place then the function is not one-to-one.

### EXAMPLE 1

These are the points in a relation: (3, 5), (6, 1), (2, 4), (3, 2), (5, 1). What type of relation is it?

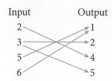

We map the inputs to their corresponding outputs.

It is a many-to-many relation.

### EXAMPLE 2

Use the vertical line test to show that this is not the graph of a function.

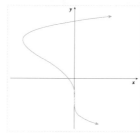

This vertical line cuts the graph in two places, so it is not a function.

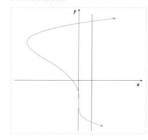

It is possible to draw a vertical line that cuts the graph in just one place but that does not make it a function. Because it is possible to draw a line that cuts the graph in more than one place it is not a function.

### EXAMPLE 3

Is this function one-to-one? Justify your answer.

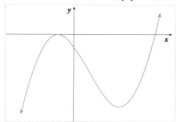

No, it is a one-to-many function because a horizontal line cuts the graph more than once.

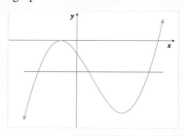

'Many' might only be two or three. It doesn't mean that there has to be lots of values.

→ **PRACTICE**

1   These are the points in a relation: $(2, 1)$, $(5, 3)$, $(3, 1)$, $(4, 3)$, $(1, 1)$, $(6, 2)$. What type of relation is it?

..........................................................................

2   Use the vertical line test to show that this is not the graph of a function.

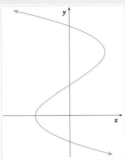

3   Is this function one-to-one? Justify your answer.

..........................................................................

4*  What type of function or relation, (one-to-one, one-to many, many-to-one or many-to-many) is defined by the rule $y = 2x^2 - 3$?

Answers ⊃ p. 41

## 5 Even and odd functions

→   A function is **even** if $f(-x) = f(x)$ for all values of $x$. The graph of an even function is symmetrical about the $y$-axis.

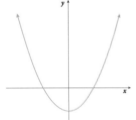

→   A function is **odd** if $f(-x) = -f(x)$ for all values of $x$. The graph of an odd function has **point symmetry** about the origin.

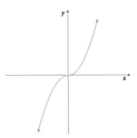

→   A function might be **neither even nor odd**.

**EXAMPLE 1**

Determine whether $f(x) = x^4 - 9x^2 + 7$ is even, odd or neither.

$$f(x) = x^4 - 9x^2 + 7$$
$$f(-x) = (-x)^4 - 9 \times (-x)^2 + 7$$
$$= x^4 - 9x^2 + 7$$
$$= f(x)$$

∴ the function is even.

> Replace every $x$ in $f(x)$ with $-x$ to find $f(-x)$.

**EXAMPLE 2**

Determine whether $f(x) = x^2 - 3x$ is even, odd or neither.

$$f(x) = x^2 - 3x$$
$$f(-x) = (-x)^2 - 3 \times (-x)$$
$$= x^2 + 3x$$

∴ the function is neither even nor odd.

> If $f(-x)$ is not equal to either $f(x)$ or $-f(x)$ the function is not even or odd.

**EXAMPLE 3**

Determine whether $f(x) = \dfrac{x}{x^2 - 1}$ is even, odd or neither.

$$f(x) = \frac{x}{x^2 - 1}$$
$$f(-x) = \frac{-x}{(-x)^2 - 1}$$
$$= \frac{-x}{x^2 - 1}$$
$$= -f(x)$$

∴ the function is odd.

> This function is an example of one that is not continuous. There will be a gap in the graph when $x = \pm 1$.

→ **PRACTICE**

1   Determine whether $f(x) = x^3 + 2$ is even, odd or neither.

..........................................................................

2   Determine whether $f(x) = x + \dfrac{1}{x}$ is even, odd or neither.

..........................................................................

3   Determine whether $f(x) = x^4 - 2x^2$ is even, odd or neither.

4* The diagram shows part of the graph of $y = f(x)$.

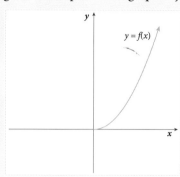

Copy and complete the graph given that $f(x)$ is:

a   an even function

b   an odd function

Answers ⊃ p. 41

## 6 Sum, difference, product and quotient of functions

→ Functions can be **added** together to find their **sum** or one function can be **subtracted** from another to find the **difference**.

→ The **product** of two functions is found by **multiplying** them together. A product might simply be given in **factorised form**.

→ The **quotient** of two functions is the result when one is **divided** by the other. It might not be possible to actually divide some functions so the quotient might just be given in **fractional form**.

### EXAMPLE 1

If $f(x) = 3x^2 - 2x + 5$ and $g(x) = 2x^2 + 6x - 7$ find the sum of the functions.

$f(x) + g(x) = 3x^2 - 2x + 5 + 2x^2 + 6x - 7$
$\qquad\qquad = 5x^2 + 4x - 2$

Collect like terms.

### EXAMPLE 2

Find $f(x) - g(x)$ if $f(x) = 8x^2 - 5x + 6$ and $g(x) = 5 - x^2$.

$f(x) - g(x) = 8x^2 - 5x + 6 - (5 - x^2)$
$\qquad\qquad = 8x^2 - 5x + 6 - 5 + x^2$
$\qquad\qquad = 9x^2 - 5x + 1$

Take care to subtract in the required order. $g(x) - f(x)$ will give the negative of this answer.

### EXAMPLE 3

Find the product of $f(x) = 2x^2 - 3$ and $g(x) = x^3 + 5x - 2$.

$(2x^2 - 3)(x^3 + 5x - 2) = 2x^5 + 10x^3 - 4x^2 - 3x^3 - 15x + 6$
$\qquad\qquad\qquad\qquad\quad = 2x^5 + 7x^3 - 4x^2 - 15x + 6$

Every term in the second set of brackets must be multiplied by each term in the first.

### EXAMPLE 4

Find $f(x) \div g(x)$ if $f(x) = x^2 + 2x - 15$ and $g(x) = x^2 - 5x + 6$.

$$\frac{f(x)}{g(x)} = \frac{x^2 + 2x - 15}{x^2 - 5x + 6}$$

$$= \frac{(x+5)(x-3)}{(x-2)(x-3)}$$

$$= \frac{x+5}{x-2}$$

Only cancel common factors.

### → PRACTICE

1   If $f(x) = 2x^2 + 3x - 8$ and $g(x) = x^2 + 4x + 3$ find the sum of the functions.

2   Find $f(x) - g(x)$ if $f(x) = 2x^3 + 5x - 4$ and $g(x) = 6 + 2x - 3x^2$.

3   Find the product of $f(x) = 3x - 7$ and $g(x) = x^4 - 9x^2 - 4x$.

4   Find $f(x) \div g(x)$ if $f(x) = x^2 - 13x + 40$ and $g(x) = x^2 - 5x - 24$.

5*  If $f(x) = \dfrac{x}{1-x^2}$ and $g(x) = x - \dfrac{1}{x}$, find their product.

Answers ⊃ pp. 41–42

## 7 Composite functions

→ A composite function can also be referred to as a **function of a function**.

→ In a composite function, the **variable** is **replaced** with another **function**; for example,

if $f(x) = x^2$ and $g(x) = 3x - 2$ then $f(g(x)) = (3x - 2)^2$.

→ The **order** in which the functions are applied is **important**. $f(g(x))$ and $g(f(x))$ are not usually the same. In the above example $g(f(x)) = 3x^2 - 2$.

## EXAMPLE 1

Find $f(g(x))$ if $f(x) = x^2 + 2x$ and $g(x) = 3x - 1$.

$f(x) = x^2 + 2x \quad g(x) = 3x - 1$
$f(g(x)) = (3x - 1)^2 + 2(3x - 1)$
$\qquad = 9x^2 - 6x + 1 + 6x - 2$
$\qquad = 9x^2 - 1$

> We are looking for $f(3x - 1)$. Each $x$ in $f(x)$ must be replaced by $(3x - 1)$.

## EXAMPLE 2

If $f(x) = \dfrac{x+3}{x+2}$ and $g(x) = 2 - \dfrac{1}{x}$, show that $g(f(x)) = \dfrac{x+4}{x+3}$.

$f(x) = \dfrac{x+3}{x+2} \quad g(x) = 2 - \dfrac{1}{x}$

$g(f(x)) = 2 - \dfrac{1}{\dfrac{x+3}{x+2}}$

$\qquad = 2 - \dfrac{x+2}{x+3}$

$\qquad = \dfrac{2(x+3)-(x+2)}{x+3}$

$\qquad = \dfrac{2x+6-x-2}{x+3}$

$\qquad = \dfrac{x+4}{x+3}$

> Replace $x$ in $g(x)$ with $\frac{x+3}{x+2}$ and simplify.

## EXAMPLE 3

Find the domain and range of the composite function $f(g(x))$ if $f(x) = \sqrt{x}$ and $g(x) = x - 2$.

$f(x) = \sqrt{x} \quad g(x) = x - 2$
$f(g(x)) = \sqrt{x-2}$
domain: $x - 2 \geq 0$
$\qquad\quad x \geq 2$
range: $y \geq 0$

> The domain of $f(g(x))$ will be a subset of the domain of $g(x)$.

## → PRACTICE

1  Find $f(g(x))$ if $f(x) = x^2 - 3x$ and $g(x) = 2x - 7$.

2  If $f(x) = \dfrac{x-4}{x+1}$ and $g(x) = 3 + \dfrac{1}{x}$, show that
$g(f(x)) = \dfrac{4x-11}{x-4}$.

3  Find the domain and range of the composite function $f(g(x))$ if $f(x) = \sqrt{5-x}$ and $g(x) = x^2 - 4$.

4*  If $f(x) = x^2 - 2x$ and $g(x) = x + 2$ find $f(g(x)) - g(f(x))$.

Answers ⊃ p. 42

## 8  If $f(x) = 0$

→ The **solutions of the equation $f(x) = 0$** are the values of $x$ where the curve $y = f(x)$ meets the $x$-axis.

→ If a curve $y = f(x)$ cuts the $x$-axis at $x = a$, then $f(a) = 0$.

→ If there are **no solutions to the equation $f(x) = 0$** then the curve $y = f(x)$ **will not meet** the $x$-axis.

## EXAMPLE 1

Find the coordinates of the points where the curve $y = f(x)$ meets the $x$-axis, if $f(x) = x^3 - 2x^2 - 15x$.

$x^3 - 2x^2 - 15x = 0$
$x(x^2 - 2x - 15) = 0$
$x(x - 5)(x + 3) = 0$
$x = 0$ or $x = 5$ or $x = -3$
So the curve $y = f(x)$ meets the $x$-axis at $(0, 0)$, $(5, 0)$ and $(-3, 0)$.

> Take care to answer the actual question. Here, we were asked for the points.

## EXAMPLE 2

Show that the curve $y = x^4 + 5$ does not cut the $x$-axis.

If $x^4 + 5 = 0$
then $\quad x^4 = -5$
But $x^4 \geq 0$ for all real values of $x$.
So $x^4 + 5 \neq 0$
∴ the curve does not cut the $x$-axis.

> We assume that the function is equal to zero and show that there is no solution.

## EXAMPLE 3

The diagram shows the graph of $y = f(x)$ where $f(x) = 8 + 2x - x^2$.

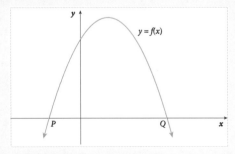

What are the coordinates of $P$ and $Q$?

When $f(x) = 0$
$8 + 2x - x^2 = 0$
$(4 - x)(2 + x) = 0$
$x = 4$ or $x = -2$
$\therefore P$ is the point $(-2, 0)$ and $Q$ is the point $(4, 0)$.

*Refer to the diagram to distinguish between the two points.*

## → PRACTICE

1  Find the coordinates of the points where the curve $y = f(x)$ meets the $x$-axis, if $f(x) = x^3 + 3x^2 - 10x$.

2  Show that the curve $y = x^2 + 3$ does not cut the $x$-axis.

3  The diagram shows the graph of $y = -x^2 + 6x - 5$.

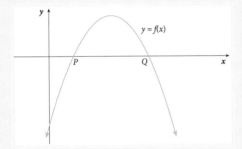

What are the coordinates of $P$ and $Q$?

4*  The curve $y = x^4 - kx^3 + 3x^2$ cuts the $x$-axis at $x = 1$.
   a  What is the value of $k$?
   b  Where else does the curve meet the $x$-axis?

Answers ⊃ p. 42

## Linear, quadratic and cubic functions

### 1 Direct variation

→  A direct variation relationship between two variables means that the value of one variable **varies directly** with the other. For example, if one variable doubles, the other variable will also double.

→  If one variable varies directly with another then the **graph** of the relationship is a **straight line**, with positive gradient, passing through the origin.

→  A straight-line graph can be used to **model practical problems**.

## EXAMPLE 1

The number of matches needed to make a pattern of 'houses' varies directly with the number of houses. 100 matches are needed to make 20 houses. How many matches are needed to make 35 houses?

number of matches per house $= 100 \div 20$
$= 5$
number of matches for 35 houses $= 5 \times 35$
$= 175$

*The direct variation means that every house has the same number of matches, five. If $m$ is the number of matches and $h$ the number of houses, then $m = 5h$.*

## EXAMPLE 2

At a constant speed, the distance ($d$ km in $h$ hours) covered by a vehicle is shown in the graph.

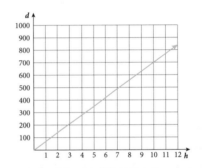

a  How far has the vehicle travelled in 5 hours?
b  What is the constant speed?
c  Write an equation for the distance travelled over time.

a  The vehicle has travelled 350 km in 5 hours.

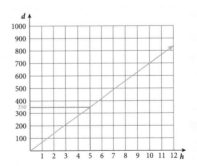

b  speed $= 350$ km $\div 5$ h
$= 70$ km/h

c  $d = 70h$

*There are no negative values shown on the graph because it makes no sense to consider negative distances or a negative period of time.*

## → PRACTICE

1  The number of bolts needed to make a particular type of bookshelf varies directly with the number of bookshelves. 500 bolts are needed to make 25 bookshelves. How many bolts are needed to make 15 bookshelves?

2  At a constant rate, the volume ($V$ litres in $m$ minutes) flowing into a tank is shown in the graph.

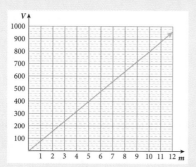

  a  How many litres have flowed in 8 minutes?
  b  What is the constant rate?
  c  Write an equation for the volume over time.

3*  A graph has been drawn to convert litres to gallons and vice versa.

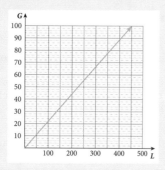

  a  What is the capacity in gallons of a container that holds 300 litres?
  b  What is the capacity in litres of a container that holds 90 gallons?
  c  Mick has 25 drums that each hold 40 gallons. How many litres in total will the 25 drums hold?
  d  Katy has a tank that holds 20 000 litres. She looks at the graph and finds that 200 litres is about 44 gallons so concludes that her tank will hold approximately 4400 gallons. Is she correct? Justify your answer.

Answers ⊃ pp. 42–43

## 2 Gradient and y-intercept

→  The equation $y = mx + c$ is a **linear equation**. It is the graph of a **straight line**.

→  The line $y = mx + c$ has **gradient $m$ and $y$-intercept $c$**.

→  The gradient of a line is its **slope**. It is the measure of how steep the line is.

$$\text{gradient} = \frac{\text{change in vertical position (rise)}}{\text{change in vertical position (run)}}$$

If the line leans to the right (/) the gradient is **positive** and if the line leans to the left (\) the gradient is **negative**.

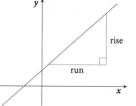

→  The **$y$-intercept** is where the line cuts the $y$-axis.

### EXAMPLE 1

Write down the gradient and $y$-intercept for the line $y = x - 3$.

gradient $= 1$
$y$-intercept $= -3$

Think of the line as $y = 1x + (-3)$.

### EXAMPLE 2

Write down the equation of the line with gradient $\frac{2}{3}$ and $y$-intercept $-4$.

$m = \dfrac{2}{3}$,  $c = -4$

Equation is $y = \dfrac{2}{3}x - 4$.

A gradient of $\frac{2}{3}$ means that from any point on the line running across 3 units to the right and rising up 2 units will give another point on the line.

### EXAMPLE 3

Find the gradient and $y$-intercept for this line and give its equation.

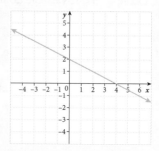

$m = -\dfrac{1}{2}$,  $c = 2$

Equation is $y = -\dfrac{1}{2}x + 2$.

From any point on the line, run across 2 units and move down 1 unit to find another point. So the 'rise' is negative.

## EXAMPLE 4

Write down the gradient and $y$-intercept and graph the line $y = 2x - 1$.

$y = 2x - 1$
gradient: $m = 2$
$y$-intercept: $c = -1$

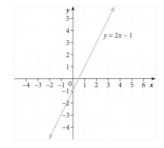

Begin from the $y$-intercept, in this case the point $(0, -1)$. The gradient is $2\left(\dfrac{2}{1}\right)$, so run across 1 unit and rise up 2 units to find another point on the line.

### → PRACTICE

1   Write down the gradient and $y$-intercept for the line $y = -2x$.

2   Write down the equation of the line with gradient $\dfrac{3}{5}$ and $y$-intercept 7.

3   Find the gradient and $y$-intercept for this line and give its equation.

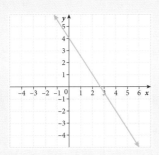

4   Write down the gradient and $y$-intercept and graph the line $y = 3x - 2$.

5*  Find the gradient and $y$-intercept of the line whose equation is $3x + 4y - 2 = 0$.

Answers ⊃ p. 43

## 3 Formulas for the gradient and the equation of a line

→   A line **parallel to the $x$-axis** has zero gradient, $m = 0$. A line **parallel to the $y$-axis** has infinite slope, $m$ **is undefined**.

→   When finding the gradient, the change in the vertical position will be the **difference** between the $y$-**coordinate**s and the change in the horizontal position will be the **difference** between the $x$-**coordinates**. So the gradient of the line joining the points $(x_1, y_1)$ and $(x_2, y_2)$ is given by the **formula**

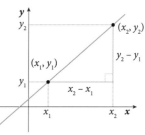

$$m = \frac{y_2 - y_1}{x_2 - x_1} \quad (x_1 \neq x_2).$$

→   The equation of a line through the **point** $(x_1, y_1)$ with **gradient** $m$ is given by the point-gradient **formula**: $y - y_1 = m(x - x_1)$.

→   The equation of a line through any **two points** can be found by first finding the gradient and then using the point-gradient formula.

### EXAMPLE 1

Find the gradient of the line joining $(2, 9)$ to $(7, -1)$.

$(2, 9), \quad (7, -1)$

$$m = \frac{y_2 - y_1}{x_2 - x_1}$$

$$= \frac{-1 - 9}{7 - 2}$$

$$= -2$$

It doesn't matter which point is first and which is second because the gradient will be the same. But $x_1$ and $y_1$ must be from the same point and $x_2$ and $y_2$ from the other point.

### EXAMPLE 2

The gradient of the line joining $P(-7, 1)$ to $Q(2, y)$ is $\dfrac{1}{3}$. Find $y$.

$P(-7, 1), \quad Q(2, y), \quad m = \dfrac{1}{3}$

$$m = \frac{y_2 - y_1}{x_2 - x_1}$$

$$\frac{1}{3} = \frac{y - 1}{2 - (-7)}$$

$$\frac{1}{3} = \frac{y - 1}{9}$$

$$3 = y - 1$$

$$y = 4$$

Solve an equation. Multiply everything by the common denominator to get rid of the fractions.

## EXAMPLE 3

Find the equation of the line through (3, 4) with gradient 2.

$(3, 4), \quad m = 2$
$y - y_1 = m(x - x_1)$
$y - 4 = 2(x - 3)$
$y - 4 = 2x - 6$
$\quad y = 2x - 2$

It is easy to check that the answer is correct. The coefficient of $x$ should be the gradient and the coordinates of the point should satisfy the equation.

## EXAMPLE 4

A line has gradient $\frac{1}{2}$ and passes through the point (5, –1). Find the coordinates of the point where the line cuts the $y$-axis.

$(5, -1), \quad m = \frac{1}{2}$
$y - y_1 = m(x - x_1)$
$y - (-1) = \frac{1}{2}(x - 5)$
$y + 1 = \frac{1}{2}x - 2\frac{1}{2}$
$y = \frac{1}{2}x - 3\frac{1}{2}$
$y\text{-intercept} = -3\frac{1}{2}$
$\therefore$ the line cuts the $y$-axis at $(0, -3\frac{1}{2})$.

First find the equation of the line in order to find the $y$-intercept.

## EXAMPLE 5

Find the equation of the line that passes through (1, 8) and (–2, –1).

$(1, 8), \quad (-2, -1)$
$m = \frac{y_2 - y_1}{x_2 - x_1}$
$\quad = \frac{-1 - 8}{-2 - 1}$
$\quad = 3$
$y - y_1 = m(x - x_1)$
$y - 8 = 3(x - 1)$
$y - 8 = 3x - 3$
$\quad y = 3x + 5$

Check that both points satisfy the equation. If they do, the answer must be right.

→ PRACTICE

1   Find the gradient of the line joining (4, 3) to (5, –2).

2   The gradient of the line joining $P(-3, -2)$ to $Q(1, y)$ is $\frac{5}{2}$. Find $y$.

3   Find the equation of the line through (2, 5) with gradient 3.

4   A line with gradient –2 cuts the $x$-axis at (7, 0). Find the coordinates of the point where the line cuts the $y$-axis.

5   Find the equation of the line that passes through (–6, –7) and (–3, 8).

6*  Show that the point (1, 7) lies on the line joining (–3, –1) to (4, 13).

Answers ⊃ p. 43

## 4 Parallel and perpendicular lines

→ **Parallel lines** have the **same gradient**. If the gradient of a line is $m_1$ and the gradient of a different line is $m_2$ then if $m_1 = m_2$ the two lines must be parallel, and if the lines are parallel then $m_1 = m_2$.

→ **Perpendicular lines** meet at **right angles**.

→ **Perpendicular lines** have gradients that are **negative reciprocals**. If the gradient of a line is $m_1$ and the gradient of a different line is $m_2$ then if $m_1 m_2 = -1$ the two lines must be perpendicular, and if the lines are perpendicular then $m_1 m_2 = -1$.

## EXAMPLE 1

Find the equation of the line through (2, –3) parallel to $y = \frac{1}{2}x - 3$.

$y = \frac{1}{2}x - 3$ has gradient $\frac{1}{2}$.
$\therefore$ parallel lines have $m = \frac{1}{2}$.
$y - y_1 = m(x - x_1)$
$y - (-3) = \frac{1}{2}(x - 2)$
$y + 3 = \frac{1}{2}x - 1$
$y = \frac{1}{2}x - 4$

The only difference in the equation is the $y$-intercept.

## EXAMPLE 2

Show that the lines $y = 5 - 2x$ and $y = \dfrac{x}{2}$ are perpendicular.

$y = 5 - 2x$ has gradient $m_1 = -2$.

$y = \dfrac{x}{2}$ has gradient $m_2 = \dfrac{1}{2}$.

Now $m_1 m_2 = -2 \times \dfrac{1}{2}$

$\qquad\qquad = -1$

$y = 5 - 2x$ is the same equation as $y = -2x + 5$;
$y = \dfrac{x}{2}$ is the same as $y = \dfrac{1}{2}x$.

$\therefore$ the lines are perpendicular.

## EXAMPLE 3

Find the equation of the line through $(-1, 4)$, perpendicular to the line $3x + 2y + 7 = 0$.

$3x + 2y + 7 = 0$

$\qquad 2y = -3x - 7$

$\qquad\quad y = -\dfrac{3}{2}x - \dfrac{7}{2}$

This line has gradient $-\dfrac{3}{2}$.

So a perpendicular line has gradient $m = \dfrac{2}{3}$.

$y - y_1 = m(x - x_1)$

$y - 4 = \dfrac{2}{3}(x - (-1))$

$y - 4 = \dfrac{2}{3}x + \dfrac{2}{3}$

$\qquad\qquad$ In general form this is the line $2x - 3y + 14 = 0$.

$y = \dfrac{2}{3}x + 4\dfrac{2}{3}$

### → PRACTICE

1   Find the equation of the line through $(-4, -1)$ parallel to $y = -3x + 5$.

2   Show that the lines $y = 3x + 4$ and $y = 4 - \dfrac{x}{3}$ are perpendicular.

3   Find the equation of the line through $(5, -2)$, perpendicular to the line $2x - y - 3 = 0$.

4*  $P$ and $Q$ are the points $(5, 6)$ and $(-3, 0)$ respectively. The point $N$ lies on the $y$-axis. Find the coordinates of $N$ if $PQ$ is perpendicular to $QN$.

Answers ➲ pp. 43–44

## 5 Quadratic functions

→ A quadratic function is of the form $f(x) = ax^2 + bx + c$, $a \neq 0$.

→ The graph of a quadratic function is a **parabola**.

→ $a$ will determine the **concavity** of the parabola. If $a > 0$, the curve is concave up: $\smile$. If $a < 0$, the curve is concave down: $\frown$. The value of $a$ will also determine how **wide or narrow** the curve will be.

→ The $y$-intercept is $c$.

→ The **turning point** of the parabola is called the **vertex**. It lies on the **axis of symmetry**.

## EXAMPLE 1

The diagram shows the graph of a parabola.

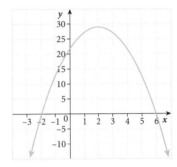

a   Is the parabola concave up or concave down?

b   What are the coordinates of the vertex?

c   What is the equation of the axis of symmetry?

d   What is the $y$-intercept?

e   Where does the curve cut the $x$-axis?

a   concave down

b   $(2, 29)$

c   $x = 2$

$\qquad\qquad$ We can just read the values from the graph.

d   22

e   $(-2, 0)$ and $(6, 0)$

## EXAMPLE 2

The diagram shows a sketch of the parabolas $y = 2x^2 - 2$ and $y = 4 - x^2$.

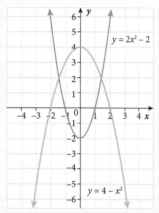

Briefly explain the important features of each parabola and comment on any similarities or differences.

$y = 2x^2 - 2$ is concave up. Its vertex is at $(0, -2)$ and it cuts the $x$-axis at $(1, 0)$ and $(-1, 0)$. $y = 4 - x^2$ is concave down and has its vertex at $(0, 4)$ and it cuts the $x$-axis at $(2, 0)$ and $(-2, 0)$. Both parabolas have the same axis of symmetry, the $y$-axis. $y = 2x^2 - 2$ is narrower than $y = 4 - x^2$.

Consider the concavity, intercepts, vertex and axis of symmetry.

### → PRACTICE

1  The diagram shows the graph of a parabola.

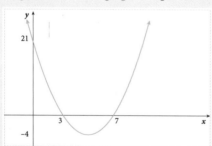

  a  Is the parabola concave up or concave down?
  b  What are the coordinates of the vertex?
  c  What is the equation of the axis of symmetry?
  d  What is the $y$-intercept?
  e  Where does the curve cut the $x$-axis?

---

2  The diagram shows a sketch of the parabolas $y = x^2 - 1$ and $y = 1 - \dfrac{x^2}{4}$.

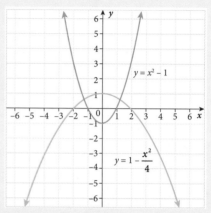

Briefly explain the important features of each parabola and comment on any similarities or differences.

3*  A parabola has its vertex at $(-2, -1)$ and its $y$-intercept is 4. Is the parabola concave up or concave down? Justify your answer.

Answers ⊃ p. 44

### 6 Finding the intercepts and vertex

→  The **$x$-intercepts** of the parabola $y = ax^2 + bx + c$ are the solutions of the quadratic equation $ax^2 + bx + c = 0$.

→  The **solutions of quadratic equations** can be found by factorising, completing the square, or using the quadratic formula $\left( x = \dfrac{-b \pm \sqrt{b^2 - 4ac}}{2a} \right)$.

→  The **axis of symmetry** is found midway between the $x$-intercepts.

→  The **vertex** will lie on the axis of symmetry.

→  The $y$-coordinate of the vertex will be the **least value** of the parabola if the parabola is concave up or the **greatest value** if the parabola is concave down.

### EXAMPLE 1

Find the $x$- and $y$-intercepts and the vertex of the parabola $y = x^2 + 10x + 16$.

$$y = x^2 + 10x + 16$$
$$x^2 + 10x + 16 = 0$$
$$(x + 2)(x + 8) = 0$$
$$x + 2 = 0 \quad \text{or} \quad x + 8 = 0$$
$$x = -2 \quad \text{or} \quad x = -8$$

So the $x$-intercepts are $-2$ and $-8$.

The $y$-intercept is 16.

axis: $x = \dfrac{-2+(-8)}{2}$

The axis is a line so its equation is the equation of a line. To find its position find the average of the $x$-intercepts.

$x = -5$

When $x = -5$,

$y = (-5)^2 + 10(-5) + 16$

$= -9$

The vertex is $(-5, -9)$.

## EXAMPLE 2

**Use the method of completing the square to find the $x$-intercepts of the parabola $y = 25x^2 - 20x - 12$.**

$25x^2 - 20x - 12 = 0$

$25x^2 - 20x + 4 = 16$

$(5x - 2)^2 = 16$

$5x - 2 = -4$   or   $5x - 2 = 4$

The quadratic equation could have been factorised, $(5x + 2)(5x - 6)$, but we must use the method asked for in the question.

$5x = -2$   or   $5x = 6$

$x = -\dfrac{2}{5}$   or   $x = 1\dfrac{1}{5}$

The $x$-intercepts are $-\dfrac{2}{5}$ and $1\dfrac{1}{5}$.

## EXAMPLE 3

a   **Use the quadratic formula to find the $x$-intercepts of the parabola $y = 2x^2 + 8x + 3$.**

b   **Find the coordinates of the vertex.**

a   $2x^2 + 8x + 3 = 0$

$a = 2, \quad b = 8, \quad c = 3$

$x = \dfrac{-b \pm \sqrt{b^2 - 4ac}}{2a}$

$= \dfrac{-8 \pm \sqrt{8^2 - 4 \times 2 \times 3}}{2 \times 2}$

$= \dfrac{-8 \pm \sqrt{40}}{4}$

$= \dfrac{-8 \pm 2\sqrt{10}}{4}$

$= \dfrac{2\left(-4 \pm \sqrt{10}\right)}{4}$

$= \dfrac{-4 \pm \sqrt{10}}{2}$

The $x$-intercepts of the parabola are $\dfrac{-4 - \sqrt{10}}{2}$ and $\dfrac{-4 + \sqrt{10}}{2}$.

b   axis: $x = \dfrac{\dfrac{-4-\sqrt{10}}{2} + \dfrac{-4+\sqrt{10}}{2}}{2}$

$x = -2$

When $x = -2$,

$y = 2 \times (-2)^2 + 8 \times -2 + 3$

$= -5$

The vertex is at $(-2, -5)$.

The equation of the axis of symmetry can often be obvious.

Midway between $-2 + \dfrac{\sqrt{10}}{2}$ and $-2 - \dfrac{\sqrt{10}}{2}$ must be $-2$.

Alternatively we can use the formula $x = \dfrac{-b}{2a}$.

## EXAMPLE 4

**Consider the parabola $y = 4x^2 + 16x + 15$.**

a   **Is the parabola concave up or concave down?**

b   **Where does the parabola cut the $y$-axis?**

c   **Find the coordinates of the points where the parabola cuts the $x$-axis.**

d   **Find the coordinates of the vertex.**

e   **Sketch the parabola.**

$y = 4x^2 + 16x + 15$

a   concave up           $a > 0$

b   $y$-intercept $= 15$

The parabola cuts the $y$-axis at $(0, 15)$.

c        $4x^2 + 16x + 15 = 0$

$4x^2 + 6x + 10x + 15 = 0$

$2x(2x + 3) + 5(2x + 3) = 0$

$(2x + 3)(2x + 5) = 0$

$2x = -3$   or   $2x = -5$

$x = -1.5$   or   $x = -2.5$

It may not be obvious that a quadratic expression can be factorised. The quadratic formula could be used.

The parabola cuts the $x$-axis at $(-1.5, 0)$ and $(-2.5, 0)$.

d   axis: $x = \dfrac{-1.5 + (-2.5)}{2}$

$x = -2$

When $x = -2$,

$y = 4 \times (-2)^2 + 16 \times (-2) + 15$

$= -1$

The vertex is at $(-2, -1)$.

e  $y = 4x^2 + 16x + 15$

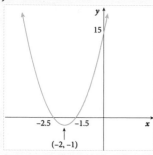

Using this information a sketch of the parabola can be made. It is only a sketch, so it is not intended that a great deal of time has to be taken to draw an accurate graph.

## EXAMPLE 5

Express $x^2 - 4x + 11 = 0$ in the form $(x - p)^2 + q = 0$ and hence find the minimum value of $x^2 - 4x + 11$.

$$x^2 - 4x + 11 = 0$$
$$x^2 - 4x + 4 + 7 = 0$$
$$(x - 2)^2 + 7 = 0$$

Now $(x - 2)^2 \geq 0$ for all real values of $x$.
∴ $(x - 2)^2 + 7 \geq 7$
∴ the minimum value of $x^2 - 4x + 11$ is 7.

This occurs when $(x - 2)^2 = 0$; that is, when $x = 2$.

### → PRACTICE

1  Find the $x$- and $y$-intercepts and the vertex of the parabola $y = x^2 - 6x - 16$.

2  Use the method of completing the square to find the $x$-intercepts of the parabola $y = 9x^2 - 18x + 8$.

3  a  Use the quadratic formula to find the $x$-intercepts of the parabola $y = x^2 - 6x + 2$.
   b  Find the coordinates of the vertex.

4  Consider the parabola $y = 4x^2 - 16x + 7$.
   a  Is the parabola concave up or concave down?
   b  Where does the parabola cut the $y$-axis?
   c  Find the coordinates of the points where the parabola cuts the $x$-axis.
   d  Find the coordinates of the vertex.
   e  Sketch the parabola.

5  Express $x^2 + 8x + 25 = 0$ in the form $(x - p)^2 + q = 0$ and hence find the minimum value of the expression $x^2 + 8x + 25$.

6*  By completing the square, find the vertex of $y = -x^2 + 2x - 9$ and hence show that $-x^2 + 2x - 9$ is always negative.

Answers ⊃ pp. 44–45

## 7 The discriminant

→ If $y = ax^2 + bx + c$, a value of $x$ for which $y = 0$ is called a **root of the quadratic equation** $ax^2 + bx + c = 0$.

→ $\Delta = b^2 - 4ac$ is called the **discriminant**. It is that part of the quadratic formula that is under the square root sign and is used to **discriminate** between the **types of roots** of the equation $ax^2 + bx + c = 0$.

→ If $\Delta \geq 0$, the roots are **real**.
   If $\Delta < 0$, the roots are **not real**.
   If $\Delta = 0$, the roots are **equal**.
   If $\Delta$ **is a perfect square**, the roots are **rational**.

### EXAMPLE 1

Find the discriminant and hence determine whether the roots of $3x^2 - 5x - 1 = 0$ are real. If the roots are real, determine whether they are rational or irrational, and equal or unequal.

$$3x^2 - 5x - 1 = 0$$
$$\Delta = b^2 - 4ac$$
$$= (-5)^2 - 4 \times 3 \times -1$$
$$= 37$$

The discriminant is positive so the roots are real (and not equal), but it is not a perfect square so the roots are irrational.

∴ the roots are real, irrational and unequal.

### EXAMPLE 2

Show that $x^2 + 3x + 5 = 0$ does not have real roots.

$$x^2 + 3x + 5 = 0$$
$$\Delta = b^2 - 4ac$$
$$= 3^2 - 4 \times 1 \times 5$$
$$= -11$$

We cannot have the square root of a negative number.

∴ the roots are not real.

Because the equation doesn't have real roots there is no solution to the equation.

### EXAMPLE 3

Show that $4x^2 - 5x - 6 = 0$ has rational roots.

$$4x^2 - 5x - 6 = 0$$
$$\Delta = b^2 - 4ac$$
$$= (-5)^2 - 4 \times 4 \times -6$$
$$= 121$$
$$= 11^2$$

If the roots are rational, it means that the expression could be factorised.

∴ the roots are rational.

## EXAMPLE 4

Find the values of $m$ for which $3x^2 - mx + m = 0$ has equal roots.

$3x^2 - mx + m = 0$
$\Delta = b^2 - 4ac$
$\quad = (-m)^2 - 4 \times 3 \times m$
$\quad = m^2 - 12m$
The roots are equal when $\Delta = 0$,
i.e. $m^2 - 12m = 0$
$\quad m(m - 12) = 0$
$\quad m = 0 \ $ or $\ m = 12$

*If $b^2 - 4ac = 0$, the quadratic formula gives just one value for $x$ so the equation has just one distinct root. We say that the two roots are equal.*

## EXAMPLE 5

For what values of $p$ will the expression $5x^2 - 4x + p$ always be positive?

As $a > 0$ the expression will always be positive if $5x^2 - 4x + p = 0$ has no real roots.
$\Delta = b^2 - 4ac$
$\quad = (-4)^2 - 4 \times 5 \times p$
$\quad = 16 - 20p$
If $16 - 20p < 0$
$\quad -20p < -16$
$\quad\quad p > 0.8$
The expression will always be positive when $p > 0.8$.

*The parabola $y = 5x^2 - 4x + p$ is concave up. If there are no real roots the graph will not cross the $x$-axis and so will always be positive.*

### → PRACTICE

1   Find the discriminant and hence determine whether the roots of $4x^2 - 3x - 2 = 0$ are real. If the roots are real, determine whether they are rational or irrational, and equal or unequal.

2   Show that $2x^2 + x + 7 = 0$ does not have real roots.

3   Show that $9x^2 - 36x + 20 = 0$ has rational roots.

4   Find the values of $m$ for which $2x^2 + mx + 18 = 0$ has equal roots.

5   For what values of $k$ will the expression $9x^2 + 6x + k$ always be positive?

6*  Find the values of $n$ for which $(n - 2)x^2 + (n + 1)x + 3 = 0$ has real roots.

Answers ⊃ pp. 45–46

## 8 Finding the equation of a quadratic

→ A **quadratic polynomial** is an expression of the form $P(x) = ax^2 + bx + c \ (a \neq 0)$.

→ Using given information we can find the values of $a$, $b$ and $c$ and hence find the **unique quadratic** that satisfies certain requirements.

## EXAMPLE 1

The parabola $y = 4x^2 - bx + c$ has $y$-intercept 7 and passes through the point $(2, -9)$. Find its equation.

$y = 4x^2 - bx + c$
$y$-intercept $= 7$
$\therefore c = 7$
$\quad y = 4x^2 - bx + 7$
When $x = 2$, $y = -9$
$-9 = 4 \times 2^2 - b \times 2 + 7$
$-9 = 23 - 2b$
$2b = 32$
$\quad b = 16$
$\therefore$ the equation of the parabola is $y = 4x^2 - 16x + 7$.

*Substitute the given information into the equation and solve to find the value of the unknowns.*

## EXAMPLE 2

A parabola has $x$-intercepts 2 and $-3$ and $y$-intercept 12. Find its equation in the form $y = ax^2 + bx + c$.

The $x$-intercepts are 2 and $-3$ so the equation is of the form $y = k(x - 2)(x + 3)$.
When $x = 0$, $y = 12$
$12 = k(0 - 2)(0 + 3)$
$\quad = -6k$
$\quad k = -2$
$\quad y = -2(x - 2)(x + 3)$
$\quad = -2(x^2 + x - 6)$
$\quad = -2x^2 - 2x + 12$
The equation of the parabola is $y = -2x^2 - 2x + 12$.

*If the $x$-intercepts of the equation are $p$ and $q$ then $y = k(x - p)(x - q)$ for some constant $k$.*

## EXAMPLE 3

$P(x) = ax^2 + bx + c$. $P(0) = 8$, $P(1) = 3$ and $P(-1) = 25$. Find $P(x)$.

$P(x) = ax^2 + bx + c$
$P(0) = 8$
$\therefore 8 = a \times 0^2 + b \times 0 + c$
$\quad c = 8$
$\therefore P(x) = ax^2 + bx + 8$
$\quad P(1) = 3$
$\therefore 3 = a \times 1^2 + b \times 1 + 8$
$\quad 3 = a + b + 8$

*It may be necessary to solve equations simultaneously to find the required values.*

$a + b = -5$   (i)
$P(-1) = 25$
$\therefore 25 = a \times (-1)^2 + b \times (-1) + 8$
$25 = a - b + 8$
$a - b = 17$   (ii)
(i) + (ii):  $2a = 12$
$a = 6$
Substitute into (i):  $6 + b = -5$
$b = -11$
$\therefore P(x) = 6x^2 - 11x + 8$

## → PRACTICE

1   The parabola $y = 3x^2 + bx + c$ has
    $y$-intercept –11 and passes through the point (4, 9).
    Find its equation.

2   A parabola has $x$-intercepts 1 and 4 and $y$-intercept
    8. Find its equation in the form $y = ax^2 + bx + c$.

3   $P(x) = ax^2 + bx + c$. $P(0) = 5$, $P(1) = 3$ and
    $P(-1) = 13$. Find $P(x)$.

4*  The parabola $y = ax^2 + bx + c$ cuts the $x$-axis at
    (–2, 0) and (6, 0) and has least value –8. Find the
    values of $a$, $b$ and $c$.

Answers ⊃ p. 46

## 9 Intersections of lines and parabolas

→ The **point of intersection** of two lines, a line and a
  parabola, or two parabolas can be found by solving their
  equations simultaneously.

→ The **simultaneous solution** can be found **algebraically**,
  using either substitution or elimination methods, or
  **graphically**.

→ Often the point of intersection has some **practical
  significance**.

→ Solving the **equation** $f(x) = k$ gives the values of $x$ for
  which $y = f(x)$ **intersects the line** $y = k$.

## EXAMPLE 1

The graph shows the cost of producing tables and
the return from their sale. What is the point of
intersection? Explain its significance.

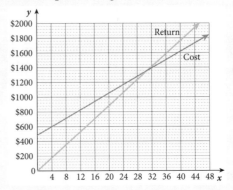

The point of intersection is where $x = 30$ and $y = \$1350$.
This is the break-even point. If 30 tables are made, the
cost to make them and the return from their sale is the
same ($1350). If more than 30 tables are made and sold,
a profit will be made.

The break-even point is simply where the
cost and return are equal. Before this point
a business will make a loss because the
cost to produce items is greater than the
return from their sale. Beyond the
break-even point a profit will be made.

## EXAMPLE 2

Find the points of intersection of the parabola
$y = x^2 - 7x + 11$ and the line $y = 3x - 5$.

$y = x^2 - 7x + 11$   (i)
$y = 3x - 5$          (ii)
At any point of intersection
$x^2 - 7x + 11 = 3x - 5$
$x^2 - 10x + 16 = 0$
$(x - 2)(x - 8) = 0$
$x - 2 = 0$  or  $x - 8 = 0$
$x = 2$  or      $x = 8$
Substitute into (ii)
When $x = 2$,  $y = 3 \times 2 - 5$
$= 1$
When $x = 8$,  $y = 3 \times 8 - 5$
$= 19$

Unless a graph has already been drawn
it is usually less time consuming to
solve the equations algebraically.

The points of intersection are (2, 1) and (8, 19).

## → PRACTICE

1 The graph shows the cost charged by two different contractors for each hour of work. What is the point of intersection and what is its significance?

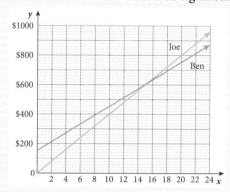

2 Find the points of intersection of the parabola $y = x^2 - 5x + 21$ and the line $y = 4x + 3$.

3* Find the value of $x$, $x > 0$, for which $3x^2 - 5x - 2 = x^2 + 2x + 7$.

Answers ⊃ p. 46

## 10 Cubic functions

→ A **cubic function** is one involving terms that include $x^3$, where the highest power of $x$ is 3.

→ The **graph of $y = kx^3$** passes through the origin, where it changes concavity, and through the point $(1, k)$.

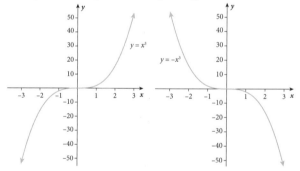

→ The graph of $y = k(x - b)^3 + c$ changes concavity when $x = b$. It is the graph of $y = kx^3$ moved across $b$ units and up $c$ units.

→ The **graph of $y = k(x - a)(x - b)(x - c)$** intercepts the $x$-axis at $a$, $b$ and $c$.

## EXAMPLE 1

a Where does the curve $y = \dfrac{x^3}{2} + 4$ cut the $x$-axis?

b Sketch the curve.

a $y = \dfrac{x^3}{2} + 4$

The curve cuts the $x$-axis when $y = 0$.

i.e. $\dfrac{x^3}{2} + 4 = 0$

$$\dfrac{x^3}{2} = -4$$
$$x^3 = -8$$
$$x = -2$$

b

In curves of the form $y = kx^3 + c$, $k$ determines the width of the curve and $c$ is the $y$-intercept.

## EXAMPLE 2

Consider the curve $y = 1 - (x - 2)^3$.

a What is the $y$-intercept?

b Where does the curve cut the $x$-axis?

c What happens to the value of $y$ for very large positive values of $x$?

d What happens to the value of $y$ for very large negative values of $x$?

e Sketch the curve.

a $y = 1 - (x - 2)^3$

When $x = 0$,

$y = 1 - (0 - 2)^3$

$= 9$

The cubic function needs to be of the form $y = ax^3 + bx^2 + cx + d$ for the constant term to be the $y$-intercept.

The $y$-intercept is 9.

b When $y = 0$,

$1 - (x - 2)^3 = 0$

$(x - 2)^3 = 1$

$x - 2 = 1$

$x = 3$

The curve cuts the $x$-axis at $(3, 0)$.

c When $x$ is a large positive number, $y$ will be a large negative number.

d When $x$ is a large negative number, $y$ will be a large positive number.

e

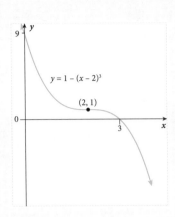

$y = 1 - (x - 2)^3$

(2, 1)

This is the curve $y = -x^3$ moved 2 units to the right and 1 unit up.

## EXAMPLE 3

**Sketch the curve $y = (x + 1)(x - 2)(x - 5)$.**

$y = (x + 1)(x - 2)(x - 5)$
When $x = 0$,
$y = (0 + 1)(0 - 2)(0 - 5)$
$\quad = 10$
When $y = 0$,
$x + 1 = 0$ or $x - 2 = 0$ or $x - 5 = 0$
$\quad x = -1$ or $\quad x = 2$ or $\quad x = 5$
When $x$ is a large positive number, $y$ is large and positive.

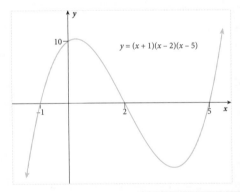

$y = (x + 1)(x - 2)(x - 5)$

The curve must have a turning point between $x = -1$ and $x = 2$ and another between $x = 2$ and $x = 5$. Without further investigation it is not possible to tell exactly where these lie.

→ **PRACTICE**

1  a  Where does the curve $y = 2x^3 - 2$ cut the $x$-axis?
   b  Sketch the curve.

2  Consider the curve $y = 8 - (x - 1)^3$.
   a  What is the $y$-intercept?
   b  Where does the curve cut the $x$-axis?

c  What happens to the value of $y$ for very large positive values of $x$?
d  What happens to the value of $y$ for very large negative values of $x$?
e  Sketch the curve.

3  Sketch the curve $y = (x + 4)(x + 2)(x - 3)$.

4*  Without sketching, explain the features of the curve $y = -4x(x + 2)(x - 4)$.

Answers ⊃ pp. 46–47

## Further functions and relations

### 1 Polynomials

→ A **polynomial, $P(x)$,** is an expression involving, exclusively, the sum of (non-negative integral) powers of $x$. It is any expression of the form $a_n x^n + a_{n-1} x^{n-1} + \dots + a_2 x^2 + a_1 x + a_0$ ($a_n \neq 0$), where $n$ is a positive integer.

→ The **degree** of a polynomial is the highest power of $x$. $a_n, a_{n-1} \dots a_2, a_1$ and $a_0$ are the **coefficients** of the different powers and must be real numbers. The coefficient of the highest power is called the **leading coefficient**.

→ The graph of $y = P(x)$ is a **continuous curve**. To sketch the graph we can find the $y$-intercept and, if the polynomial can easily be factorised, the $x$-intercepts. We can determine whether the function is even or odd and hence symmetrical and consider the behaviour for very large positive and negative values of $x$.

## EXAMPLE 1

**Consider $P(x) = 3x^5 + 7x^4 + 6x^3 - 2x^2 + 7x - 5$. Write down the degree of the polynomial, the leading coefficient and the constant term.**

$P(x) = 3x^5 + 7x^4 + 6x^3 - 2x^2 + 7x - 5$
degree = 5
leading coefficient = 3
constant term = −5

The leading term is the term involving the highest power of $x$. It might not be the first term in the expression.

## EXAMPLE 2

**Consider the curve $y = (x + 3)(x + 1)(x - 1)(x - 3)$.**
a  What is the $y$-intercept?
b  What are the $x$-intercepts?
c  Show that it is an even function.
d  Sketch the curve.

$y = (x + 3)(x + 1)(x - 1)(x - 3)$

a   When $x = 0$,
$y = (0 + 3)(0 + 1)(0 - 1)(0 - 3)$
$\quad = 9$
The $y$-intercept is 9.

b   $y = 0$ when $x + 3 = 0$ or $x + 1 = 0$ or $x - 1 = 0$
or $x - 3 = 0$
The $x$-intercepts are $-3$, $-1$, $1$ and $3$.

c   $f(x) = (x + 3)(x + 1)(x - 1)(x - 3)$
$\quad = (x + 3)(x - 3)(x + 1)(x - 1)$
$\quad = (x^2 - 9)(x^2 - 1)$
$f(-x) = ((-x)^2 - 9)((-x)^2 - 1)$
$\quad = (x^2 - 9)(x^2 - 1)$
$\quad = f(x)$
$\therefore$ the function is even.

d
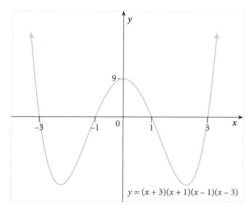

It does not have to be an accurate graph, just a sketch showing the essential features.

→ PRACTICE

1   Consider $P(x) = 7x^6 - x^5 + 2x^4 - 6x^2 + 9x - 3$. Write down the degree of the polynomial, the leading coefficient and the constant term.

2   Consider the curve $y = (x + 4)(x + 2)(x - 4)(x - 2)$.
   a   What is the $y$-intercept?
   b   What are the $x$-intercepts?
   c   Show that it is an even function.
   d   Sketch the curve.

3*  Consider $P(x) = 8 - 8x + x^3 - x^4$.
   a   What is the degree?
   b   What is the leading coefficient?
   c   What are the $x$ and $y$-intercepts of $y = P(x)$?

Answers ⊃ p. 47

## 2 Hyperbolas

→ If two quantities **vary inversely** with one another, then one would get larger as the other gets smaller.

→ Any function of the form $f(x) = \dfrac{k}{x}$, where $k$ is a constant, represents **inverse variation**.

→ The graph of $y = \dfrac{k}{x}$ is a **hyperbola**. It consists of two branches in opposite quadrants of the number plane. The $x$ and $y$ axes are **asymptotes** of the curve. (An asymptote is a line that a curve gets closer and closer to.)

### EXAMPLE 1

**The cost per person to go on a bus trip varies inversely with the number of people travelling. If 24 people go on the trip the cost per person is \$42. What is the cost per person if 28 people go on the trip?**

Let $x$ be the number of people travelling and \$C the cost per person.

$C = \dfrac{k}{x}$

When $x = 24$, $C = 42$

$42 = \dfrac{k}{24}$

$k = 1008$

$\therefore C = \dfrac{1008}{x}$

When $x = 28$,

$C = \dfrac{1008}{28}$

$\quad = 36$

$\therefore$ the cost would be \$36 per person.

Because this is an example of inverse variation, we know it is of the form $f(x) = \dfrac{k}{x}$. We first use the given information to find the value of the constant.

### EXAMPLE 2

**Sketch the graph of $y = \dfrac{12}{x}$.**

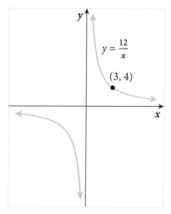

We need to show at least one point to identify that particular hyperbola.

## EXAMPLE 3

Sketch the graph of $y = -\dfrac{60}{x}$.

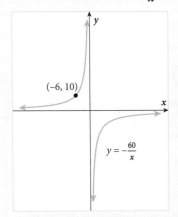

(−6, 10)

$y = -\dfrac{60}{x}$

The negative in the equation means that the curve must lie in the two quadrants of the number plane where $x$ and $y$ have different signs.

### → PRACTICE

1  The cost per person to go on a cruise varies inversely with the number of people travelling. If 60 people go on the trip the cost per person is $96. What is the cost per person if 144 people go on the trip?

2  Sketch the graph of $y = \dfrac{15}{x}$.

3  Sketch the graph of $y = -\dfrac{24}{x}$.

4*  As shown in the diagram, the line $y = 2x + 1$ intersects the hyperbola $y = \dfrac{k}{x}$ when $x = 3.5$.

   What is the value of $k$?

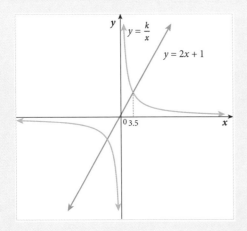

$y = \dfrac{k}{x}$

$y = 2x + 1$

0  3.5

Answers ⊃ p. 48

## 3 Absolute values

→ $|x|$ means the **absolute value** of $x$. The absolute value of a number is its **magnitude** regardless of its sign (that is, the size of the number without considering whether it is positive or negative). So $|3| = 3$ and $|-3| = 3$.

→ We have the **definition:** $|a| = \begin{cases} a \text{ if } a \geq 0 \\ -a \text{ if } a < 0 \end{cases}$

   (If $a$ is negative, $-a$ will be positive.)

→ Geometrically $|x|$ is the **distance of $x$ from 0** on the number line.

→ The **graph** of an absolute value expression consists of **two branches**, both of which are **straight lines**, that meet on the $x$-axis.

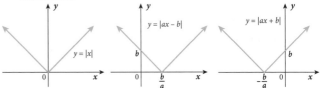

### EXAMPLE 1

Find $|-5| - |-9|$

$|-5| - |-9| = 5 - 9$

$\qquad\qquad = -4$

The answer to a calculation involving absolute values can be negative.

### EXAMPLE 2

Graph on the number line $|x| < 4$.

$|x| < 4$

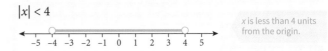

$x$ is less than 4 units from the origin.

### EXAMPLE 3

Graph on the number line $|x| \geq 2$.

$|x| \geq 2$

$x$ is 2 or more units from the origin.

## EXAMPLE 4

Sketch the graph of $y = |x - 3|$.

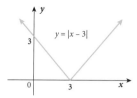

If $x \geq 3$, $y = x - 3$.
If $x < 3$, $y = -(x - 3) = -x + 3$.

## EXAMPLE 5

Sketch the graph of $y = |3x + 2|$.

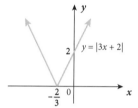

When $y = 0$, $x = -\frac{2}{3}$. If $x \geq -\frac{2}{3}$,

$y = 3x + 2$; if $x < -\frac{2}{3}$, $y = -3x - 2$.

---

### → PRACTICE

1  Find $|-2| - |-8|$.

2  Graph on the number line $|x| \leq 3$.

3  Graph on the number line $|x| > 1$.

4  Sketch the graph of $y = |x + 2|$.

5  Sketch the graph of $y = |2x - 5|$.

6*  Describe the features of the graph of $y = |4x + 1|$.

Answers ⊃ p. 48

---

## 4 Equations involving absolute values

→ Equations involving absolute values can be solved either **algebraically or graphically**.

→ Algebraically, we consider the **two cases** (whether the expression of which the absolute value has been taken is positive or negative) separately.

→ Geometrically, $|x - y|$ is the **distance** of $y$ from $x$ on the number line.

→ We can **graph $y = |ax \pm b|$** and use it to solve equations of the form $|ax \pm b| = k$ ($k \geq 0$).

## EXAMPLE 1

Use a number line to find the values of $x$ for which $|x + 2| = 3$.

$$|x + 2| = 3$$

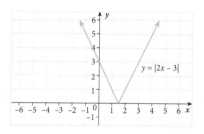

$|x + 2| = |x - (-2)|$. So $x$ is 3 units from −2.

$\therefore x = -5$ or $x = 1$

## EXAMPLE 2

Solve algebraically $|3x - 1| = 7$.

$$|3x - 1| = 7$$

| $3x - 1 = 7$ | or | $3x - 1 = -7$ |
|---|---|---|
| $3x = 8$ | | $3x = -6$ |
| $x = 2\frac{2}{3}$ | or | $x = -2$ |

Substitute each answer back into the original equation to see if it is satisfied.

## EXAMPLE 3

By drawing the graph of $y = |2x - 3|$, find all solutions to $|2x - 3| = 5$.

$y = |2x - 3|$

$\therefore |2x - 3| = 5$ when $x = -1$ or $x = 4$.

The graph needs to be accurate to be sure of getting the correct answer.

## EXAMPLE 4

Solve $|4x + 7| = 13$.

If the method is not specified, then any method can be used.

| $|4x + 7| = 13$ | | |
|---|---|---|
| $4x + 7 = 13$ | or | $4x + 7 = -13$ |
| $4x = 6$ | or | $4x = -20$ |
| $x = 1.5$ | or | $x = -5$ |

→ **PRACTICE**

1   Use a number line to find the values of $x$ for which $|x - 4| = 2$.

......................................................

2   Solve algebraically $|5x + 3| = 17$.

......................................................

3   By drawing the graph of $y = |2x + 1|$, find all solutions to $|2x + 1| = 7$.

......................................................

4   Solve $|3x + 8| = 10$.

......................................................

5*  Solve $|3 - 2a| = 7$.

Answers ⊃ pp. 48–49

## 5 Graphs and their reflections

→  The graph of $y = -f(x)$ is the **reflection** of $y = f(x)$ in the **$x$-axis**.

→  The graph of $y = f(-x)$ is the **reflection** of $y = f(x)$ in the **$y$-axis**.

→  The graph of $y = -f(-x)$ is the reflection of $y = f(x)$ in both the $x$-axis and $y$-axis. It is a **rotation of 180°** about the origin.

### EXAMPLE 1

The graph shows $y = f(x)$.

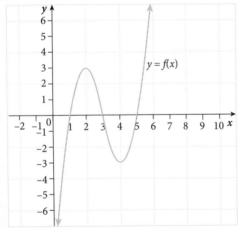

Copy the graph and on the same diagram sketch $y = -f(x)$.

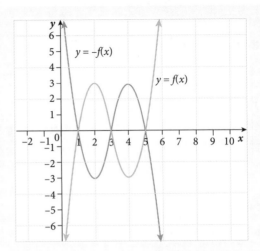

It doesn't matter what the original graph looks like; the graph of $y = -f(x)$ will always be the same as the original graph flipped over the $x$-axis.

### EXAMPLE 2

a   On the same diagram sketch the graphs of $y = 4x - x^2$, $y = x^2 + 4x$ and $y = -x^2 - 4x$.

b   Comment on any similarities and differences between the curves.

a

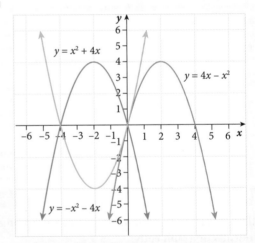

b   All the curves are exactly the same shape.
$y = -x^2 - 4x$ is the curve $y = x^2 + 4x$ reflected in the $x$-axis or the curve $y = 4x - x^2$ reflected in the $y$-axis. A rotation of 180° about the origin would mean that $y = 4x - x^2$ would map onto $y = x^2 + 4x$.

Because each curve is symmetrical, a translation or rotation could produce the same result as a reflection.

1  The graph shows $y = f(x)$.

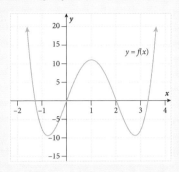

Copy the graph and on the same diagram sketch
$y = -f(x)$.

2  a  On the same diagram sketch the graphs of
      $y = 1 - x^3$, $y = x^3 + 1$ and $y = x^3 - 1$.
   b  Comment on any similarities and differences
      between the curves.

3*  The diagram shows the graph of $y = f(x)$.

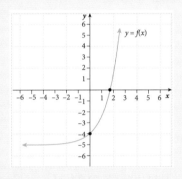

On separate diagrams sketch:

a  $y = f(-x)$
b  $y = -f(x)$
c  $y = -f(-x)$

Answers ⊃ p. 49

## 6 Circles

→ A circle is defined as the **set of points** in the plane which
  are **equidistant** from a **fixed point** (the centre).

→ The **equation of a circle** with centre at the origin and
  radius $r$ units is given by: $x^2 + y^2 = r^2$.

→ The equation of a circle
  comes directly from
  **Pythagoras' theorem.**

→ The equation of a circle
  with centre $(a, b)$ and radius
  $r$ units is given by
  $(x - a)^2 + (y - b)^2 = r^2$.

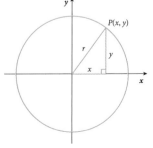

It might be necessary to **complete squares** in order to
find the centre and radius.

→ If we know the **centre and any point** on a circle we can
  find the equation and the radius.

## EXAMPLE 1

**Describe the features of the graph of $x^2 + y^2 = 49$.**

$x^2 + y^2 = 7^2$
The graph is a circle, centre $(0, 0)$,
radius 7 units.

A circle is not a
function.

## EXAMPLE 2

**Find the equation of this circle.**

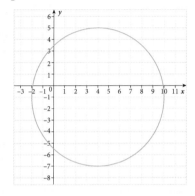

Centre $(4, -1)$ and radius 6 units.
$(x - a)^2 + (y - b)^2 = r^2$
$(x - 4)^2 + (y - (-1)^2 = 6^2$
$(x - 4)^2 + (y + 1)^2 = 36$

The equation is usually left in
this form, without expanding
the squares.

## EXAMPLE 3

**Sketch the graph of $(x + 2)^2 + (y - 5)^2 = 25$.**

$(x + 2)^2 + (y - 5)^2 = 25$
$(x - (-2))^2 + (y - 5)^2 = 5^2$
Circle: centre $(-2, 5)$, $r = 5$

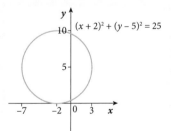

## EXAMPLE 4

Draw the graph of $x^2 + y^2 - 4x + 10y + 20 = 0$.

$$x^2 + y^2 - 4x + 10y + 20 = 0$$
$$x^2 - 4x + y^2 + 10y = -20$$
$$x^2 - 4x + 4 + y^2 + 10y + 25 = -20 + 29$$
$$(x - 2)^2 + (y + 5)^2 = 9$$

The graph is a circle, centre (2, -5), radius 3 units.

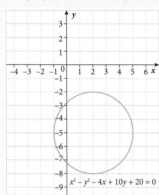

We complete the square on $x$ and on $y$ separately.

## EXAMPLE 5

The circle, centre (-7, 5), passes through the point (8, -3). Find the radius.

Centre (-7, 5)
$$(x - (-7))^2 + (y - 5)^2 = r^2$$
$$(x + 7)^2 + (y - 5)^2 = r^2$$
When $x = 8$ and $y = -3$,
$$(8 + 7)^2 + (-3 - 5)^2 = r^2$$
$$289 = r^2$$
$$17 = r \quad (r > 0)$$

Alternatively the distance formula could be used.

∴ the radius is 17 units.

### → PRACTICE

1   Describe the features of the graph of $x^2 + y^2 = 121$.

2   What is the equation of this circle?

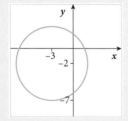

3   Sketch the graph of $(x - 1)^2 + (y + 3)^2 = 16$.

4   Draw the graph of $x^2 + y^2 + 22x - 2y + 41 = 0$.

5   The circle, centre (-2, 4), passes through the point (10, 9). Find the radius.

6*  Find the centre and radius of the circle $x^2 + y^2 = 2x - 8y$.

Answers ⊃ pp. 49–50

## 7 Semicircles

→ A **circle** is **not a function** (because for most values of $x$ there are two values of $y$). However, any circle can be divided into two semicircles, both of which are functions, by a horizontal line.

→ For a circle with centre the origin and radius $r$ units the two **semicircular functions** are $y = \sqrt{r^2 - x^2}$ and $y = -\sqrt{r^2 - x^2}$. These equations follow from rearranging the equation of the circle.

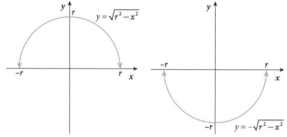

## EXAMPLE 1

Describe the function $y = -\sqrt{49 - x^2}$.

$y = -\sqrt{49 - x^2}$ is a semicircle. It is the bottom half of a circle, centre the origin, and radius 7 units.

## EXAMPLE 2

Write the equation of this semicircle.

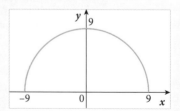

Centre (0, 0); radius 9 units

The equation is $y = \sqrt{81 - x^2}$.

The 'centre' is the centre of the circle of which this is a semicircle, not the actual centre point of the semicircle.

## EXAMPLE 3

a What is the domain and range of $f(x) = \sqrt{25 - x^2}$?

b Draw the graph of $y = f(x)$.

a $y = \sqrt{25 - x^2}$ is a semicircle, centre $(0, 0)$ radius 5 units.

So the domain is $-5 \le x \le 5$ and the range is $0 \le y \le 5$.

> The domain can be determined by solving the equation $25 - x^2 \ge 0$, but it is simpler to use our knowledge of semicircles.

b

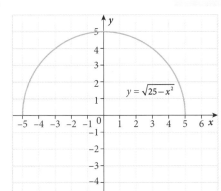

$y = \sqrt{25 - x^2}$

→ PRACTICE

1 Describe the function $y = \sqrt{64 - x^2}$.

2 Write the equation of this semicircle.

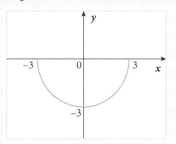

3 a What is the domain and range of $f(x) = \sqrt{16 - x^2}$?

b Draw the graph of $y = f(x)$.

4* Find the domain and range of the function $y = -\sqrt{36 - x^2}$.

Answers ⊃ p. 50

---

**A QUICK NOTE!** To help you study effectively we have made the **Examples** and **Practice** questions with the same numbers very similar to each other or you will require very similar skills to solve them.

- Please see the sample below: it shows that the **Example 1** question is similar to the **Practice 1** question and the **Example 2** question is similar to the **Practice 2** question.
  - » This is to enable you to **practise** what you have just read in an **Example**.
  - » You can also refer to the **Examples** when you are answering the **Practice** questions as their worked solutions and tips will help you answer the questions.

- The **Practice** questions that have an **asterisk (*)** are different to the other **Practice** questions. They do not match any particular **Example** but are designed to provide you with extra practice.
  - » You can see in the sample below that the **Practice 3** question is a different type to the other questions and is not directly related to any example. It is to give you further practice.

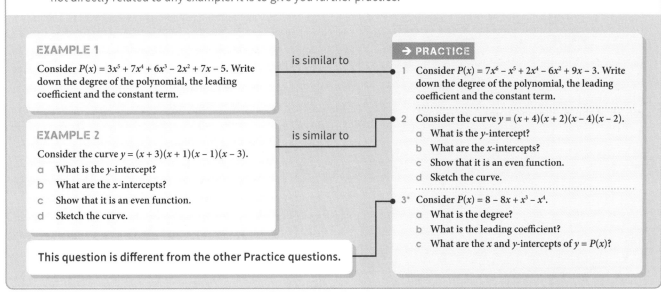

### EXAMPLE 1

Consider $P(x) = 3x^5 + 7x^4 + 6x^3 - 2x^2 + 7x - 5$. Write down the degree of the polynomial, the leading coefficient and the constant term.

*is similar to*

### EXAMPLE 2

Consider the curve $y = (x + 3)(x + 1)(x - 1)(x - 3)$.

a What is the $y$-intercept?

b What are the $x$-intercepts?

c Show that it is an even function.

d Sketch the curve.

*is similar to*

This question is different from the other Practice questions.

→ PRACTICE

1 Consider $P(x) = 7x^6 - x^5 + 2x^4 - 6x^2 + 9x - 3$. Write down the degree of the polynomial, the leading coefficient and the constant term.

2 Consider the curve $y = (x + 4)(x + 2)(x - 4)(x - 2)$.

a What is the $y$-intercept?

b What are the $x$-intercepts?

c Show that it is an even function.

d Sketch the curve.

3* Consider $P(x) = 8 - 8x + x^3 - x^4$.

a What is the degree?

b What is the leading coefficient?

c What are the $x$ and $y$-intercepts of $y = P(x)$?

Now for the real thing! The following questions are modelled on the types of questions you will face in the yearly examination in Year 11. Think about it: if you get extensive practice at answering these sorts of questions, you will be more confident in answering them in the yearly examination. It makes sense, doesn't it?

Remember the Answer section is located straight after this section so that you can check the answers readily. There are worked solutions and also ticks that indicate the mark allocation for all questions. Both these features will help you to strive for full marks.

Make sure also that when you check your work you highlight any questions you found difficult and earmark these areas for extra study.

## Total marks: 50

### PART A

(Suggested time: 15 minutes)

(1 mark each)

1  What are the solutions to $x^2 + 10x - 24 = 0$?

 A   $x = 4$ and $x = 6$          B   $x = -4$ and $x = -6$
 C   $x = -2$ and $x = 12$       D   $x = 2$ and $x = -12$

2  Which of these is equal to $\dfrac{1}{\sqrt{5}-3}$?

 A   $\dfrac{\sqrt{5}+3}{2}$          B   $\dfrac{\sqrt{5}-3}{2}$

 C   $\dfrac{-\sqrt{5}+3}{4}$          D   $\dfrac{-\sqrt{5}-3}{4}$

3  Which is **not** the graph of a function?

 A 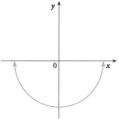     B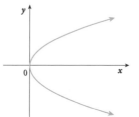

 C 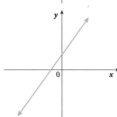     D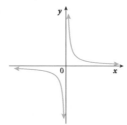

4  Which of these relations is **not** one-to-one?

 A 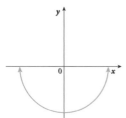     B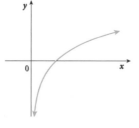

C 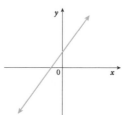     D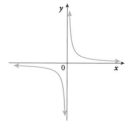

5  Which is an odd function?

 A   $y = x^2$          B   $y = \dfrac{1}{x}$

 C   $y = x^3 + 1$          D   $y = x^0$

6  What is the range of the function $y = \sqrt{9 - x^2}$?

 A   $-3 \le y \le 3$          B   $y \ge 3$
 C   $0 \le y \le 3$          D   $-3 \le y \le 0$

7  Which is the graph of $y = |x - 2|$?

 A 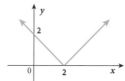     B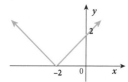

 C 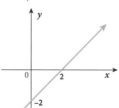     D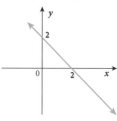

8  If $f(x) = \begin{cases} x^2 + 1 & \text{for } x \ge 0 \\ -x & \text{for } x < 0 \end{cases}$ what is the value of $f(-2)$?

 A   $-2$          B   $-5$          C   $2$          D   $5$

9  What is the equation of this circle?

 A   $(x - 2)^2 + (y + 1)^2 = 3$
 B   $(x + 2)^2 + (y - 1)^2 = 3$
 C   $(x - 2)^2 + (y + 1)^2 = 9$
 D   $(x + 2)^2 + (y - 1)^2 = 9$

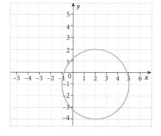

10 If $f(x) = 2 - 5x$ and $g(x) = x^2$, what is $g(f(x))$?

    **A**   $2x^2 - 5x^3$          **B**   $4 - 25x^2$

    **C**   $2 - 5x^2$             **D**   $(2 - 5x)^2$

11 Which of these could be the graph of
$y = x(x - 2)(x + 4)$?

   **A** 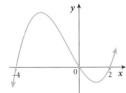    **B**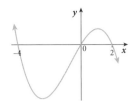

   **C** 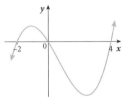    **D**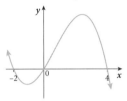

12 The discriminant of a particular quadratic expression is 9. How could the roots be described?

    **A**   real, rational and equal

    **B**   real, rational but not equal

    **C**   real, but not rational

    **D**   not real

## PART B
(Suggested time: 50 minutes)

Show all working.

13 Simplify 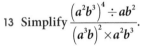.      (2 marks)

14 Find integers $x$ and $y$ such that
$\left(6 - \sqrt{3}\right)^2 = x + y\sqrt{3}$.      (2 marks)

15 Express $\dfrac{2}{x^2 + 2x} - \dfrac{3}{x^2 + 3x}$ as a single fraction in simplest form.      (2 marks)

16 The graph shows the cost of producing gift baskets and the return from their sale.

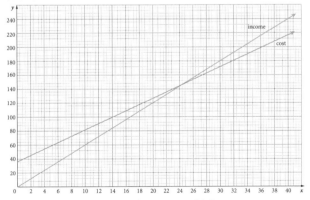

   **a**   How much is each gift basket sold for?    (1 mark)

   **b**   What is the equation of the line representing the cost?    (2 marks)

   **c**   What is the break-even point?    (1 mark)

17 Solve $2x^2 - 6x + 1 = 0$, giving the answers in simplest surd form.      (2 marks)

18 Consider $P(x) = 2x^4 - 5x^3 + 7x^2 - 3x - 1$.

   **a**   What is the degree of the polynomial?    (1 mark)

   **b**   What is the leading coefficient?    (1 mark)

19 Find the equation of the line that is perpendicular to the line $y = 1 - 3x$ and which meets it on the $y$-axis.      (2 marks)

20 Without sketching, determine whether the curve $y = 3x^2 - 8x + 5$ will cross the $x$-axis.      (2 marks)

21  **a**   Sketch $y = |4x + 3|$.    (1 mark)

   **b**   Write down the solutions of $|4x + 3| = 5$.    (1 mark)

22 Given $f(x) = x^2 + x$:

   **a**   find $f(x + h) - f(x)$    (1 mark)

   **b**   simplify $\dfrac{f(x+h) - f(x)}{h}$    (1 mark)

23 Find the equation of the straight line through $(3, -3)$ and $(-1, 5)$.      (2 marks)

24 A function is defined as $f(x) = \begin{cases} x+1 & \text{for } x < 0 \\ 1 & \text{for } 0 \leq x < 1 \\ x & \text{for } x \geq 1 \end{cases}$

   **a**   Evaluate $f(2) + f(-2)$.    (1 mark)

   **b**   Sketch $y = f(x)$.    (2 marks)

25  **a**   Express $y = x^2 - 10x + 23$ in the form $y = (x - p)^2 + q$.    (1 mark)

   **b**   What are the coordinates of the vertex of the parabola?    (1 mark)

   **c**   Will the parabola cut the $x$-axis? Justify your answer.    (1 mark)

26 If $f(x) = x^2 - 1$ and $g(x) = 1 - x$, find:

   **a**   $f(x) - g(x)$    (1 mark)

   **b**   $\dfrac{f(x)}{g(x)}$    (1 mark)

   **c**   $f(g(x))$    (2 marks)

27 Given $f(x) = 2x^2 - 8$ determine the domain and range of the function.      (2 marks)

28 Find the coordinates of the centre and the length of the radius of the circle $x^2 + y^2 = 8x - 6y$.      (2 marks)

### ALGEBRAIC TECHNIQUES

**1 Revision—basic algebra ⊃ p. 4**

1  $9mn - 4m + n - 6n + 7m$
   $= \mathbf{9mn + 3m - 5n}$

2  $6p(4p - 1) - 5(3p^2 + 5p - 2)$
   $= 24p^2 - 6p - 15p^2 - 25p + 10$
   $= \mathbf{9p^2 - 31p + 10}$

3  $(5a + 2b)^2 = (5a)^2 + 2 \times 5a \times 2b + (2b)^2$
   $\qquad = \mathbf{25a^2 + 20ab + 4b^2}$

4  $(3x + 2)(2x - 5) + (5x - 1)(x + 4)$
   $= 6x^2 - 15x + 4x - 10 + 5x^2 + 20x - x - 4$
   $= \mathbf{11x^2 + 8x - 14}$

5  $(n + 3)(n - 3) - (n - 2)^2$
   $= n^2 - 9 - (n^2 - 4n + 4)$
   $= n^2 - 9 - n^2 + 4n - 4$
   $= \mathbf{4n - 13}$

6  $(3m + 5n)(m^2 - n) - (4mn - 2)$
   $= 3m^3 - 3mn + 5m^2n - 5n^2 - 4mn + 2$
   $= \mathbf{3m^3 - 7mn + 5m^2n - 5n^2 + 2}$

**2 Review of factorisation ⊃ p. 5**

1  $p^2 + pq - p - q = p(p + q) - 1(p + q)$
   $\qquad\qquad\qquad = \mathbf{(p + q)(p - 1)}$

2  $x^3 + 12x^2 + 36x = x(x^2 + 12x + 36)$
   $\qquad\qquad\qquad = \mathbf{x(x + 6)^2}$

3  $1000x^3 - y^3 = \mathbf{(10x - y)(100x^2 + 10xy + y^2)}$

4  $3x^2 + 23x - 8 = 3x^2 + 24x - x - 8$
   $\qquad\qquad\quad = 3x(x + 8) - 1(x + 8)$
   $\qquad\qquad\quad = \mathbf{(x + 8)(3x - 1)}$

5  $k^2 - 9 + 7km - 21m = (k + 3)(k - 3) + 7m(k - 3)$
   $\qquad\qquad\qquad\qquad = \mathbf{(k - 3)(k + 3 + 7m)}$

6  $14x(2x + 3)^3 + 35x^2(2x + 3)^2$
   $= 7x(2x + 3)^2[2(2x + 3) + 5x]$
   $= 7x(2x + 3)^2(9x + 6)$
   $= \mathbf{21x(3x + 2)(2x + 3)^2}$

**3 Index laws ⊃ p. 6**

1  $(2a^3)^2 \times 5(a^2)^7 = 4a^6 \times 5a^{14}$
   $\qquad\qquad\qquad = \mathbf{20a^{20}}$

2  $\dfrac{35x^3y^8 \div 7x^2y^6}{5x \times 2xy} = \dfrac{5xy^2}{10x^2y}$
   $\qquad\qquad\qquad = \dfrac{\mathbf{y}}{\mathbf{2x}}$

3  $a^3b^7 - a^4b^6 = \mathbf{a^3b^6(b - a)}$

4  $\dfrac{1}{x\sqrt{x}} = \dfrac{1}{x \times x^{\frac{1}{2}}}$
   $\qquad = \dfrac{1}{x^{\frac{3}{2}}}$
   $\qquad = \mathbf{x^{-\frac{3}{2}}}$

5  $27^x \times 3^x = \dfrac{1}{9}$
   $(3^3)^x \times 3^x = \dfrac{1}{3^2}$
   $3^{3x} \times 3^x = 3^{-2}$
   $\qquad 3^{4x} = 3^{-2}$
   $\qquad 4x = -2$
   $\qquad x = \mathbf{-\dfrac{1}{2}}$

6  $8^{k-5} \times 4^{3-k} = 1$
   $(2^3)^{k-5} \times (2^2)^{3-k} = 1$
   $2^{3k-15} \times 2^{6-2k} = 2^0$
   $\qquad 2^{k-9} = 2^0$
   $\qquad k - 9 = 0$
   $\qquad k = \mathbf{9}$

**4 Surds ⊃ p. 7**

1  $4\sqrt{6} + \sqrt{6} = \mathbf{5\sqrt{6}}$

2  $8 - 3\sqrt{7} + 7\sqrt{2} - 2 + \sqrt{7}$
   $= \mathbf{6 - 2\sqrt{7} + 7\sqrt{2}}$

3  $3\sqrt{6} \times 7\sqrt{6} = 21 \times 6$
   $\qquad\qquad = \mathbf{126}$

4  $3\sqrt{40} = 3 \times \sqrt{4} \times \sqrt{10}$
   $\qquad = 3 \times 2 \times \sqrt{10}$
   $\qquad = \mathbf{6\sqrt{10}}$

5  $\sqrt{98} + \sqrt{72} = \sqrt{49} \times \sqrt{2} + \sqrt{36} \times \sqrt{2}$
   $\qquad\qquad = 7\sqrt{2} + 6\sqrt{2}$
   $\qquad\qquad = \mathbf{13\sqrt{2}}$

6  $2\sqrt{6} \times 3\sqrt{2} = 6\sqrt{12}$
   $\qquad\qquad = 6 \times \sqrt{4} \times \sqrt{3}$
   $\qquad\qquad = \mathbf{12\sqrt{3}}$

**5 Rationalising the denominator ⊃ p. 8**

1  $(5 - \sqrt{3})(2\sqrt{3} - 4) = 10\sqrt{3} - 20 - 6 + 4\sqrt{3}$
   $\qquad\qquad\qquad\quad = \mathbf{14\sqrt{3} - 26}$

2  $(2\sqrt{7} + 1)(2\sqrt{7} - 1) = 28 - 1$
   $\qquad\qquad\qquad\quad = \mathbf{27}$

3  $\dfrac{10}{\sqrt{5}} = \dfrac{10}{\sqrt{5}} \times \dfrac{\sqrt{5}}{\sqrt{5}}$

$\phantom{\dfrac{10}{\sqrt{5}}} = \dfrac{10\sqrt{5}}{5}$

$\phantom{\dfrac{10}{\sqrt{5}}} = \mathbf{2\sqrt{5}}$

4  $\dfrac{3}{4+\sqrt{7}} = \dfrac{3}{4+\sqrt{7}} \times \dfrac{4-\sqrt{7}}{4-\sqrt{7}}$

$\phantom{\dfrac{3}{4+\sqrt{7}}} = \dfrac{3\left(4-\sqrt{7}\right)}{16-7}$

$\phantom{\dfrac{3}{4+\sqrt{7}}} = \dfrac{3\left(4-\sqrt{7}\right)}{9}$

$\phantom{\dfrac{3}{4+\sqrt{7}}} = \dfrac{\mathbf{4-\sqrt{7}}}{\mathbf{3}}$

5  $\dfrac{\sqrt{2}-\sqrt{3}}{\sqrt{2}+\sqrt{3}} = \dfrac{\sqrt{2}-\sqrt{3}}{\sqrt{2}+\sqrt{3}} \times \dfrac{\sqrt{2}-\sqrt{3}}{\sqrt{2}-\sqrt{3}}$

$\phantom{\dfrac{\sqrt{2}-\sqrt{3}}{\sqrt{2}+\sqrt{3}}} = \dfrac{2-2\sqrt{6}+3}{2-3}$

$\phantom{\dfrac{\sqrt{2}-\sqrt{3}}{\sqrt{2}+\sqrt{3}}} = \dfrac{5-2\sqrt{6}}{-1}$

$\phantom{\dfrac{\sqrt{2}-\sqrt{3}}{\sqrt{2}+\sqrt{3}}} = \mathbf{-5+2\sqrt{6}}$

6  $\dfrac{7}{5-3\sqrt{2}} = a + \sqrt{b}$

$\dfrac{7}{5-3\sqrt{2}} = \dfrac{7}{5-3\sqrt{2}} \times \dfrac{5+3\sqrt{2}}{5+3\sqrt{2}}$

$\phantom{\dfrac{7}{5-3\sqrt{2}}} = \dfrac{7\left(5+3\sqrt{2}\right)}{25-18}$

$\phantom{\dfrac{7}{5-3\sqrt{2}}} = \dfrac{7\left(5+3\sqrt{2}\right)}{7}$

$\phantom{\dfrac{7}{5-3\sqrt{2}}} = 5 + 3\sqrt{2}$

$\phantom{\dfrac{7}{5-3\sqrt{2}}} = 5 + \sqrt{9} \times \sqrt{2}$

$\phantom{\dfrac{7}{5-3\sqrt{2}}} = 5 + \sqrt{18}$

$\therefore \mathbf{a = 5 \text{ and } b = 18}$

## 6 Algebraic fractions ⊃ p. 9

1  $\dfrac{x^2+4x+3}{x^2-4x-21} = \dfrac{(x+3)(x+1)}{(x-7)(x+3)}$

$\phantom{\dfrac{x^2+4x+3}{x^2-4x-21}} = \dfrac{\mathbf{x+1}}{\mathbf{x-7}}$

2  $\dfrac{8m-7}{15} - \dfrac{3m+7}{10} = \dfrac{2(8m-7)-3(3m+7)}{30}$

$\phantom{\dfrac{8m-7}{15} - \dfrac{3m+7}{10}} = \dfrac{16m-14-9m-21}{30}$

$\phantom{\dfrac{8m-7}{15} - \dfrac{3m+7}{10}} = \dfrac{\mathbf{7m-35}}{\mathbf{30}}$

3  $\dfrac{2a+3}{a^2+a} + \dfrac{a-4}{a^2-1} = \dfrac{2a+3}{a(a+1)} + \dfrac{a-4}{(a+1)(a-1)}$

$\phantom{\dfrac{2a+3}{a^2+a} + \dfrac{a-4}{a^2-1}} = \dfrac{(2a+3)(a-1)+a(a-4)}{a(a+1)(a-1)}$

$\phantom{\dfrac{2a+3}{a^2+a} + \dfrac{a-4}{a^2-1}} = \dfrac{2a^2+a-3+a^2-4a}{a(a+1)(a-1)}$

$\phantom{\dfrac{2a+3}{a^2+a} + \dfrac{a-4}{a^2-1}} = \dfrac{3a^2-3a-3}{a(a+1)(a-1)}$

$\phantom{\dfrac{2a+3}{a^2+a} + \dfrac{a-4}{a^2-1}} = \dfrac{\mathbf{3\left(a^2-a-1\right)}}{\mathbf{a(a+1)(a-1)}}$

4  $\dfrac{x^2+4x}{3x+7} \times \dfrac{5x+10}{x^2+6x+8} = \dfrac{x(x+4)}{3x+7} \times \dfrac{5(x+2)}{(x+4)(x+2)}$

$\phantom{\dfrac{x^2+4x}{3x+7} \times \dfrac{5x+10}{x^2+6x+8}} = \dfrac{\mathbf{5x}}{\mathbf{3x+7}}$

5  $\dfrac{x^2+6x}{x^2+5x-6} \div \dfrac{x^2+9x+8}{x^2-1} = \dfrac{x^2+6x}{x^2+5x-6} \times \dfrac{x^2-1}{x^2+9x+8}$

$\phantom{\dfrac{x^2+6x}{x^2+5x-6} \div \dfrac{x^2+9x+8}{x^2-1}} = \dfrac{x(x+6)}{(x+6)(x-1)} \times \dfrac{(x+1)(x-1)}{(x+8)(x+1)}$

$\phantom{\dfrac{x^2+6x}{x^2+5x-6} \div \dfrac{x^2+9x+8}{x^2-1}} = \dfrac{\mathbf{x}}{\mathbf{x+8}}$

6  $\dfrac{x^2+5x-14}{x^2+2x-8} \times \dfrac{x^2-x-20}{x^2+2x-35} = \dfrac{(x+7)(x-2)}{(x+4)(x-2)} \times \dfrac{(x-5)(x+4)}{(x+7)(x-5)}$

$\phantom{\dfrac{x^2+5x-14}{x^2+2x-8} \times \dfrac{x^2-x-20}{x^2+2x-35}} = \mathbf{1}$

## 7 Quadratic equations ⊃ p. 10

1  $x^2 - 10x + 16 = 0$
$(x - 8)(x - 2) = 0$
$x - 8 = 0 \quad \text{or} \quad x - 2 = 0$
$\quad \mathbf{x = 8} \quad \textbf{or} \quad \mathbf{x = 2}$

2  $(x + 3)(x - 4) = 18$
$\quad x^2 - x - 12 = 18$
$\quad x^2 - x - 30 = 0$
$(x - 6)(x + 5) = 0$
$x - 6 = 0 \quad \text{or} \quad x + 5 = 0$
$\quad \mathbf{x = 6} \quad \textbf{or} \quad \mathbf{x = -5}$

3  $\quad 4x^2 + 28x = -47$
$4x^2 + 28x + 49 = -47 + 49$
$\quad (2x + 7)^2 = 2$
$\quad 2x + 7 = \pm\sqrt{2}$
$\quad 2x = -7 \pm \sqrt{2}$
$\quad \mathbf{x = \dfrac{-7 \pm \sqrt{2}}{2}}$

4  $x^2 - 9x + 11 = 0$
$a = 1, \quad b = -9, \quad c = 11$

$x = \dfrac{-b \pm \sqrt{b^2 - 4ac}}{2a}$

$\phantom{x} = \dfrac{-(-9) \pm \sqrt{(-9)^2 - 4 \times 1 \times 11}}{2 \times 1}$

$\phantom{x} = \dfrac{9 \pm \sqrt{37}}{2}$

$x = \dfrac{9 + \sqrt{37}}{2} \quad \text{or} \quad x = \dfrac{9 - \sqrt{37}}{2}$

$x = 7.541\,381\,26\ldots \quad \text{or} \quad x = 1.458\,618\,73\ldots$

$\mathbf{x = 7.541} \quad \textbf{or} \quad \mathbf{x = 1.459} \quad \text{correct to 3 decimal places}$

5  $2x^2 - 8x - 3 = 0$

$a = 2, \quad b = -8, \quad c = -3$

$x = \dfrac{-b \pm \sqrt{b^2 - 4ac}}{2a}$

$= \dfrac{-(-8) \pm \sqrt{(-8)^2 - 4 \times 2 \times -3}}{2 \times 2}$

$= \dfrac{8 \pm \sqrt{88}}{4}$

$= \dfrac{8 \pm \sqrt{4} \times \sqrt{22}}{4}$

$= \dfrac{8 \pm 2\sqrt{22}}{4}$

$= \dfrac{2\left(4 \pm \sqrt{22}\right)}{4}$

$= \dfrac{\mathbf{4 \pm \sqrt{22}}}{\mathbf{2}}$

6  $\qquad\qquad 7x^2 = 25x + 12$

$\qquad\qquad 7x^2 - 25x - 12 = 0$

$\qquad 7x^2 - 28x + 3x - 12 = 0$

$\qquad 7x(x - 4) + 3(x - 4) = 0$

$\qquad\qquad (x - 4)(7x + 3) = 0$

$x - 4 = 0 \quad$ or $\quad 7x + 3 = 0$

$\quad\; x = 4 \quad$ or $\qquad 7x = -3$

$\quad\; \mathbf{x = 4} \quad$ **or** $\qquad \mathbf{x = -\dfrac{3}{7}}$

## INTRODUCTION TO FUNCTIONS

### 1 Relations and functions ⊃ p. 11

1  $y = 8x + 7$

| $x$ | 0 | 1 | 2 | 3 | 4 |
|---|---|---|---|---|---|
| $y$ | 7 | 15 | 23 | 31 | 39 |

2  To be a function there can only be one value of $y$ for every value of $x$ so **this is a function**. It doesn't matter how many values of $x$ have the same value of $y$.

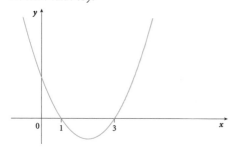

3  $(1, 1), (4, 2), (9, 3), (1, -1), (9, -3)$ and $(4, -2)$. **This relation is not a function** because when $x = 1$ there are two different values of $y$ and when $x = 4$ there are two different values of $y$. To be a function there can only be one value of $y$ for every value of $x$.

### 2 Function notation ⊃ p. 12

1  $f(x) = 2x^2 + x - 4$

a  $f(2) = 2 \times 2^2 + 2 - 4$

$\qquad = \mathbf{6}$

b  $f(-3) = 2 \times (-3)^2 + (-3) - 4$

$\qquad = \mathbf{11}$

c  $f\left(\dfrac{1}{2}\right) = 2 \times \left(\dfrac{1}{2}\right)^2 + \dfrac{1}{2} - 4$

$\qquad = \mathbf{-3}$

2  $f(x) = \begin{cases} 3x - 4 & \text{for } x < 2 \\ x & \text{for } 2 \le x \le 3 \\ x^2 - 6 & \text{for } x > 3 \end{cases}$

a  $f(5) = 5^2 - 6$

$\qquad = \mathbf{19}$

b  $f(-1) = 3 \times (-1) - 4$

$\qquad = \mathbf{-7}$

c  $f(2.5) = \mathbf{2.5}$

3  $f(x) = x^2 + 4x$

$\dfrac{f(x+h) - f(x)}{h} = \dfrac{(x+h)^2 + 4(x+h) - (x^2 + 4x)}{h}$

$= \dfrac{x^2 + 2xh + h^2 + 4x + 4h - x^2 - 4x}{h}$

$= \dfrac{2xh + h^2 + 4h}{h}$

$= \dfrac{h(2x + h + 4)}{h}$

$= \mathbf{2x + h + 4}$

4.  $p(n) = 3n^2 - 5n$

$p(-1) = 3 \times (-1)^2 - 5 \times (-1)$

$\qquad = \mathbf{8}$

5  $f(u) = \dfrac{u - 1}{u + 1}$

$f\left(\dfrac{1}{u}\right) = \dfrac{\dfrac{1}{u} - 1}{\dfrac{1}{u} + 1}$

$= \dfrac{\dfrac{1 - u}{u}}{\dfrac{1 + u}{u}}$

$= \dfrac{1 - u}{u} \times \dfrac{u}{1 + u}$

$= \dfrac{1 - u}{1 + u}$

$= \dfrac{-(u - 1)}{u + 1}$

$= \mathbf{-f(u)}$

### 3 Domain and range ⊃ p. 13

1  $y = \dfrac{1}{x + 3}$

Now $x + 3 \ne 0$

$\qquad x \ne -3$

**The domain is all real $x$ except $x = -3$.**

2  $2x - y + 3 = 0, -1 \le x \le 5$

When $x = -1$,

$2 \times (-1) - y + 3 = 0$

$\qquad\qquad y = 1$

When $x = 5$,
$2 \times 5 - y + 3 = 0$
$y = 13$
**The range is $1 \leq y \leq 13$.**

3　$y = x^2 - 7$
**domain: all real $x$**
Now $x^2 \geq 0$ for all real values of $x$.
So $x^2 - 7 \geq -7$ for all $x$.
**The range is $y \geq -7$.**

4　$f(x) = 1 - 2x$, $(-4, 4]$
$f(-4) = 1 - 2 \times (-4)$
$\quad = 9$
$f(4) = 1 - 2 \times 4$
$\quad = -7$
**The range is $[-7, 9)$.**

5　$y = \sqrt{1 - x^2}$
Now $1 - x^2 \geq 0$
$\quad \therefore x^2 \leq 1$
$\quad$ So $-1 \leq x \leq 1$
**The domain is $-1 \leq x \leq 1$.**
When $x = \pm 1$, $y = 0$
When $x = 0$, $y = 1$
**The range is $0 \leq y \leq 1$.**

**4 Types of relations and functions ➲ p. 14**

1　(2, 1), (5, 3), (3, 1), (4, 3), (1, 1), (6, 2)

The relation is a function because there is just one value of $y$ for each value of $x$. **It is a one-to-many function** because there is more than one value of $x$ for some values of $y$.

2　**The vertical line test shows that there is more than one value of $y$ for a value of $x$ so it is not a function.**
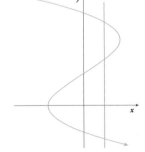

3　**This function is not one-to-one.**
The horizontal line test shows that there are values of $y$ for which there are more than one value of $x$.
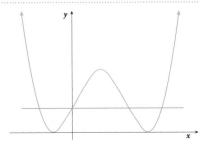

4　$y = 2x^2 - 3$ is a function because there is only one value of $y$ for each value of $x$. **It is a one-to-many function** because there is more than one value of $x$ for some values of $y$.

**5 Even and odd functions ➲ pp. 14–15**

1　$f(x) = x^3 + 2$
$f(-x) = (-x)^3 + 2$
$\quad = -x^3 + 2$
**The function is neither even nor odd.**

2　$f(x) = x + \dfrac{1}{x}$
$f(-x) = -x + \dfrac{1}{-x}$
$\quad = -x - \dfrac{1}{x}$
$\quad = -\left(x + \dfrac{1}{x}\right)$
$\quad = -f(x)$
$\therefore$ **the function is odd.**

3　$f(x) = x^4 - 2x^2$
$f(-x) = (-x)^4 - 2(-x)^2$
$\quad = x^4 - 2x^2$
$\quad = f(x)$
$\therefore$ **the function is even.**

4　a
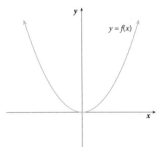

b
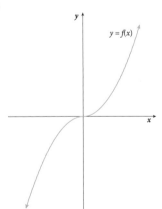

**6 Sum, difference, product and quotient of functions ➲ p. 15**

1　$f(x) + g(x) = 2x^2 + 3x - 8 + x^2 + 4x + 3$
$\quad = \mathbf{3x^2 + 7x - 5}$

2　$f(x) - g(x) = 2x^3 + 5x - 4 - (6 + 2x - 3x^2)$
$\quad = 2x^3 + 5x - 4 - 6 - 2x + 3x^2$
$\quad = \mathbf{2x^3 + 3x^2 + 3x - 10}$

3   $f(x) \times g(x) = (3x - 7)(x^4 - 9x^2 - 4x)$
$$= 3x^5 - 27x^3 - 12x^2 - 7x^4 + 63x^2 + 28x$$
$$= \mathbf{3x^5 - 7x^4 - 27x^3 + 51x^2 + 28x}$$

4   $f(x) \div g(x) = \dfrac{x^2 - 13x + 40}{x^2 - 5x - 24}$
$$= \dfrac{(x-8)(x-5)}{(x-8)(x+3)}$$
$$= \dfrac{\boldsymbol{x-5}}{\boldsymbol{x+3}}$$

5   $f(x) \times g(x) = \dfrac{x}{1-x^2}\left(x - \dfrac{1}{x}\right)$
$$= \dfrac{x^2}{1-x^2} - \dfrac{1}{1-x^2}$$
$$= \dfrac{x^2 - 1}{1 - x^2}$$
$$= \mathbf{-1}$$

## 7 Composite functions ➲ p. 15

1   $f(x) = x^2 - 3x \quad g(x) = 2x - 7$
$f(g(x)) = (2x - 7)^2 - 3(2x - 7)$
$$= 4x^2 - 28x + 49 - 6x + 21$$
$$= \mathbf{4x^2 - 34x + 70}$$

2   $f(x) = \dfrac{x-4}{x+1} \quad g(x) = 3 + \dfrac{1}{x}$
$g(f(x)) = 3 + \dfrac{1}{\dfrac{x-4}{x+1}}$
$$= 3 + \dfrac{x+1}{x-4}$$
$$= \dfrac{3(x-4) + x + 1}{x-4}$$
$$= \dfrac{3x - 12 + x + 1}{x - 4}$$
$$= \dfrac{\boldsymbol{4x - 11}}{\boldsymbol{x - 4}}$$

3   $f(x) = \sqrt{5-x} \quad g(x) = x^2 - 4$
$f(g(x)) = \sqrt{5 - (x^2 - 4)}$
$$= \sqrt{5 - x^2 + 4}$$
$$= \sqrt{9 - x^2}$$
Now $9 - x^2 \geq 0$
$$\therefore x^2 \leq 9$$
**domain: $-3 \leq x \leq 3$**
When $x = 3$, $y = 0$
When $x = 0$, $y = 3$
**range: $0 \leq y \leq 3$**

4   $f(x) = x^2 - 2x \quad g(x) = x + 2$
$f(g(x)) = (x + 2)^2 - 2(x + 2)$
$$= x^2 + 4x + 4 - 2x - 4$$
$$= x^2 + 2x$$
$g(f(x)) = x^2 - 2x + 2$
$f(g(x)) - g(f(x)) = x^2 + 2x - (x^2 - 2x + 2)$
$$= x^2 + 2x - x^2 + 2x - 2$$
$$= \mathbf{4x - 2}$$

## 8 If $f(x) = 0$ ➲ p. 17

1   $f(x) = 0$
$$x^3 + 3x^2 - 10x = 0$$
$$x(x^2 + 3x - 10) = 0$$
$$x(x + 5)(x - 2) = 0$$
$$x = 0 \text{ or } x = -5 \text{ or } x = 2$$
**The curve meets the $x$-axis at $(0, 0)$, $(-5, 0)$ and $(2, 0)$.**

2   $y = x^2 + 3$
Now $x^2 \geq 0$ for all real values of $x$.
So $x^2 + 3 \geq 3$
**As $y \geq 3$ for all values of $x$ the curve does not cut the $x$-axis.**

3   $y = -x^2 + 6x - 5$
At $P$ and at $Q$ $y = 0$
i.e.      $0 = -x^2 + 6x - 5$
$$x^2 - 6x + 5 = 0$$
$$(x - 1)(x - 5) = 0$$
$$x = 1 \text{ or } x = 5$$
**So $P$ is the point $(1, 0)$ and**
**$Q$ is $(5, 0)$.**

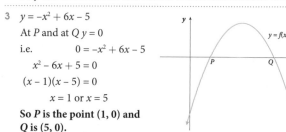

4   a   $y = x^4 - kx^3 + 3x^2$
When $x = 1$, $y = 0$
$$0 = 1^4 - k \times 1^3 + 3 \times 1^2$$
$$0 = 4 - k$$
$$\mathbf{k = 4}$$
   b   $y = x^4 - 4x^3 + 3x^2$
When $y = 0$,
$$x^4 - 4x^3 + 3x^2 = 0$$
$$x^2(x^2 - 4x + 3) = 0$$
$$x^2(x - 1)(x - 3) = 0$$
$$x = 0, \quad x = 1 \quad \text{or} \quad x = 3$$
**The curve also meets the $x$-axis at $x = 0$ and $x = 3$.**

## LINEAR, QUADRATIC AND CUBIC FUNCTIONS

### 1 Direct variation ➲ p. 18

1   Let $b$ be the number of bolts and $s$ the number of shelves.
So $b = ks$ where $k$ is a constant.
When $s = 25$, $b = 500$
$$500 = k \times 25$$
$$k = 20$$
$$\therefore b = 20s$$
When $s = 15$,
$$b = 20 \times 15$$
$$= 300$$
**300 bolts are needed for 15 bookshelves.**

2   a   **In 8 minutes 640 litres have flowed into the tank.**
   b   rate $= \dfrac{640}{8}$ L/min
$$= \mathbf{80 \text{ L/min}}$$
   c   $\boldsymbol{V = 80m}$

3  a  **300 litres is about 66 gallons.**

   b  **90 gallons is about 410 litres.**

   c  40 gallons is about 180 litres.

   total capacity $\approx 25 \times 180$ L

   $= 4500$ L

   d  **Yes, Katy is correct.** There is a direct variation relationship between the number of litres and the number of gallons.

2 Gradient and *y*-intercept ⊃ p. 19

1  $y = -2x$

   gradient: $m = -2$

   *y*-intercept: $c = 0$

2  $m = \dfrac{3}{5}, \quad c = 7$

   The equation is $y = \dfrac{3}{5}x + 7$.

3  $m = -\dfrac{3}{2}, \quad c = 4$

   $y = -\dfrac{3}{2}x + 4$

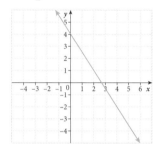

4  $y = 3x - 2$

   gradient: $m = 3$

   *y*-intercept: $c = -2$

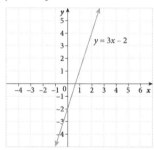

5  $3x + 4y - 2 = 0$

   $4y = -3x + 2$

   $y = -\dfrac{3}{4}x + \dfrac{1}{2}$

   **So the gradient is $-\dfrac{3}{4}$ and the *y*-intercept is $\dfrac{1}{2}$.**

3 Formulas for the gradient and the equation of a line ⊃ p. 20

1  $(4, 3), \quad (5, -2)$

   $m = \dfrac{y_2 - y_1}{x_2 - x_1}$

   $= \dfrac{-2 - 3}{5 - 4}$

   $= -5$

2  $P(-3, -2), \quad Q(1, y), \quad m = \dfrac{5}{2}$

   $m = \dfrac{y_2 - y_1}{x_2 - x_1}$

   $\dfrac{5}{2} = \dfrac{y - (-2)}{1 - (-3)}$

   $= \dfrac{y + 2}{4}$

   So $y + 2 = 10$

   $y = 8$

3  $(2, 5), \quad m = 3$

   $y - y_1 = m(x - x_1)$

   $y - 5 = 3(x - 2)$

   $y - 5 = 3x - 6$

   $y = 3x - 1$

4  $m = -2, \quad (7, 0)$

   $y - y_1 = m(x - x_1)$

   $y - 0 = -2(x - 7)$

   $y = -2x + 14$

   The *y*-intercept is 14.

   The line cuts the *y*-axis at **(0, 14)**.

5  $(-6, -7), \quad (-3, 8)$

   $m = \dfrac{y_2 - y_1}{x_2 - x_1}$

   $= \dfrac{8 - (-7)}{-3 - (-6)}$

   $= 5$

   $y - y_1 = m(x - x_1)$

   $y - (-7) = 5(x - (-6))$

   $y + 7 = 5x + 30$

   $y = 5x + 23$

6  $(-3, -1), \quad (4, 13)$

   $m = \dfrac{y_2 - y_1}{x_2 - x_1}$

   $= \dfrac{13 - (-1)}{4 - (-3)}$

   $= 2$

   $y - y_1 = m(x - x_1)$

   $y - (-1) = 2(x - (-3))$

   $y + 1 = 2x + 6$

   $y = 2x + 5$

   When $x = 1$,

   $y = 2 \times 1 + 5$

   $= 7$

   **∴ the point (1, 7) lies on the line joining (-3, -1) to (4, 13).**

4 Parallel and perpendicular lines ⊃ p. 21

1  $y = -3x + 5$ has gradient $-3$.

   ∴ parallel line has gradient $-3$.

   $(-4, -1), \quad m = -3$

   $y - y_1 = m(x - x_1)$

   $y - (-1) = -3(x - (-4))$

   $y + 1 = -3x - 12$

   $y = -3x - 13$

**2**  $y = 3x + 4$

$m_1 = 3$

$y = 4 - \dfrac{x}{3}$

$\quad = -\dfrac{1}{3}x + 4$

$m_2 = -\dfrac{1}{3}$

Now $m_1 m_2 = 3 \times -\dfrac{1}{3}$

$\qquad\qquad = -1$

∴ **the lines are perpendicular.**

**3**  $2x - y - 3 = 0$

$\quad 2x - 3 = y$

The gradient is 2.

The perpendicular line has gradient $-\dfrac{1}{2}$.

$(5, -2), \qquad m = -\dfrac{1}{2}$

$y - y_1 = m(x - x_1)$

$y - (-2) = -\dfrac{1}{2}(x - 5)$

$y + 2 = -\dfrac{1}{2}x + 2\dfrac{1}{2}$

$y = -\dfrac{1}{2}x + \dfrac{1}{2}$

**4**  $P(5, 6), \quad Q(-3, 0)$

$m = \dfrac{y_2 - y_1}{x_2 - x_1}$

$\quad = \dfrac{0 - 6}{-3 - 5}$

$\quad = \dfrac{3}{4}$

$Q(-3, 0), \quad N(0, y)$

$m = \dfrac{y_2 - y_1}{x_2 - x_1}$

$\quad = \dfrac{y - 0}{0 - (-3)}$

$\quad = \dfrac{y}{3}$

Now $PQ$ is perpendicular to $QN$.

So $\dfrac{3}{4} \times \dfrac{y}{3} = -1$

$\dfrac{y}{4} = -1$

$y = -4$

**$N$ is the point $(0, -4)$.**

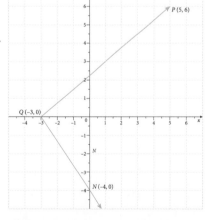

**5 Quadratic functions ⊃ p. 22**

**1  a  concave up**

  b  The vertex is **$(5, -4)$**.

  c  axis of symmetry: **$x = 5$**

  d  $y$-intercept = **21**

  e  The curve cuts the $x$-axis at **$(3, 0)$** and **$(7, 0)$**.

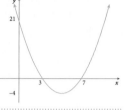

**2**  $y = x^2 - 1$ is concave up. It cuts the $x$-axis at $(-1, 0)$ and $(1, 0)$ and has $y$-intercept $-1$.

$y = 1 - \dfrac{x^2}{4}$ is concave down. It cuts the $x$-axis at $(-2, 0)$ and $(2, 0)$ and has $y$-intercept 1.

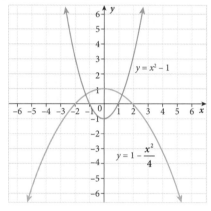

Both curves have the same axis of symmetry. $y = 1 - \dfrac{x^2}{4}$ is wider than $y = x^2 - 1$.

**3**  **The parabola is concave up.** Its turning point is at $(-2, -1)$ and the $y$-intercept, 4, is greater than the $y$-value of the vertex.

**6 Finding the intercepts and vertex ⊃ p. 24**

**1**  $y = x^2 - 6x - 16$

$y$-intercept = $-16$

$x^2 - 6x - 16 = 0$

$(x + 2)(x - 8) = 0$

$x + 2 = 0 \quad$ or $\quad x - 8 = 0$

$\qquad x = -2 \quad$ or $\qquad x = 8$

**The $x$-intercepts are $-2$ and 8.**

axis: $\quad x = \dfrac{-2 + 8}{2}$

$\qquad\qquad x = 3$

When $x = 3$,

$y = 3^2 - 6 \times 3 - 16$

$\quad = -25$

**The vertex is $(3, -25)$.**

**2**  $y = 9x^2 - 18x + 8$

When $y = 0$,

$9x^2 - 18x + 8 = 0$

$9x^2 - 18x + 9 = 1$

$(3x - 3)^2 = 1$

$3x - 3 = -1 \quad$ or $\quad 3x - 3 = 1$

$3x = 2 \quad$ or $\qquad 3x = 4$

$x = \dfrac{2}{3} \qquad$ *or* $\qquad x = 1\dfrac{1}{3}$

3 a $x^2 - 6x + 2 = 0$

$a = 1 \quad b = -6 \quad c = 2$

$x = \dfrac{-b \pm \sqrt{b^2 - 4ac}}{2a}$

$\phantom{x} = \dfrac{-(-6) \pm \sqrt{(-6)^2 - 4 \times 1 \times 2}}{2 \times 1}$

$\phantom{x} = \dfrac{6 \pm \sqrt{28}}{2}$

$\phantom{x} = \dfrac{6 \pm 2\sqrt{7}}{2}$

$\phantom{x} = \dfrac{2(3 \pm \sqrt{7})}{2}$

$\phantom{x} = 3 \pm \sqrt{7}$

The x-intercepts of the parabola are **$3 + \sqrt{7}$ and $3 - \sqrt{7}$.**

b axis: $x = \dfrac{3 + \sqrt{7} + 3 - \sqrt{7}}{2}$

$\phantom{axis:} x = 3$

When $x = 3$,

$y = 3^2 - 6 \times 3 + 2$

$\phantom{y} = -7$

The vertex is at **(3, –7).**

4 $y = 4x^2 - 16x + 7$

a The parabola is **concave up**.

b The parabola cuts the y-axis at **(0, 7)**.

c $4x^2 - 16x + 7 = 0$

$4x^2 - 2x - 14x + 7 = 0$

$2x(2x - 1) - 7(2x - 1) = 0$

$(2x - 1)(2x - 7) = 0$

$x = \dfrac{1}{2}$ or $x = 3\dfrac{1}{2}$

The parabola cuts the x-axis at $\left(\dfrac{1}{2}, 0\right)$ and $\left(3\dfrac{1}{2}, 0\right)$.

d axis: $x = \dfrac{\frac{1}{2} + 3\frac{1}{2}}{2}$

$\phantom{axis:} x = 2$

When $x = 2$,

$y = 4 \times 2^2 - 16 \times 2 + 7$

$\phantom{y} = -9$

The vertex is **(2, –9)**.

e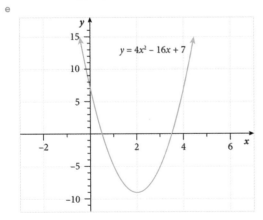

5 $x^2 + 8x + 25 = 0$

$x^2 + 8x + 16 + 9 = 0$

$(x + 4)^2 + 9 = 0$

Now $(x + 4)^2 \geq 0$ for all real values of x.

$(x + 4)^2 + 9 \geq 9$

**The minimum value of $x^2 + 8x + 25$ is 9.**

6 $y = -x^2 + 2x - 9$

$-x^2 + 2x - 9 = -(x^2 - 2x + 9)$

$\phantom{-x^2 + 2x - 9} = -(x^2 - 2x + 1 + 8)$

$\phantom{-x^2 + 2x - 9} = -((x - 1)^2 + 8)$

$\phantom{-x^2 + 2x - 9} = -(x - 1)^2 - 8$

∴ the vertex is (1, –8).

As the parabola is concave down the greatest value is –8.

**∴ $-x^2 + 2x - 9$ is always negative.**

## 7 The discriminant ⊃ p. 25

1 $4x^2 - 3x - 2 = 0$

$a = 4, \quad b = -3, \quad c = -2$

$\Delta = b^2 - 4ac$

$\phantom{\Delta} = (-3)^2 - 4 \times 4 \times -2$

$\phantom{\Delta} = 41$

∴ **the roots are real, irrational and unequal.**

2 $2x^2 + x + 7 = 0$

$a = 2, \quad b = 1, \quad c = 7$

$\Delta = b^2 - 4ac$

$\phantom{\Delta} = 1^2 - 4 \times 2 \times 7$

$\phantom{\Delta} = -55$

∴ **the equation does not have real roots.**

3 $9x^2 - 36x + 20 = 0$

$a = 9, \quad b = -36, \quad c = 20$

$\Delta = b^2 - 4ac$

$\phantom{\Delta} = (-36)^2 - 4 \times 9 \times 20$

$\phantom{\Delta} = 576$

$\phantom{\Delta} = 24^2$

∴ **the roots are rational.**

4 $2x^2 + mx + 18 = 0$

$a = 2, \quad b = m, \quad c = 18$

$\Delta = b^2 - 4ac$

$\phantom{\Delta} = m^2 - 4 \times 2 \times 18$

$\phantom{\Delta} = m^2 - 144$

The roots are equal when $\Delta = 0$,

i.e. $m^2 - 144 = 0$

$\phantom{i.e.} m^2 = 144$

$\phantom{i.e.} \mathbf{m = \pm 12}$

5 $9x^2 + 6x + k$

$a = 9, \quad b = 6, \quad c = k$

$\Delta = b^2 - 4ac$

$\phantom{\Delta} = 6^2 - 4 \times 9 \times k$

$\phantom{\Delta} = 36 - 36k$

Now $a > 0$ so the expression will always be positive if there are no real roots,

i.e. $36 - 36k < 0$

$\phantom{i.e.} 36k > 36$

$\phantom{i.e.} k > 1$

**The expression will always be positive if $k > 1$.**

**6** $(n-2)x^2 + (n+1)x + 3 = 0$

$a = n - 2, \quad b = n + 1, \quad c = 3$

$\Delta = b^2 - 4ac$

$\quad = (n+1)^2 - 4 \times (n-2) \times 3$

$\quad = n^2 + 2n + 1 - 12n + 24$

$\quad = n^2 - 10n + 25$

$\quad = (n-5)^2$

**Now $(n-5)^2 \geq 0$ for all real values of $n$.**

So the equation will always have real roots.

## 8 Finding the equation of a quadratic ⊃ p. 26

**1** $y = 3x^2 + bx + c$

$y$-intercept $= -11$

So $c = -11$

$y = 3x^2 + bx - 11$

When $x = 4$, $y = 9$.

$\quad 9 = 3 \times 4^2 + b \times 4 - 11$

$\quad 9 = 37 + 4b$

$4b = -28$

$\quad b = -7$

So $\boldsymbol{y = 3x^2 - 7x - 11}$.

**2** The $x$-intercepts are 1 and 4.

The equation is of the form $y = k(x-1)(x-4)$.

When $x = 0$, $y = 8$

$8 = k(0-1)(0-4)$

$\quad = 4k$

$k = 2$

$y = 2(x-1)(x-4)$

$\quad = 2(x^2 - 5x + 4)$

$\boldsymbol{y = 2x^2 - 10x + 8}$

**3** $P(x) = ax^2 + bx + c$

$P(0) = 5$

$\therefore c = 5$

$P(x) = ax^2 + bx + 5$

$P(1) = 3$

$\quad 3 = a \times 1^2 + b \times 1 + 5$

$a + b = -2 \quad$ (i)

$P(-1) = 13$

$\quad 13 = a \times (-1)^2 + b \times (-1) + 5$

$a - b = 8 \quad$ (ii)

(i) + (ii) $\quad 2a = 6$

$\qquad\qquad a = 3$

Substitute into (i):

$\quad 3 + b = -2$

$\qquad b = -5$

$\therefore \boldsymbol{P(x) = 3x^2 - 5x + 5}$

**4** $x$-intercepts are $-2$ and 6.

So $y = k(x+2)(x-6)$

Now axis: $\quad x = \dfrac{-2+6}{2}$

$\qquad\qquad x = 2$

The least value is $-8$ so the vertex is $(2, -8)$.

When $x = 2$, $y = -8$

$-8 = k(2+2)(2-6)$

$\quad = -16k$

$k = \dfrac{1}{2}$

$y = \dfrac{1}{2}(x+2)(x-6)$

$\quad = \dfrac{1}{2}(x^2 - 4x - 12)$

$\quad = \dfrac{1}{2}x^2 - 2x - 6$

$\therefore \boldsymbol{a = \dfrac{1}{2}, \, b = -2 \text{ and } c = -6}$.

## 9 Intersections of lines and parabolas ⊃ p. 27

**1** **The point of intersection is when $x = 15$ and $y = 600$. It is the point where both contractors charge the same price for the same number of hours.**

**2** $\quad x^2 - 5x + 21 = 4x + 3$

$\quad x^2 - 9x + 18 = 0$

$(x-3)(x-6) = 0$

$\qquad x = 3 \quad$ or $\quad x = 6$

$y = 4x + 3$

When $x = 3$,

$y = 4 \times 3 + 3$

$\quad = 15$

When $x = 6$,

$y = 4 \times 6 + 3$

$\quad = 27$

**The points of intersection are (3, 15) and (6, 27).**

**3** $\qquad 3x^2 - 5x - 2 = x^2 + 2x + 7$

$\qquad\qquad 2x^2 - 7x - 9 = 0$

$\qquad 2x^2 + 2x - 9x - 9 = 0$

$\qquad 2x(x+1) - 9(x+1) = 0$

$\qquad\quad (x+1)(2x-9) = 0$

$\quad x + 1 = 0 \quad$ or $\quad 2x - 9 = 0$

$\qquad\qquad x = -1 \quad$ or $\qquad x = 4.5$

But $x > 0$ so $\boldsymbol{x = 4.5}$.

## 10 Cubic functions ⊃ p. 28

**1 a** $y = 2x^3 - 2$

When $y = 0$,

$2x^3 - 2 = 0$

$\quad 2x^3 = 2$

$\quad x^3 = 1$

$\quad x = 1$

**The curve cuts the $x$-axis at (1, 0).**

b

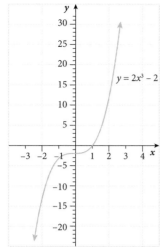

2  $y = 8 - (x - 1)^3$

a  When $x = 0$,
$$y = 8 - (0 - 1)^3$$
$$= 9$$
The $y$-intercept is 9.

b  When $y = 0$,
$$(x - 1)^3 = 8$$
$$x - 1 = 2$$
$$x = 3$$
The curve cuts the $x$-axis at $(3, 0)$.

c  $y$ has a very large negative value for very large positive values of $x$.

d  $y$ has a very large positive value for very large negative values of $x$.

e

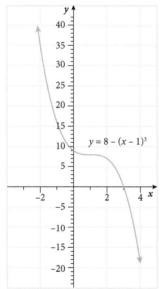

3  $y = (x + 4)(x + 2)(x - 3)$
When $x = 0$,
$$y = (0 + 4)(0 + 2)(0 - 3)$$
$$= -24$$
When $y = 0$, $x = -4, -2$ or $3$
For very large positive values of $x$, $y$ is very large and positive.

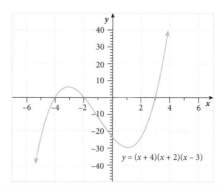

4  $y = -4x(x + 2)(x - 4)$
The curve is a cubic curve. The $y$-intercept is 0 and the $x$-intercepts are 0, –2 and 4. For very large positive values of $x$, $y$ is very large but negative.

FURTHER FUNCTIONS AND RELATIONS

1 Polynomials ⊃ p. 29

1  $P(x) = 7x^6 - x^5 + 2x^4 - 6x^2 + 9x - 3$
The degree is 6, the leading coefficient is 7 and the constant term is –3.

2  $y = (x + 4)(x + 2)(x - 4)(x - 2)$

a  When $x = 0$,
$$y = (0 + 4)(0 + 2)(0 - 4)(0 - 2)$$
$$= 64$$
The $y$-intercept is 64.

b  The $x$-intercepts are –4, –2, 4 and 2.

c  $P(x) = (x + 4)(x + 2)(x - 4)(x - 2)$
$$= (x + 4)(x - 4)(x + 2)(x - 2)$$
$$= (x^2 - 16)(x^2 - 4)$$
$P(-x) = ((-x)^2 - 16)((-x)^2 - 4)$
$$= (x^2 - 16)(x^2 - 4)$$
$$= P(x)$$
∴ the function is even.

d

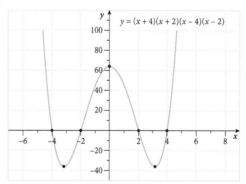

**3** $P(x) = 8 - 8x + x^3 - x^4$

   **a** The degree is **4**.

   **b** The leading coefficient is **–1**.

   **c** The $y$-intercept is **8**.

   When $y = 0$,

$$8 - 8x + x^3 - x^4 = 0$$
$$8(1 - x) + x^3(1 - x) = 0$$
$$(1 - x)(8 + x^3) = 0$$
$$1 - x = 0 \quad \text{or} \quad 8 + x^3 = 0$$
$$x = 1 \quad \text{or} \quad x^3 = -8$$
$$x = -2$$

   **The $x$-intercepts are –2 and 1.**

## 2 Hyperbolas ⊃ p. 30

**1** Let \$$C$ be the cost per person and let $n$ be the number of people travelling.

Now $C = \dfrac{k}{n}$ for some constant $k$.

When $n = 60$, $C = 96$

$$96 = \frac{k}{60}$$
$$k = 5760$$

So $C = \dfrac{5760}{n}$

When $n = 144$,

$$C = \frac{5760}{144}$$
$$= 40$$

∴ **when 144 people go on the trip the cost per person is \$40.**

**2**

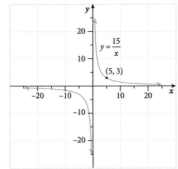

**3**

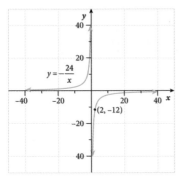

**4** $y = 2x + 1$

When $x = 3.5$,

$$y = 2 \times 3.5 + 1$$
$$= 8$$

So the hyperbola passes through the point (3.5, 8).

Now $y = \dfrac{k}{x}$

$$8 = \frac{k}{3.5}$$
$$k = \mathbf{28}$$

## 3 Absolute values ⊃ p. 31

**1** $|-2| - |-8| = 2 - 8$

                $= \mathbf{-6}$

**2** $|x| \le 3$

**3** $|x| > 1$

**4**

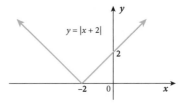

**5**

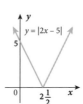

**6** The graph of $y = |4x + 1|$ is made up of two straight lines that meet on the $x$-axis when $x = -\dfrac{1}{4}$ forming a V shape. When $x \ge -\dfrac{1}{4}$, $y = 4x + 1$ but when $x < -\dfrac{1}{4}$, $y = -(4x + 1) = -4x - 1$.

## 4 Equations involving absolute values ⊃ p. 32

**1** $|x - 4| = 2$

The distance of $x$ from 4 on the number line is 2 units.

So **$x = 2$ or $x = 6$**.

**2**             $|5x + 3| = 17$

$$5x + 3 = 17 \quad \text{or} \quad 5x + 3 = -17$$
$$5x = 14 \qquad\qquad 5x = -20$$
$$x = \mathbf{2.8} \quad \text{or} \quad x = \mathbf{-4}$$

3  From the graph $|2x + 1| = 7$ when $x = -4$ and $x = 3$.

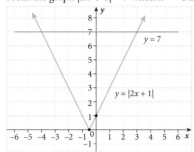

4  $|3x + 8| = 10$

$3x + 8 = 10$   or   $3x + 8 = -10$

$3x = 2$   or   $3x = -18$

$x = \dfrac{2}{3}$   or   $x = -6$

5  $|3 - 2a| = 7$

$3 - 2a = 7$   or   $3 - 2a = -7$

$2a = -4$   or   $2a = 10$

$a = -2$   or   $a = 5$

## 5 Graphs and their reflections ⊃ p. 33

1

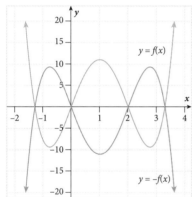

2  a

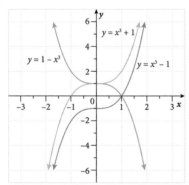

   b  All the curves are exactly the same shape and size.
      $y = x^3 + 1$ is the reflection of $y = 1 - x^3$ in the $y$-axis. $y = x^3 - 1$
      is the reflection of $y = 1 - x^3$ in the $x$-axis. If $y = x^3 + 1$ was
      rotated through $180°$ about the origin it would map onto
      $y = x^3 - 1$.

3  a

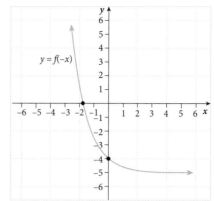

   b

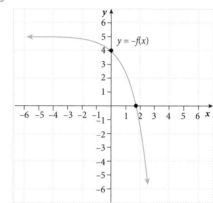

   c

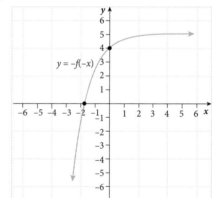

## 6 Circles ⊃ p. 34

1  $x^2 + y^2 = 121$ is a circle centre the
   origin, radius 11 units.

2  Centre $(-3, -2)$, radius 5 units
   Equation: $(x + 3)^2 + (y + 2)^2 = 5^2$

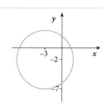

**3**  $(x-1)^2 + (y+3)^2 = 16$

Circle: centre $(1, -3)$, radius 4 units.

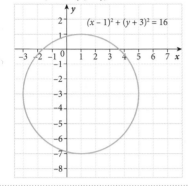

**4**  $x^2 + y^2 + 22x - 2y + 41 = 0$

$$x^2 + 22x + y^2 - 2y = -41$$

$$x^2 + 22x + 121 + y^2 - 2y + 1 = 81$$

$$(x+11)^2 + (y-1)^2 = 9^2$$

Circle: centre $(-11, 1)$, radius 9 units

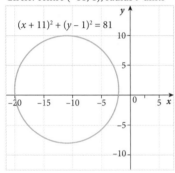

**5**  Circle, centre $(-2, 4)$

$$(x+2)^2 + (y-4)^2 = r^2$$

When $x = 10$, $y = 9$.

$$(10+2)^2 + (9-4)^2 = r^2$$

$$r^2 = 169$$

$$r = 13 \quad (r > 0)$$

**The radius is 13 units.**

**6**  $\qquad\qquad x^2 + y^2 = 2x - 8y$

$$x^2 - 2x + y^2 + 8y = 0$$

$$x^2 - 2x + 1 + y^2 + 8y + 16 = 17$$

$$(x-1)^2 + (y+4)^2 = 17$$

**Circle: centre $(1, -4)$, radius $\sqrt{17}$ units**

**7 Semicircles ⊃ p. 35**

**1**  $y = \sqrt{64 - x^2}$ **is a semicircle. It is the top half of a circle, centre the origin, and radius 8 units.**

**2**  Centre origin, radius 3 units

$$y = -\sqrt{9 - x^2}$$

**3**  a  $f(x) = \sqrt{16 - x^2}$

   **Domain: $-4 \le x \le 4$**

   **Range: $0 \le y \le 4$**

b

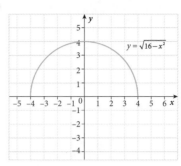

**4**  $y = -\sqrt{36 - x^2}$

   **Domain: $-6 \le x \le 6$**

   **Range: $-6 \le y \le 0$**

## YEAR 11 EXAM-TYPE QUESTIONS

### Part A

**1**  **D.**  $x^2 + 10x - 24 = 0$

$$(x-2)(x+12) = 0$$

$$x - 2 = 0 \quad \text{or} \quad x + 12 = 0$$

$$x = 2 \quad \text{or} \qquad x = -12$$

**2**  **D.**  $\dfrac{1}{\sqrt{5}-3} = \dfrac{1}{\sqrt{5}-3} \times \dfrac{\sqrt{5}+3}{\sqrt{5}+3}$

$$= \dfrac{\sqrt{5}+3}{5-9}$$

$$= \dfrac{\sqrt{5}+3}{-4}$$

$$= \dfrac{-\sqrt{5}-3}{4}$$

**3**  **B.**  is not the graph of a function because there is more than one value of $y$ for most values of $x$.

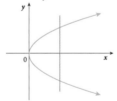

**4**  **A.**  is not one-to-one because there is more than one value of $x$ for some values of $y$.

**5**  **B.**  If $f(x) = \dfrac{1}{x}$

$$f(-x) = \dfrac{1}{-x}$$

$$= -\dfrac{1}{x}$$

$$= -f(x)$$

So $y = \dfrac{1}{x}$ is an odd function.

**6** **C.** $y = \sqrt{9 - x^2}$

Semicircle, radius 3 units

Range: $0 \le y \le 3$

**7** **A.** $y = 0$ when $x = 2$

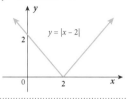

**8** **C.** $f(x) = \begin{cases} x^2 + 1 & \text{for } x \ge 0 \\ -x & \text{for } x < 0 \end{cases}$

$f(-2) = -(-2)$

$\quad\quad = 2$

**9** **C.** Centre $(2, -1)$, radius 3 units

$(x - 2)^2 + (y + 1)^2 = 9$

**10** **D.** $f(x) = 2 - 5x \quad g(x) = x^2$

$g(f(x)) = (2 - 5x)^2$

**11** **A.** $y = x(x - 2)(x + 4)$

$x$-intercepts are 0, 2 and $-4$.

If $x$ is a large positive
value $y$ is also
a large positive value.

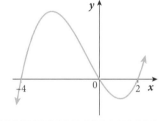

**12** **B.** $\Delta = 9$

The roots are real, rational but not equal.

## Part B

**13** $\dfrac{\left(a^2b^3\right)^4 \div ab^2}{\left(a^3b\right)^2 \times a^2b^3} = \dfrac{a^8b^{12} \div ab^2}{a^6b^2 \times a^2b^3}$  ✓

$\quad = \dfrac{a^7b^{10}}{a^8b^5}$

$\quad = \dfrac{b^5}{a}$  ✓

**14** $\left(6 - \sqrt{3}\right)^2 = x + y\sqrt{3}$

$\left(6 - \sqrt{3}\right)^2 = 36 - 12\sqrt{3} + 3$

$\quad\quad\quad = 39 - 12\sqrt{3}$  ✓

$\therefore x = \mathbf{39} \quad \text{and} \quad y = \mathbf{-12}$  ✓

**15** $\dfrac{2}{x^2 + 2x} - \dfrac{3}{x^2 + 3x} = \dfrac{2}{x(x + 2)} - \dfrac{3}{x(x + 3)}$

$\quad = \dfrac{2(x + 3) - 3(x + 2)}{x(x + 2)(x + 3)}$  ✓

$\quad = \dfrac{2x + 6 - 3x - 6}{x(x + 2)(x + 3)}$

$\quad = \dfrac{-x}{x(x + 2)(x + 3)}$

$\quad = \dfrac{-1}{(x + 2)(x + 3)}$  ✓

**16** **a** 10 baskets sell for \$60

$\therefore$ each basket sells for **\$6**.  ✓

**b** $y$-intercept $= 36$

The cost for 12 baskets is \$90.

$\text{gradient} = \dfrac{90 - 36}{12}$

$\quad\quad\quad = 4.5$  ✓

The equation of the line representing the cost is
$y = \mathbf{4.5x + 36}$  ✓

**c** The break-even point is **when 24 baskets are sold
for \$144**.  ✓

**17** $2x^2 - 6x + 1 = 0$

$a = 2 \quad b = -6 \quad c = 1$

$x = \dfrac{-b \pm \sqrt{b^2 - 4ac}}{2a}$

$\quad = \dfrac{-(-6) \pm \sqrt{(-6)^2 - 4 \times 2 \times 1}}{2 \times 2}$  ✓

$\quad = \dfrac{6 \pm \sqrt{28}}{4}$

$\quad = \dfrac{6 \pm 2\sqrt{7}}{4}$

$\quad = \dfrac{\mathbf{3 \pm \sqrt{7}}}{\mathbf{2}}$  ✓

**18** $P(x) = 2x^4 - 5x^3 + 7x^2 - 3x - 1$

**a** The degree of the polynomial is **4**.  ✓

**b** The leading coefficient is **2**.  ✓

**19** $y = 1 - 3x$

gradient $-3$, $y$-intercept $= 1$

Perpendicular line has gradient $\dfrac{1}{3}$.  ✓

The lines meet on the $y$-axis so have the same $y$-intercept.

Equation of perpendicular line is $y = \dfrac{1}{3}x + 1$.  ✓

**20** $3x^2 - 8x + 5$

$\Delta = b^2 - 4ac$

$\quad = (-8)^2 - 4 \times 3 \times 5$

$\quad = 4$  ✓

$\therefore$ the equation $3x^2 - 8x + 5 = 0$ has real roots.

**The parabola $y = 3x^2 - 8x + 5$ will cross the $x$-axis.**  ✓

**21** **a**

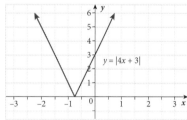

**b** From the graph $|4x + 3| = 5$ when $x = \mathbf{-2}$ and $x = \mathbf{0.5}$.  ✓

**22 a** $f(x) = x^2 + x$

$f(x+h) - f(x) = (x+h)^2 + (x+h) - (x^2 + x)$
$$= x^2 + 2xh + h^2 + x + h - x^2 - x$$
$$= \mathbf{2xh + h^2 + h} \quad \checkmark$$

**b** $\dfrac{f(x+h) - f(x)}{h} = \dfrac{2xh + h^2 + h}{h}$

$$= \dfrac{h(2x + h + 1)}{h}$$

$$= \mathbf{2x + h + 1} \quad \checkmark$$

**23** $(3, -3), \quad (-1, 5)$

$m = \dfrac{y_2 - y_1}{x_2 - x_1}$

$\quad = \dfrac{5 - (-3)}{-1 - 3}$

$\quad = -2 \quad \checkmark$

$y - y_1 = m(x - x_1)$
$y - (-3) = -2(x - 3)$
$y + 3 = -2x + 6$
$\quad\quad \mathbf{y = -2x + 3} \quad \checkmark$

**24 a** $f(x) = \begin{cases} x+1 & \text{for } x < 0 \\ 1 & \text{for } 0 \le x < 1 \\ x & \text{for } x \ge 1 \end{cases}$

$f(2) + f(-2) = 2 + (-2 + 1)$
$$= \mathbf{1} \quad \checkmark$$

**b**

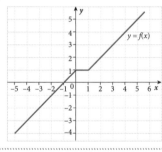

$\checkmark\checkmark$

**25 a** $y = x^2 - 10x + 23$
$$= x^2 - 10x + 25 - 2$$
$$= \mathbf{(x - 5)^2 - 2} \quad \checkmark$$

**b** Vertex **(5, −2)** $\checkmark$

**c** **Yes, the parabola will cut the $x$-axis. The vertex is below the $x$-axis and the curve is concave up.** $\checkmark$

**26 a** $f(x) = x^2 - 1 \quad g(x) = 1 - x$

$f(x) - g(x) = x^2 - 1 - (1 - x)$
$$= x^2 - 1 - 1 + x$$
$$= \mathbf{x^2 + x - 2} \quad \checkmark$$

**b** $\dfrac{f(x)}{g(x)} = \dfrac{x^2 - 1}{1 - x}$

$$= \dfrac{(x+1)(x-1)}{1-x}$$

$$= \dfrac{x+1}{-1}$$

$$= \mathbf{-x - 1} \quad \checkmark$$

**c** $f(g(x)) = (1 - x)^2 - 1 \quad \checkmark$
$$= 1 - 2x + x^2 - 1$$
$$= \mathbf{x^2 - 2x} \quad \checkmark$$

**27** $f(x) = 2x^2 - 8$

**Domain: all real values of $x$** $\quad \checkmark$

Now $2x^2 \ge 0$ for all real values of $x$

So $2x^2 - 8 \ge -8$

**Range is $y \ge -8$** $\quad \checkmark$

**28** $\quad\quad\quad\quad\quad\quad x^2 + y^2 = 8x - 6y$
$$x^2 - 8x + y^2 + 6y = 0$$
$$x^2 - 8x + 16 + y^2 + 6y + 9 = 25$$
$$(x - 4)^2 + (y + 3)^2 = 5^2 \quad \checkmark$$

**Centre (4, −3), radius 5 units** $\quad \checkmark$

## Trigonometry

### 1 Trigonometry of right-angled triangles

➜ Sin (sine), cos (cosine) and tan (tangent) are **trig ratios**.

➜ The side opposite the right angle, the **hypotenuse**, is always the longest side of a right-angled triangle. The **opposite** and **adjacent** sides depend upon the angle being considered.

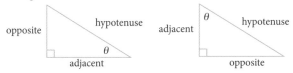

➜ $\sin \theta = \dfrac{\text{opposite}}{\text{hypotenuse}}$  $\cos \theta = \dfrac{\text{adjacent}}{\text{hypotenuse}}$  $\tan \theta = \dfrac{\text{opposite}}{\text{adjacent}}$

➜ Angles of **elevation** and **depression** are always measured from the **horizontal**.

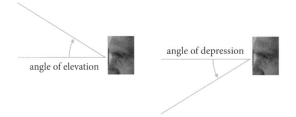

angle of elevation     angle of depression

### EXAMPLE 1

**Find the value of *x*, giving the answer correct to one decimal place.**

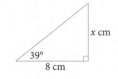

$\tan 39° = \dfrac{x}{8}$

$\quad x = 8 \times \tan 39°$

$\quad\quad = 6.478\,272\,26\dots$

$\quad\quad = 6.5 \quad (1 \text{ d.p.})$

The unknown side is opposite the given angle and the known side is adjacent to it. So we use the ratio that links opposite and adjacent: tan.

### EXAMPLE 2

**Find the length of the hypotenuse of this triangle. Give the answer to two decimal places.**

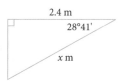

$\cos 28°41' = \dfrac{2.4}{x}$

$x \times \cos 28°41' = 2.4$

$\quad\quad x = \dfrac{2.4}{\cos 28°41'}$

$\quad\quad\quad = 2.735\,710\,47\dots$

$\quad\quad\quad = 2.74 \quad (2 \text{ d.p.})$

The length of the hypotenuse is 2.74 m, correct to two decimal places.

The second step isn't necessary but it does show how the equation should be solved. The same rules apply that work with other sorts of equations.

### EXAMPLE 3

**Find *θ*, to the nearest degree.**

$\sin \theta = \dfrac{5}{8}$

$\quad \theta = \sin^{-1}\left(\dfrac{5}{8}\right)$

$\quad\quad = 38.682\,1874\dots°$

$\quad\quad = 39° \quad (\text{nearest degree})$

The inverse (or opposite) operation to sin is $\sin^{-1}$.

### EXAMPLE 4

**Find the size of $\angle PQR$. Give the answer to the nearest minute.**

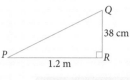

$\tan Q = \dfrac{120}{38}$

$\quad Q = \tan^{-1}\left(\dfrac{120}{38}\right)$

$\quad\quad = 72°25'43.47''$

$\quad\quad = 72°26' \quad (\text{nearest minute})$

The lengths of the sides must be in the same units.

There are 60 minutes in a degree and 60 seconds in a minute. So, if there are 30 or more seconds, you must round up to the next minute.

## EXAMPLE 5

An office building and a house are 28 m apart on level ground. From the top of the office building the angle of depression of the base of the house is 21°. How high is the office building?

Let the height of the office building be $x$ metres.

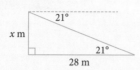

$$\tan 21° = \frac{x}{28}$$
$$x = 28 \times \tan 21°$$
$$= 10.748\,1929\ldots$$
$$= 10.7 \quad (1 \text{ d.p.})$$

∴ the office building is 10.7 m high, to one decimal place.

> When working with angles of depression, we often make use of the fact that alternate angles, formed when a transversal cuts a pair of parallel lines, are equal.

### → PRACTICE

1   Find $x$, giving the answer correct to one decimal place.

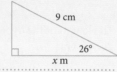

2   Find the length of the hypotenuse of this triangle. Give the answer to two decimal places.

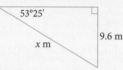

3   Find $\theta$ to the nearest degree.

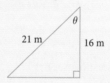

4   Find the size of $\angle ABC$. Give the answer to the nearest minute.

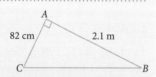

5   From the observation deck of a tower, Oliver notes that the angle of depression of his brother, Sid, on the ground is 15°. If the observation deck is 38 m above the ground, how far is Sid from the base of the tower?

6*  Find the height of a tree that casts a shadow 19 m long on level ground when the angle of elevation of the sun is 39°.

Answers ⊃ p. 82

## 2 Complementary and supplementary angles

→ **Complementary angles** add to 90°.

→ Sine and cosine are complementary ratios or **co-ratios**. The sine of any acute angle is equal to the cosine of the complementary angle. $\sin \theta = \cos(90° - \theta)$ and $\cos \theta = \sin(90° - \theta)$.

→ **Supplementary angles** add to 180°.

→ $\sin(180° - A) = \sin A$, $\cos(180° - A) = -\cos A$ and $\tan(180° - A) = -\tan A$ where $A$ is an acute angle.

### EXAMPLE 1

Simplify $\sin 37° - \cos 53°$.

$$\cos 53° = \sin(90° - 53°)$$
$$= \sin 37°$$

So $\sin 37° - \cos 53° = 0$.

> It is helpful to be able to quickly recognise complementary angles.

### EXAMPLE 2

Find $\cos 128°$ giving the answer to four decimal places.

$$\cos 128° = -0.615\,661\,475\ldots$$
$$= -0.6157 \quad (4 \text{ d.p.})$$

> The cosine of an obtuse angle is always negative.

### EXAMPLE 3

If $\sin \theta = 0.9574$ find the size of $\theta$ to the nearest minute if it is:

a   acute

b   obtuse

a   $\sin \theta = 0.9574$
$$\theta = \sin^{-1}(0.9574)$$
$$= 73°12'57.48"$$
$$= 73°13' \quad (\text{nearest minute})$$

b   If $\theta$ is obtuse:
$$\theta = 180° - 73°13'$$
$$= 106°47' \text{ to the nearest minute.}$$

> For any acute angle there is always an obtuse angle that has the same sine ratio. Those two angles will be supplementary.

### → PRACTICE

1   Simplify $\cos 41° - \sin 49°$.

2   Find $\cos 156°$ giving the answer to four decimal places.

**3** If $\sin \theta = 0.2978$ find the size of $\theta$ to the nearest minute if it is:

    **a** acute

    **b** obtuse

**4*** If $0° \leq \theta \leq 180°$, find the size of $\theta$ to the nearest degree if $\cos \theta = -0.2194$.

Answers ⊃ p. 82

## 3 Sine rule—finding sides

➔ The **sine rule** states: $\dfrac{a}{\sin A} = \dfrac{b}{\sin B} = \dfrac{c}{\sin C}$ where $a$, $b$ and $c$ are the sides opposite, respectively, angles $A$, $B$ and $C$.

➔ The sine rule is used to find the side of a triangle when **two angles and a side** are known.

➔ When using the sine rule we only use two of the three equal expressions at one time. That is, we work with **pairs of opposite sides and angles**.

### EXAMPLE 1

**Find the length of side $BC$ of this triangle, giving the answer to one decimal place.**

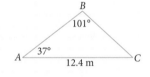

$$\frac{a}{\sin A} = \frac{b}{\sin B}$$

$$\frac{a}{\sin 37°} = \frac{12.4}{\sin 101°}$$

$$a = \frac{12.4 \sin 37°}{\sin 101°}$$

$$= 7.602\,179\,74\ldots$$

$$\therefore BC = 7.6\text{ m} \quad (1\text{ d.p.})$$

Side $BC$ is side $a$. The known side is side $b$. We use the expression that links $a$ and $b$.

### EXAMPLE 2

**Find $AB$.**

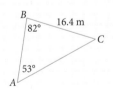

$\angle C = 180° - (82 + 53)°$
$\quad\; = 45°$

$$\frac{c}{\sin C} = \frac{a}{\sin A}$$

$$\frac{c}{\sin 45°} = \frac{16.4}{\sin 53°}$$

$$c = \frac{16.4 \sin 45°}{\sin 53°}$$

$$= 14.520\,4552\ldots$$

$$= 14.5 \quad (1\text{ d.p.})$$

$\therefore AB$ is 14.5 m to one decimal place.

$AB$ is side $c$ so we need to find the size of angle $C$. We use the fact that the angles of the triangle must add to 180°.

➔ **PRACTICE**

**1** Find the length of side $BC$ of this triangle, giving the answer to one decimal place.

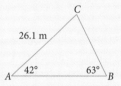

**2** Find $PQ$.

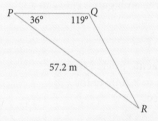

**3*** In $\triangle DEF$, $\angle D = 32°$, $\angle E = 67°$ and $DF = 114$ m. Use the sine rule to find the length of $EF$ to the nearest centimetre.

Answers ⊃ p. 82

## 4 Sine rule—finding angles

➔ When using the **sine rule to find an angle** we usually use it in inverted form:

$$\frac{\sin A}{a} = \frac{\sin B}{b} = \frac{\sin C}{c}.$$

➔ The sine rule is used to find an angle when **two sides and one angle** are known.

→ The **ambiguous** case of the sine rule needs to be considered, e.g. if, in $\triangle ABC$, $\angle A = 34°$, $AC = 8$ cm and $BC = 12$ cm there is only one possible triangle.

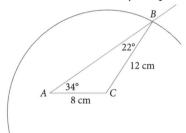

But, if, in $\triangle ABC$, $\angle A = 34°$, $AC = 12$ cm and $BC = 8$ cm then there are two possible triangles, one acute-angled and one obtuse-angled.

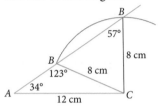

→ The sine rule will always give **two possible results** for the size of the angle: an acute and an obtuse angle. The obtuse angle will not always be valid because the angle sum of the triangle must be 180°. If the side opposite the required angle is longer than the side opposite the known angle then the ambiguous case can apply.

## EXAMPLE 1

$\triangle ABC$ is an acute-angled triangle. Find the size of $\angle BAC$ to the nearest degree.

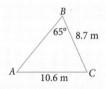

$$\frac{\sin A}{a} = \frac{\sin B}{b}$$

$$\frac{\sin A}{8.7} = \frac{\sin 65°}{10.6}$$

$$\sin A = \frac{8.7 \sin 65°}{10.6}$$

$$A = \sin^{-1}\left(\frac{8.7 \sin 65°}{10.6}\right)$$

$$= 48.060\,9654\ldots°$$

$\therefore \angle BAC = 48°$ to the nearest degree.

An acute-angled triangle has all its angles less than 90° so we don't need to consider the ambiguous case.

## EXAMPLE 2

Find, to the nearest degree, the size of $\angle ABC$.

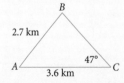

$$\frac{\sin B}{b} = \frac{\sin C}{c}$$

$$\frac{\sin B}{3.6} = \frac{\sin 47°}{2.7}$$

$$\sin B = \frac{3.6 \sin 47°}{2.7}$$

$$B = \sin^{-1}\left(\frac{3.6 \sin 47°}{2.7}\right)$$

$$= 77.197\,1334\ldots° \text{ or } 180° - 77.197\,1334\ldots°$$

$\therefore \angle ABC = 77°$ or $103°$ to the nearest degree.

Do not use the shape of the triangle to determine whether an angle is acute or obtuse, because the triangle might not be drawn to scale.

## EXAMPLE 3

Find the value of $\theta$ to the nearest minute.

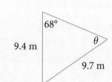

$$\frac{\sin A}{a} = \frac{\sin B}{b}$$

$$\frac{\sin \theta}{9.4} = \frac{\sin 68°}{9.7}$$

$$\sin \theta = \frac{9.4 \sin 68°}{9.7}$$

$$\theta = \sin^{-1}\left(\frac{9.4 \sin 68°}{9.7}\right)$$

$$= 63°57'45.53''$$

$$= 63°58' \quad \text{(nearest minute)}$$

Because $b > a$, $\angle B$ must be larger than $\angle A$. So $(180° - \angle A) + \angle B > 180°$ and the ambiguous case cannot apply. You should be able to easily recognise when the ambiguous case applies.

## EXAMPLE 4

Find the size of $\angle DEF$.

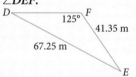

$$\frac{\sin D}{d} = \frac{\sin F}{f}$$

$$\frac{\sin D}{41.35} = \frac{\sin 125°}{67.25}$$

$$\sin D = \frac{41.35 \sin 125°}{67.25}$$

$$D = \sin^{-1}\left(\frac{41.35 \sin 125°}{67.25}\right)$$

$$= 30.243\,2314\ldots°$$

$$= 30° \text{ to the nearest degree}$$

$\therefore \angle DEF = 180° - (125 + 30)°$

$$= 25° \text{ to the nearest degree}$$

Sometimes it is necessary to use the sine rule to find a different angle to the one that is required and then use the angle sum of a triangle to find the required angle.

As $\angle F$ is obtuse, $\angle D$ and $\angle E$ must both be acute.

1   $\triangle ABC$ is an acute-angled triangle. Find the size of $\angle BAC$ to the nearest degree.

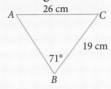

2   Find, to the nearest degree, the size of $\angle QPR$.

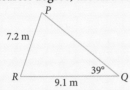

3   Find the value of $\theta$ to the nearest degree.

4   Find the size of $\angle GHI$.

5*  In $\triangle XYZ$, $XZ = 11.2$ m and $YZ = 13.5$ m.
    If $\angle XYZ = 55°15'$ find the size of $\angle YXZ$ to the nearest minute.

Answers ⊃ p. 83

## 5 Cosine rule

→ The **cosine rule** is used to find the third side of a triangle, given two sides and the included angle.

→ The cosine rule states:
   $c^2 = a^2 + b^2 - 2ab \cos C$ where
   $a$, $b$ and $c$ are the sides opposite,
   respectively, angles $A$, $B$ and $C$.

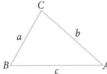

→ **Pythagoras' theorem** is a special case of the cosine rule.
   If $\angle C = 90°$, because $\cos 90° = 0$, the rule becomes
   $c^2 = a^2 + b^2$.

→ The cosine rule is also used to **find any angle** given three sides of a triangle.

→ When finding an angle, we use a rearrangement of the rule:  $\cos C = \dfrac{a^2 + b^2 - c^2}{2ab}$

## EXAMPLE 1

Find the length of $AB$.

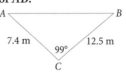

$c^2 = a^2 + b^2 - 2ab \cos C$
  $= 12.5^2 + 7.4^2 - 2 \times 12.5 \times 7.4 \times \cos 99°$
  $= 239.950\,37\ldots$
$c = \sqrt{239.950\,37\ldots}$   $(c > 0)$
  $= 15.490\,331\ldots$
  $= 15.5$   (1 d.p.)

Don't forget to take the square root. Because we are finding a length we do not need to consider the negative value of $c$.

$\therefore$ the length of $AB$ is 15.5 m, correct to one decimal place.

## EXAMPLE 2

Use the cosine rule to find the length of $XY$.

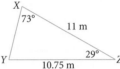

$z^2 = x^2 + y^2 - 2xy \cos Z$
  $= 10.75^2 + 11^2 - 2 \times 10.75 \times 11 \times \cos 29°$
  $= 29.714\,9392\ldots$
$z = \sqrt{29.714\,9392\ldots}$   $(z > 0)$
  $= 5.451\,141\,09\ldots$
  $= 5.5$   (1 d.p.)

We must use the angle that is included between the two known sides. We don't need to know that $\angle X = 73°$.

$\therefore$ the length of $XY$ is 5.5 m, correct to one decimal place.

## EXAMPLE 3

Find the size of $\theta$ to the nearest whole degree.

$\cos C = \dfrac{a^2 + b^2 - c^2}{2ab}$

$\cos \theta = \dfrac{3.8^2 + 7.1^2 - 5.6^2}{2 \times 3.8 \times 7.1}$

$\theta = \cos^{-1}\left(\dfrac{3.8^2 + 7.1^2 - 5.6^2}{2 \times 3.8 \times 7.1}\right)$

  $= 51.636\,7545\ldots°$
$\therefore \theta = 52°$ to the nearest degree

Make sure the measurements are used in the correct order. The side opposite the required angle is the one that is subtracted.

## EXAMPLE 4

Find the size of the largest angle of this triangle. Give the answer to the nearest minute.

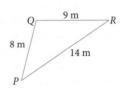

$$\cos Q = \frac{p^2 + r^2 - q^2}{2pr}$$

$$= \frac{9^2 + 8^2 - 14^2}{2 \times 9 \times 8}$$

The largest angle is always opposite the largest side.

$$Q = \cos^{-1}\left(\frac{9^2 + 8^2 - 14^2}{2 \times 9 \times 8}\right)$$

$$= 110°44'32.57''$$

$\therefore$ the largest angle is 110°45' to the nearest minute.

### → PRACTICE

1  Find the length of *AB*.

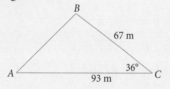

2  Use the cosine rule to find the length of *LM*. Give the answer to the nearest metre.

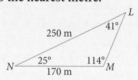

3  Find the value of $\theta$ to the nearest degree.

4  Find the size of the smallest angle of this triangle. Give the answer to the nearest minute.

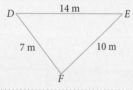

5*  Show that $\cos \theta = \frac{2}{3}$.

Answers ⊃ p. 83

## 6 Area of triangles

→ The **area of a triangle** can be found by multiplying half the base by the perpendicular height: $A = \frac{1}{2}bh$.

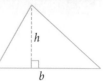

→ The area of any triangle can be found using the formula $A = \frac{1}{2}ab \sin C$ where *C* is the angle included between sides *a* and *b*. (If *h* is the perpendicular height at *B*, then $\sin C = \frac{h}{a}$ and hence $h = a \sin C$ so $\frac{1}{2}bh$ becomes $\frac{1}{2}ab \sin C$.)

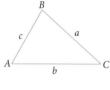

### EXAMPLE 1

Find the area of $\triangle ABC$.

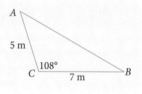

$$A = \frac{1}{2}ab \sin C$$

$$= \frac{1}{2} \times 7 \times 5 \times \sin 108°$$

$$= 16.643\,4890\ldots$$
$$= 16.6\text{ m}^2 \quad (1\text{ d.p.})$$

The angle used must always be the one between the two sides.

### EXAMPLE 2

a  Find the size of $\angle C$.
b  Find the area of the triangle.

a  $\cos C = \frac{a^2 + b^2 - c^2}{2ab}$

$$= \frac{17^2 + 9^2 - 12^2}{2 \times 17 \times 9}$$

$$C = 42.390\,9285\ldots°$$
$$= 42° \quad (\text{nearest degree})$$

b  $A = \frac{1}{2}ab \sin C$

$$= \frac{1}{2} \times 17 \times 9 \times \sin 42.390\,9285\ldots°$$

$$= 51.575\,1878\ldots$$
$$= 51.6\text{ cm}^2 \quad (1\text{ d.p.})$$

Heron's rule could also have been used to find the area of the triangle.

### → PRACTICE

1  Find the area of $\triangle PQR$.

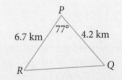

**2  a**  Find the size of $\angle C$.

   **b**  Find the area of the triangle.

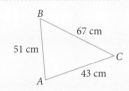

**3***  In $\triangle ABC$, $AB = 960$ m and $BC = 740$ m.
$\angle ABC = 30°$. Find the area of the triangle in hectares.

 Answers ⊃ pp. 83–84

## 7 Bearings

→ The **points of the compass** should all be known.

→ **Compass bearings** are measured from either North or South in either an easterly or westerly direction,

   e.g.   N 50° E      S 20° W      S 70° E      N 48° W

→ **True bearings** are measured in a clockwise direction from North. They are always given using three digits, e.g. the bearing of $Q$ from $P$ is:

### EXAMPLE 1

$A$ is located 23 km N 64° E of $B$. $C$ is due east of $B$ and due south of $A$. How far is it from $B$ to $C$?

$\angle ABC = 90° - 64°$
$\quad\quad\quad = 26°$
$\cos 26° = \dfrac{BC}{23}$

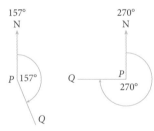

Always draw a diagram if one is not supplied. Use the correct (approximate) directions.

---

$BC = 23\cos 26°$
$\quad\quad = 20.672\,2630\ldots$
$\quad\quad = 20.7$ km   (1 d.p.)
∴ it is approximately 20.7 km from $B$ to $C$.

### EXAMPLE 2

$Q$ is 32 m south-west of $P$. $R$ is 24 m from $P$ on a bearing of 338°. How far is it, to the nearest metre, from $R$ to $Q$?

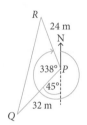

$\angle RPQ = 338° - 180° - 45°$
$\quad\quad\quad = 113°$
$p^2 = q^2 + r^2 - 2qr \cos P$
$\quad = 24^2 + 32^2 - 2 \times 24 \times 32 \times \cos 113°$
$\quad = 2200.163\,01\ldots$
$p = 46.905\,8952\ldots.$
$\quad = 47$ m   (nearest metre)

The distance from $R$ to $Q$ is 47 m to the nearest metre.

True bearings are also known as three-figure bearings.

We need to find the third side of the triangle and the other two sides and included angle are known, so we use the cosine rule.

### EXAMPLE 3

$B$ is 681 km from $A$ on a bearing of 152°. $C$ is due south of $A$ and 437 km from $B$. What is the bearing of $B$ from $C$?

$\angle BAC = 180° - 152°$
$\quad\quad\quad = 28°$
$\dfrac{\sin C}{c} = \dfrac{\sin A}{a}$
$\dfrac{\sin C}{681} = \dfrac{\sin 28°}{437}$
$\sin C = \dfrac{681 \sin 28°}{437}$
$C = \sin^{-1}\left(\dfrac{681 \sin 28°}{437}\right)$
$\quad = 47.020\,8756\ldots°$

So $\angle C = 47°$ or $133°$ to the nearest degree.

The bearing of $B$ from $C$ is either 047° or 133°.

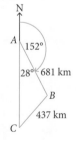

We must always consider the ambiguous case when answering questions. In a case like this we would need some further information to know which is the required bearing.

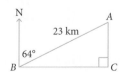

1  $P$ is located 68 km N 72° W of $Q$. $R$ is due west of $Q$ and due south of $P$. How far is it from $P$ to $R$?

2  $B$ is 57 m north-west of $A$. $C$ is 73 m from $A$ on a bearing of 205°. How far is it, to the nearest metre, from $B$ to $C$?

3  $H$ is 16.4 km from $F$ on a bearing of 163°. $G$ is due south of $F$ and 12.8 km from $H$. What is the bearing of $H$ from $G$?

4*  Point $B$ is south-east of point $A$ and at a distance of 2 km. From point $A$, a point $P$ is on a bearing of 057° and from $B$, point $P$ bears 348°. Find the distance from $A$ to $P$, giving the answer correct to the nearest 100 m.

Answers ⊃ p. 84

## 8 Problems

→ Many problems involve **combinations** of the sine rule, cosine rule, or trig ratios and may involve more than one triangle. Think carefully about how to approach the question before attempting it.

→ Always draw a **clear diagram** and show all the given information.

→ It is not always necessary to **evaluate an expression**.

→ Always use the **exact value** of a previously found variable, not a rounded-off approximation, in subsequent calculations.

### EXAMPLE 1

A person standing at $A$ finds the angle of elevation of the top of a tree is 13°. She then walks 200 m towards the tree, on level ground, and finds that the angle of elevation of the top of the tree is now 35°.

a  Find the size of $\angle ADB$.

b  Find the length of $BD$.

c  Find the height of the tree.

a  $\angle DBC = \angle ADB + \angle DAB$   (exterior angle of $\triangle$)

    $35° = \angle ADB + 13°$

  $\therefore \angle ADB = 22°$

> You might use geometry rather than trigonometry to find an angle.

b  In $\triangle ABD$,

$$\frac{a}{\sin A} = \frac{d}{\sin D}$$

$$\frac{a}{\sin 13°} = \frac{200}{\sin 22°}$$

$$a = \frac{200\sin 13°}{\sin 22°}$$

$$= 120.099\,890\ldots$$

$$\therefore BD = 120 \text{ m} \quad \text{(nearest metre)}$$

> It is helpful to state which triangle you are working in.

c  In $\triangle DBC$,

$$\sin 35° = \frac{DC}{DB}$$

$$DC = DB\sin 35°$$

$$= 68.886\,4672\ldots$$

$$= 69 \text{ m} \quad \text{(nearest metre)}$$

> Use the exact value of $DB$ from part b.

### EXAMPLE 2

a  Use the cosine rule in $\triangle ABC$ to find a simple expression for $AC^2$.

b  Find the size of $\angle ADC$.

c  Find the area of $ABCD$.

a  In $\triangle ABC$,

$$b^2 = a^2 + c^2 - 2ac\cos B$$

$$= 8^2 + 9^2 - 2 \times 8 \times 9 \times \cos 26°$$

$$\therefore AC^2 = 145 - 144\cos 26°$$

> The question asked for an expression so there is no need to evaluate $AC^2$ at this stage.

b  In $\triangle ADC$,

$$\cos D = \frac{a^2 + c^2 - d^2}{2ac}$$

$$= \frac{7^2 + 5^2 - AC^2}{2 \times 7 \times 5}$$

$$D = \cos^{-1}\left(\frac{7^2 + 5^2 - AC^2}{2 \times 7 \times 5}\right)$$

$$= 33.419\,3363\ldots°$$

$$\therefore \angle ADC = 33° \quad \text{(nearest degree)}$$

> Note that side $a$ in $\triangle ADC$ is not the same as side $a$ in $\triangle ABC$. So $a$ has a different value in this part of the question to the last.

c  Area = area of $\triangle ABC$ + area of $\triangle ADC$

$$= \frac{1}{2} \times 9 \times 8 \times \sin 26°$$

$$+ \frac{1}{2} \times 7 \times 5 \times \sin 33.419\,3363\ldots°$$

$$= 25.419\,7042\ldots$$

$$= 25.42 \text{ m}^2 \quad \text{(2 d.p.)}$$

→ **PRACTICE**

1  *AB* represents a pole. From *D*, the angle of elevation of the top of the pole is 26°. From *C*, a point 18 m closer to the pole on level ground, the angle of elevation of *A* is 64°.

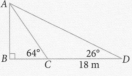

a  Find the size of ∠*DAC*.

b  Find the length of *AC*.

c  Find the height of the pole.

2  a  Use the cosine rule in △*LMN* to find a simple expression for $LN^2$.

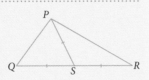

b  Find the size of ∠*LKN*.

c  Find the area of *KLMN*.

3*  *S* is a point on *QR* such that *QS* = *PS* = *RS* = 7 m. *PR* = 12 m.

a  Show that $\cos R = \dfrac{6}{7}$.

b  Find the exact length of *PQ*.

c  Find the size of ∠*QPR*.

Answers ⊃ pp. 84–85

## 9 Exact ratios

→ For some special angles the trig ratios have **exact values**.

→ If the equal sides of an **isosceles right-angled triangle** are each 1 unit in length then, by Pythagoras' theorem, the hypotenuse will be $\sqrt{2}$ units. This gives the exact values for trig ratios of 45°.

$$\sin 45° = \frac{1}{\sqrt{2}} \quad \cos 45° = \frac{1}{\sqrt{2}} \quad \tan 45° = 1$$

→ If an **equilateral triangle**, of side length 2 units, is divided in half we can find the exact values for trig ratios of angles of 30° and 60°.

$$\sin 30° = \frac{1}{2} \quad \sin 60° = \frac{\sqrt{3}}{2}$$

$$\cos 30° = \frac{\sqrt{3}}{2} \quad \cos 60° = \frac{1}{2}$$

$$\tan 30° = \frac{1}{\sqrt{3}} \quad \tan 60° = \sqrt{3}$$

## EXAMPLE 1

In the diagram, *DC* = 6 cm. ∠*ADB* = ∠*BCD* = 90°. ∠*BDC* = 45° and ∠*ABC* = 105°. Find the exact length of *AD*.

In △*BCD*,

$$\cos 45° = \frac{6}{BD}$$

$$\frac{1}{\sqrt{2}} = \frac{6}{BD}$$

$$BD = 6\sqrt{2} \text{ cm}$$

Now ∠*CBD* = 180° − (90 + 45)°  (∠ sum △)

= 45°

∠*ABD* = 105° − 45°

= 60°

In △*ABD*,

$$\tan 60° = \frac{AD}{BD}$$

$$AD = BD × \tan 60°$$

$$= 6\sqrt{2} × \sqrt{3}$$

$$= 6\sqrt{6} \text{ cm}$$

Alternatively, use the angle sum of a quadrilateral to show that ∠*DAB* = 30° and use tan 30°.

## EXAMPLE 2

In the diagram, ∠*ACB* = 30°, ∠*ABC* = 90° and *AC* = *CD*.

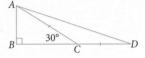

a  Show that ∠*BAD* = 75°.

b  If *AB* = 1 unit, show that $\tan 75° = 2 + \sqrt{3}$.

a  ∠*BAC* = 180° − (90 + 30)°  (∠ sum △)

= 60°

∠*ACB* = ∠*CAD* + ∠*ADC*  (ext. ∠ of △)

But ∠*CAD* = ∠*ADC*  (base ∠s isos. △)

∴ 2∠*CAD* = 30°

∠*CAD* = 15°

∠*BAD* = 60° + 15°

= 75°

b  In △*ABC*,

$$\tan 30° = \frac{AB}{BC}$$

$$\frac{1}{\sqrt{3}} = \frac{1}{BC}$$

∴ $BC = \sqrt{3}$ units

$$\sin 30° = \frac{AB}{AC}$$

$$\frac{1}{2} = \frac{1}{AC}$$

$$\therefore \quad AC = 2 \text{ units}$$

Now $CD = AC$

So $CD = 2$ units

$\therefore BD = (2 + \sqrt{3})$ units

In $\triangle ABD$,

$$\tan 75° = \frac{BD}{AB}$$

This is another exact ratio, but not one that you are expected to remember.

$$= \frac{2+\sqrt{3}}{1}$$

$$= 2 + \sqrt{3}$$

→ **PRACTICE**

1   In the diagram, $\angle ADB = \angle DCB = 90°$.
    $\angle ABD = \angle DBC = 30°$.
    $DC = 1$ unit. Find the exact length of $AB$.

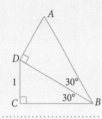

2   In the diagram, $AD = BD$. $\angle BCD = 90°$.
    $\angle DBC = 60°$. $BC = 1$ unit.

    a   Find the exact length of $AC$.
    b   Hence show that $\tan 15° = 2 - \sqrt{3}$

3*  In the diagram, $AB = 5\sqrt{2}$ cm. $\angle ABC = 45°$ and
    $\angle ACB = 30°$. Show that $BC = (5 + 5\sqrt{3})$ cm.

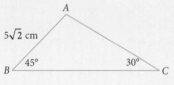

Answers ⊃ p. 85

## 10 Three-dimensional trigonometry

→ Trigonometry can also be used to solve problems in **three dimensions**.

→ A **clear diagram** is essential. If you need to show the height of something, you cannot also show north and south of the object in the same straight line.

→ In most cases you will need to use information in more than one triangle. Unless you are asked to evaluate parts as you go, work with **simplified expressions** as much as possible.

### EXAMPLE 1

The diagram shows a right pyramid of height 12 cm. The rectangular base is 18 cm long and 10 cm wide.

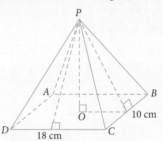

What is the size of the angle that $\triangle PBC$ makes with the base of the pyramid?

Let the midpoint of $BC$ be $Q$ and the midpoint of $DC$ be $R$.
Let the required angle be $\theta$.

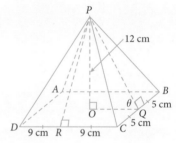

$OP = 12$ cm, $OQ = RC = 9$ cm

$$\tan \theta = \frac{12}{9}$$

$$\theta = \tan^{-1}\left(\frac{12}{9}\right)$$

Marking all the given information on the diagram helps us to see exactly what is required and how to proceed.

$$= 53.130\,1023…°$$

$$= 53° \quad \text{(nearest degree)}$$

$\therefore \triangle PBC$ makes an angle of 53°, to the nearest degree, with the base of the pyramid.

### EXAMPLE 2

Boat $C$ is 154 m from the base of a cliff and due east of it. Boat $D$ is due south of the cliff. The angle of elevation of the top of the cliff is 28° from boat $C$ and 32° from boat $D$.

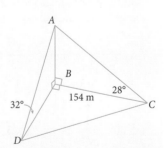

a  **Find the height of the cliff to the nearest metre.**

b  **What is the distance from the base of the cliff to boat *D*?**

c  **How far apart are the boats?**

a  In $\triangle ABC$,

$$\tan 28° = \frac{AB}{154}$$

$$AB = 154 \tan 28°$$

$$= 81.883\,2524\ldots$$

$$= 82 \text{ m} \quad \text{(nearest metre)}$$

The height of the cliff is 82 m to the nearest metre.

b  In $\triangle ABD$,

$$\tan 32° = \frac{AB}{BD}$$

$$BD = \frac{AB}{\tan 32°}$$

$$= 131.040\,596\ldots$$

$$= 131 \text{ m} \quad \text{(nearest metre)}$$

The boat is 131 m from the base of the cliff, to the nearest metre.

c  In $\triangle BCD$,

$$DC^2 = BC^2 + BD^2$$

$$= 154^2 + (131.040\,596\ldots)^2$$

$$= 40\,887.6378\ldots$$    Use the exact values, not the rounded ones from previous parts.

$$DC = 202.206\,918\ldots$$

$$= 202 \text{ m} \quad \text{(nearest metre)}$$

The distance between the boats is 202 m to the nearest metre.

## EXAMPLE 3

**Find the distance from *P* to *Q*.**

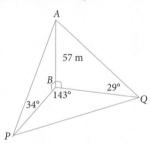

In $\triangle ABQ$,

$$\tan 29° = \frac{57}{BQ}$$

$$\therefore BQ = \frac{57}{\tan 29°}$$

In $\triangle ABP$,

$$\tan 34° = \frac{57}{PB}$$

$$\therefore PB = \frac{57}{\tan 34°}$$    There is no need to actually evaluate the length of either *BQ* or *PB*.

In $\triangle PBQ$,

$$b^2 = p^2 + q^2 - 2pq \cos 143°$$

$$PQ^2 = \left(\frac{57}{\tan 29°}\right)^2 + \left(\frac{57}{\tan 34°}\right)^2$$

$$- 2 \times \frac{57}{\tan 29°} \times \frac{57}{\tan 34°} \times \cos 143°$$

$$= 31\,595.3996\ldots$$

$$PQ = 177.750\,948\ldots$$

$$= 178 \text{ m} \quad \text{(nearest metre)}$$

The distance from *P* to *Q* is 178 m, to the nearest metre.

## EXAMPLE 4

**From *A* the angle of elevation of the top of a building (*P*) is 15° and the angle of elevation of *P* from *B* is 12°. If $\angle AQB = 120°$ (where *Q* is the foot of the building), and if *B* is 350 m from *A*, find the height of the building.**

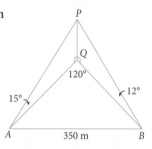

Let *h* m be the height of the building.

In $\triangle APQ$,

$$\tan 15° = \frac{h}{AQ}$$

$$AQ = \frac{h}{\tan 15°}$$

In $\triangle PQB$,

$$\tan 12° = \frac{h}{QB}$$

$$QB = \frac{h}{\tan 12°}$$

In $\triangle AQB$,

$$q^2 = a^2 + b^2 - 2ab \cos Q$$

$$350^2 = \left(\frac{h}{\tan 12°}\right)^2 + \left(\frac{h}{\tan 15°}\right)^2 -$$

$$2 \times \frac{h}{\tan 12°} \times \frac{h}{\tan 15°} \times \cos 120°$$

$$350^2 = \frac{h^2}{(\tan 12°)^2} + \frac{h^2}{(\tan 15°)^2} - \frac{2h^2}{\tan 12° \tan 15°} \times -\frac{1}{2}$$

$$350^2 = \frac{h^2}{(\tan 12°)^2} + \frac{h^2}{(\tan 15°)^2} + \frac{h^2}{\tan 12° \tan 15°}$$

$$350^2 = h^2\left(\frac{1}{(\tan12°)^2} + \frac{1}{(\tan15°)^2} + \frac{1}{\tan12°\tan15°}\right)$$

$$h^2 = 350^2 \div \left(\frac{1}{(\tan12°)^2} + \frac{1}{(\tan15°)^2} + \frac{1}{\tan12°\tan15°}\right)$$

$$= 2284.60951....$$
$$h = 47.7975890... \quad (h > 0)$$
$$= 48 \quad \text{(nearest whole number)}$$

The height of the building is 48 m, to the nearest metre.

Another way of writing $(\tan 15°)^2$ is $\tan^2 15°$.

## → PRACTICE

1  The diagram shows a right pyramid of height 16 cm. The rectangular base is 24 cm long and 20 cm wide.

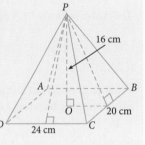

What size is the angle that $\triangle PDC$ makes with the base of the pyramid?

2  Chris is 206 m from the base, $B$, of a tower and due east of it. Dan is due south of the tower. The angle of elevation of the top, $A$, of the tower is 19° from Chris's position and 25° from Dan's.

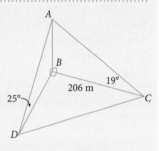

a  Find the height of the tower to the nearest metre.

b  How far is Dan from the base of the tower?

c  How far apart are Chris and Dan?

3  Find the distance from $S$ to $R$.

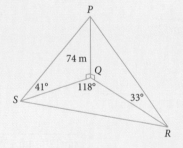

4  From $P$ the angle of elevation of the top of a cliff, $A$, is 17° and the angle of elevation of $A$ from $Q$ is 13°. If $\angle PBQ = 120°$ (where $B$ is the foot of the cliff) and if $Q$ is 775 m from $P$, find the height of the cliff.

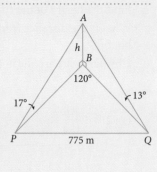

5*  In the diagram, $PQ$ represents a cliff of height 75 m. $A$ is due north of $Q$ and $B$ is due east of $Q$ ($\angle PQA = \angle PQB = 90°$). From $A$ the angle of elevation of $P$ is 45° and from $B$ the angle of elevation of $P$ is 30°.

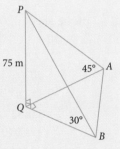

a  Show that the exact length of $QB$ is $75\sqrt{3}$ m.

b  Find the distance from $A$ to $B$.

c  Find the bearing of $A$ from $B$.

Answers ⊃ pp. 85–86

## 11 Angles of any magnitude

→  The **unit circle** is a circle of radius 1 unit. It has equation $x^2 + y^2 = 1$.

→  The **trig ratios** can be redefined using the unit circle:

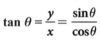

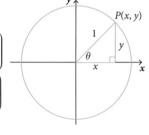

$$\sin\theta = y \quad \left(\frac{\text{opposite}}{\text{hypotenuse}} = \frac{y}{1}\right)$$

$$\cos\theta = x \quad \left(\frac{\text{adjacent}}{\text{hypotenuse}} = \frac{x}{1}\right)$$

$$\tan\theta = \frac{y}{x} = \frac{\sin\theta}{\cos\theta}$$

→  Using the unit circle the definitions of the trig ratios can be extended to **angles of any magnitude**.

In the 2nd quadrant, $y$ is positive but $x$ is negative. So, if $0° < \theta < 90°$, $\sin(180° - \theta)$ is positive, $\cos(180° - \theta)$ is negative and $\tan(180° - \theta)$ is negative.

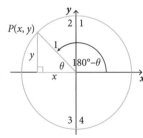

In the 3rd quadrant, $x$ and $y$ are both negative. So, if $0° < \theta < 90°$, $\sin(180° + \theta)$ is negative, $\cos(180° + \theta)$ is negative and $\tan(180° + \theta)$ is positive.

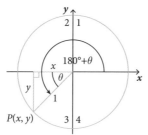

In the 4th quadrant, $x$ is positive but $y$ is negative. So, if $0° < \theta < 90°$, $\sin(360° - \theta)$ is negative, $\cos(360° - \theta)$ is positive and $\tan(360° - \theta)$ is negative.

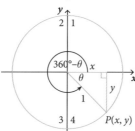

## EXAMPLE 1

Find the exact value of:

a   $\sin 135°$

b   $\tan 300°$

a   $\sin 135° = \sin(180 - 45)°$

       $= \sin 45°$

       $= \dfrac{1}{\sqrt{2}}$

*135° lies in the 2nd quadrant so sin is positive.*

b   $\tan 300° = \tan(360 - 60)°$

       $= -\tan 60°$

       $= -\sqrt{3}$

*300° lies in the 4th quadrant so tan is negative.*

## EXAMPLE 2

Find all values of $\theta$, $0° \leq \theta \leq 360°$, for which:

a   $\cos \theta = 0.2588$

b   $\tan \theta = -1$

a           $\cos \theta = 0.2588$

   $\cos^{-1}(0.2588) = 75.0011296\ldots°$

             $= 75°$   (nearest degree)

cos is positive in the 1st and 4th quadrants.

So $\theta = 75°$ or $360° - 75°$

    $\theta = 75°$ or $285°$

*We first find the acute angle and then apply our knowledge of angles of any magnitude to find all the possible answers.*

b           $\tan \theta = -1$

Now $\tan^{-1}(1) = 45°$

tan is negative in the 2nd and 4th quadrants.

So $\theta = 180° - 45°$ or $360° - 45°$

    $\theta = 135°$ or $315°$

*Most calculators give a negative value for tan⁻¹(−1). It is easier to find the acute angle than to work with a negative angle.*

## EXAMPLE 3

Find all values of $\theta$, $0° \leq \theta \leq 720°$, for which $\sin \theta = 0.6157$.

$\sin \theta = 0.6157$

$\sin^{-1}(0.6157) = 38.0028011\ldots°$

            $= 38°$   (nearest degree)

sin is positive in the 1st and 2nd quadrants.

So $\theta = 38°$ or $180° - 38°$ or $360° + 38°$ or $540° - 38°$

    $\theta = 38°$ or $142°$ or $398°$ or $502°$

*Angles greater than 360° have completed more than one revolution.*

## EXAMPLE 4

Find, to the nearest degree, the values of $x$ for which $\cos x = 0.891$ if $-180° \leq x \leq 180°$.

$\cos x = 0.891$

$\cos^{-1}(0.891) = 27.0008233\ldots°$

           $= 27°$   (nearest degree)

cos is positive in the 1st and 4th quadrants.

So $x = 27°$ or $0° - 27°$

   $x = 27°$ or $-27°$

*A negative angle has rotated in a clockwise direction from the positive x-axis.*

### → PRACTICE

1   Find the exact value of:

   a   $\cos 330°$

   b   $\tan 150°$

2   Find all values of $\theta$, $0° \leq \theta \leq 360°$, for which:

   a   $\cos \theta = 0.5299$

   b   $\tan \theta = -1.932$

3   Find all values of $\theta$, $0° \leq \theta \leq 720°$, for which $\sin \theta = 0.5$.

4   Find, to the nearest degree, the values of $x$ for which $\cos x = 0.375$ if $-180° \leq x \leq 180°$.

5*  Find, to the nearest minute, the values of $\theta$, $0° \leq \theta \leq 360°$, for which $\sin \theta = -0.7503$.

Answers ⮌ pp. 86–87

## 12 Graphs of trig ratios

→ The graphs of the trig ratios are **periodic**, i.e. they repeat after a given interval.

→ The graph of $y = \sin x°$ has period 360°.

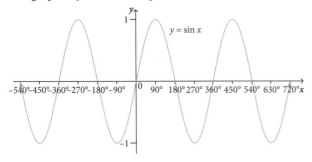

→ The graph of $y = \cos x°$ has period 360°.

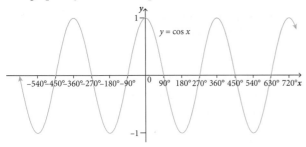

→ The graph of $y = \tan x°$ has period 180°. Because tan $x$ is undefined whenever cos $x$ = 0 ($\pm90°$, $\pm270°$, $\pm450°$ …) the graph of $y = \tan x$ has asymptotes at those values.

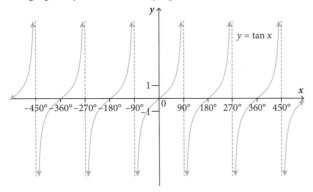

### EXAMPLE 1

Sketch $y = \sin x$ for $0° \leq x \leq 360°$.

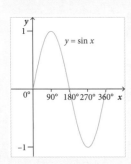

Take care to sketch the curve over the given domain.

### EXAMPLE 2

Consider the curve $y = \cos x$ for $0° \leq x \leq 1080°$.

a   How many times does the curve repeat?

b   What happens to the curve whenever $y = 0$?

a   The curve repeats every 360°.
   Now 1080 ÷ 360 = 3.
   So the curve repeats 3 times.

   You should be able to visualise what the graph looks like.

b   Whenever $y = 0$ the curve changes concavity.

### EXAMPLE 3

Briefly explain what happens to the graph of $y = \tan x$ as $x$ gets closer and closer to 90°.

The graph of $y = \tan x$ has an asymptote at $x = 90°$. As $x$ gets closer to 90° from below, the value of $y$ gets larger and larger. As $x$ gets closer and closer to 90° from above, the value of $y$ is negative but gets larger and larger negatively.

As $x \to 90°^-$, $y \to \infty$.
As $x \to 90°^+$, $y \to -\infty$.

### → PRACTICE

1   Sketch $y = \cos x$ for $0° \leq x \leq 360°$.

2   Consider the curve $y = \sin x$ for $0° \leq x \leq 1440°$.
   a   How many times does the curve repeat?
   b   What happens to the curve whenever $y = 0$?

3   Briefly explain what happens to the graph of $y = \tan x$ as $x$ gets closer and closer to 270°.

4*  Briefly comment on any similarities and differences between the graphs of $y = \sin x$ and $y = \cos x$.

Answers ⊃ p. 87

# Radians

## 1 Introduction to radians

→ Degrees are one measure of angle size. Another is **circular measure**, which is the measure of an angle in radians.

→ **One radian** is the size of the angle subtended at the centre of a **unit circle** by an **arc** of length **1 unit**.

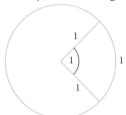

→ The circumference of any circle is given by the formula $C = 2\pi r$. So the circumference of a unit circle is $2\pi$ units. This gives us a conversion scale between angles and degrees. An angle that is a complete revolution (360°) subtends an arc of length $2\pi$ units, and so is equal to $2\pi$ radians. **$\pi$ radians = 180°**

→ In many cases radians are **expressed in terms of $\pi$**.

→ You should be familiar with the **conversions** of common angle sizes.

| Degrees | 0° | 30° | 45° | 60° | 90° | 180° | 360° |
|---------|-----|-----|-----|-----|-----|------|------|
| Radians | 0 | $\dfrac{\pi}{6}$ | $\dfrac{\pi}{4}$ | $\dfrac{\pi}{3}$ | $\dfrac{\pi}{2}$ | $\pi$ | $2\pi$ |

### EXAMPLE 1

Change 80° to radians. Give the answer correct to one decimal place.

$$80° = 80° \times \frac{\pi}{180°}$$
$$= 1.396\,263\,40\ldots$$
$$= 1.4 \quad (1\ \text{d.p.})$$

To change an angle in degrees to one in radians multiply by $\frac{\pi}{180°}$.

### EXAMPLE 2

Convert 50° to radians. Give the answer in terms of $\pi$.

$$50° = 50° \times \frac{\pi}{180°}$$
$$= \frac{5\pi}{18}$$

The answer is left as a fraction involving $\pi$.

### EXAMPLE 3

Find the size of 1 radian in degrees to the nearest degree.

$$1 = 1 \times \frac{180°}{\pi}$$
$$= 57.295\,7795\ldots°$$
$$= 57° \quad (\text{nearest degree})$$

To change an angle in radians to one in degrees multiply by $\frac{180°}{\pi}$.

### EXAMPLE 4

An angle has measure $\dfrac{7\pi}{6}$. What is its size in degrees?

$$\frac{7\pi}{6} = \frac{7 \times 180°}{6}$$
$$= 210°$$

As $\pi$ radians is 180° we can just substitute 180° for $\pi$.

### → PRACTICE

1. Change 35° to radians. Give the answer to two decimal places.

..................................................................

2. Express 120° in radians in terms of $\pi$.

..................................................................

3. Find the size of 0.8 radians in degrees to the nearest degree.

..................................................................

4. An angle has measure $\dfrac{3\pi}{5}$. What is its size in degrees?

5*. Find the exact size in radians of an angle of 225°.

Answers ⊃ p. 87

## 2 The trig ratios with radians

→ Because angles can be measured in either of two ways (degrees or radians) your **calculator** needs to know **which measurement** you are using. It is not necessary to convert from degrees to radians or vice versa because the calculator can find the trig ratio using either degrees or radians but it must be in the **correct mode**.

→ Make sure you know how to change your calculator from **degrees mode** to **radians mode** and vice versa.

→ **Always check** that your calculator is in the correct mode before using it in a calculation.

### EXAMPLE 1

Find cos 3.8. Give the answer correct to four decimal places.

$$\cos 3.8 = -0.790\,967\,711\ldots$$
$$= -0.7910 \quad (4\ \text{d.p.})$$

3.8 radians could be written as 3.8ᶜ, but that notation is rarely used. If there is no symbol the measure is radians.

## EXAMPLE 2

Find $\dfrac{5.9\sin 1.2}{7.4}$ correct to three decimal places.

$\dfrac{5.9\sin 1.2}{7.4} = 0.743\,112\,244\ldots$

As 1.2 has no units it must be radians so the calculator must be in radians mode.

$\qquad\qquad = 0.743 \quad \text{(3 d.p.)}$

## EXAMPLE 3

Find $\tan\left(\dfrac{4\pi}{3}\right)$ to three decimal places.

$\tan\left(\dfrac{4\pi}{3}\right) = 1.732\,050\,80\ldots$

If an angle is expressed in terms of $\pi$, take care to find the trig ratio of the whole expression. (Use brackets to be sure.)

$\qquad\qquad = 1.732 \quad \text{(3 d.p.)}$

### → PRACTICE

1  Find tan 0.6, giving the answer to four decimal places.

2  Find the value of $\dfrac{9.2\sin(0.75)}{8.75}$ giving the answer correct to three decimal places.

3  Find $\cos\left(\dfrac{5\pi}{3}\right)$.

4*  Find the value of $\dfrac{3.7\sin\dfrac{\pi}{5}}{\sin\dfrac{\pi}{4}}$. Give the answer correct to two decimal places.

Answers ⤳ p. 87

## 3 Further values with radians

→ The **exact values** of the trig ratios should also be known for angles measured in **radians**.

$\sin\dfrac{\pi}{4} = \dfrac{1}{\sqrt{2}} \qquad \cos\dfrac{\pi}{4} = \dfrac{1}{\sqrt{2}} \qquad \tan\dfrac{\pi}{4} = 1$

$\sin\dfrac{\pi}{6} = \dfrac{1}{2} \qquad \cos\dfrac{\pi}{6} = \dfrac{\sqrt{3}}{2} \qquad \tan\dfrac{\pi}{6} = \dfrac{1}{\sqrt{3}}$

$\sin\dfrac{\pi}{3} = \dfrac{\sqrt{3}}{2} \qquad \cos\dfrac{\pi}{3} = \dfrac{1}{2} \qquad \tan\dfrac{\pi}{3} = \sqrt{3}$

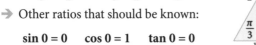

→ Other ratios that should be known:

$\sin 0 = 0 \qquad \cos 0 = 1 \qquad \tan 0 = 0$

$\sin\dfrac{\pi}{2} = 1 \qquad \cos\dfrac{\pi}{2} = 0 \qquad \tan\dfrac{\pi}{2}$ is undefined

---

→ The results for angles of any magnitude also apply to angles measured in radians: $\cos\theta = x$ and $\sin\theta = y$.

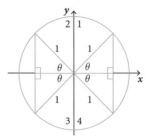

- In the **first** quadrant all ratios are **positive**.
- In the **second** quadrant sin is positive, but cos and tan are negative.

  $\sin(\pi - \theta) = \sin\theta$
  $\cos(\pi - \theta) = -\cos\theta$
  $\tan(\pi - \theta) = -\tan\theta$

- In the **third** quadrant tan is positive, but sin and cos are negative.

  $\sin(\pi + \theta) = -\sin\theta$
  $\cos(\pi + \theta) = -\cos\theta$
  $\tan(\pi + \theta) = \tan\theta$

- In the **fourth** quadrant cos is positive but sin and tan are negative.

  $\sin(2\pi - \theta) = -\sin\theta$
  $\cos(2\pi - \theta) = \cos\theta$
  $\tan(2\pi - \theta) = -\tan\theta$

## EXAMPLE 1

Find the exact value of:

a  $\cos\dfrac{3\pi}{4}$

b  $\sin\dfrac{5\pi}{3}$

a  $\cos\dfrac{3\pi}{4} = \cos\left(\pi - \dfrac{\pi}{4}\right)$

$\qquad = -\cos\dfrac{\pi}{4}$

The angle lies in the second quadrant, so cos is negative.

$\qquad = -\dfrac{1}{\sqrt{2}}$

b  $\sin\dfrac{5\pi}{3} = \sin\left(2\pi - \dfrac{\pi}{3}\right)$

$\qquad = -\sin\dfrac{\pi}{3}$

The angle lies in the fourth quadrant, so sin is negative.

$\qquad = -\dfrac{\sqrt{3}}{2}$

## EXAMPLE 2

Find the values of $\theta$, $0 \leq \theta \leq 2\pi$, for which $\cos \theta = \dfrac{3}{5}$.
Give the answers correct to four decimal places.

$\cos \theta = \dfrac{3}{5}$

Now $\cos^{-1}\left(\dfrac{3}{5}\right) = 0.927\,295\,21\ldots$

Because we are asked for values between 0 and $2\pi$ we know that radians are required. The calculator must be in radians mode.

cos is positive in the 1st and
4th quadrants
$\therefore \theta = 0.927\,295\,21\ldots$ or $\quad \theta = 2\pi - 0.927\,295\,21\ldots$
$\qquad\qquad\qquad\qquad\qquad\qquad = 5.355\,890\,08\ldots$
$\therefore \theta = 0.9273 \qquad$ or $\quad \theta = 5.3559 \quad$ (4 d.p.)

## EXAMPLE 3

Find all values of $\theta$, $0 \leq \theta \leq 2\pi$, for which $\tan \theta = -2$.
Give the answers correct to three decimal places.

$\tan \theta = -2$
Now $\tan^{-1}2 = 1.107\,148\,71\ldots$
tan is negative in the 2nd and 4th quadrants.
$\therefore \quad \theta = \pi - 1.107\,1487\ldots$ or $\quad \theta = 2\pi - 1.107\,148\,71\ldots$
$\quad \theta = 2.034\,443\,93\ldots$ or $\quad \theta = 5.176\,036\,58\ldots$
$\quad \theta = 2.034 \qquad$ or $\qquad \theta = 5.176 \quad$ (3 d.p.)

The size of the angle could be found in degrees (with the calculator in degrees mode) and then converted to radians, but it is much easier and quicker to have the calculator in radians mode.

### → PRACTICE

1 Find the exact value of:

a $\tan \dfrac{2\pi}{3}$

b $\sin \dfrac{7\pi}{4}$

2 Find the values of $\theta$, $0 \leq \theta \leq 2\pi$, for which $\tan \theta = \dfrac{5}{6}$. Give the answers correct to four decimal places.

3 Find all values of $\theta$, $0 \leq \theta \leq 2\pi$, for which $\sin \theta = -0.8$. Give the answers correct to three decimal places.

4* Find all values of $\theta$, $-\pi \leq \theta \leq \pi$, for which $\cos \theta = -0.8765$. Give the answers correct to four decimal places.

Answers ⊃ pp. 87–88

## 4 The graphs of $y = \sin x$, $y = \cos x$ and $y = \tan x$

→ $y = \sin x$ is a **function** of a real variable. The **domain** is the set of all real numbers. For any real number $x$, $\sin x$ is the sine of an angle of size $x$ radians. The **range** is $-1 \leq y \leq 1$.

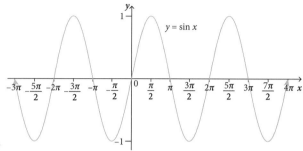

→ $y = \cos x$ is a **function** of a real variable. The **domain** is the set of all real numbers. For any real number $x$, $\cos x$ is the cosine of an angle of size $x$ radians. The **range** is $-1 \leq y \leq 1$.

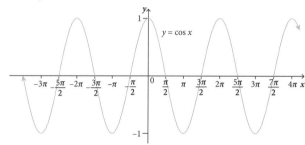

→ $y = \tan x$ is a **function** of a real variable. Because $\tan x = \dfrac{\sin x}{\cos x}$, $y = \tan x$ is **undefined** whenever $\cos x = 0$, i.e. $x = \pm\dfrac{\pi}{2}, \pm\dfrac{3\pi}{2}, \pm\dfrac{5\pi}{2}\ldots$

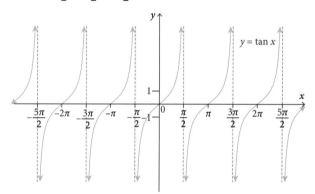

→ The graphs of the trigonometric functions are **periodic**. $y = \sin x$ and $y = \cos x$ have period $2\pi$. (The curves repeat every $2\pi$ radians.) $y = \tan x$ has period $\pi$.

→ The **amplitude** is the distance from the central position to the maximum (or minimum) value of a sine or cosine curve. (Because it is a distance, the amplitude is always positive.) The amplitude of $y = \sin x$ is 1 and the amplitude of $y = \cos x$ is 1.

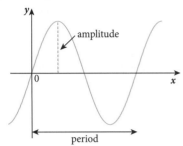

→ The graph of $y = a \sin nx$ has period $\dfrac{2\pi}{n}$ and amplitude $|a|$. The graph of $y = a \cos nx$ has period $\dfrac{2\pi}{n}$ and amplitude $|a|$. $y = a \tan nx$ has period $\dfrac{\pi}{n}$, the variable $a$ will be the value of the function when $nx = \dfrac{\pi}{4}$ (since $\tan \dfrac{\pi}{4} = 1$).

## EXAMPLE 1

**Sketch $y = 3 \sin 2x$.**

$y = 3 \sin 2x$
Amplitude = 3
Period $= \dfrac{2\pi}{2} = \pi$

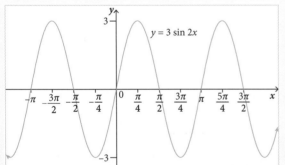

Because the amplitude is 3, the range is $-3 \leq y \leq 3$. The graph repeats every $\pi$ radians. All sine curves have the same form.

## EXAMPLE 2

**Sketch $y = 2 \cos\left(\dfrac{x}{2}\right)$, $-4\pi \leq x \leq 4\pi$.**

$y = 2 \cos\left(\dfrac{x}{2}\right)$

Amplitude = 2

Period $= \dfrac{2\pi}{\dfrac{1}{2}} = 4\pi$

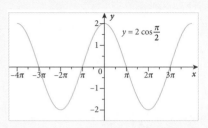

The value $n$ in $y = a \cos nx$ tells us how many times the curve repeats in $2\pi$ radians.

## EXAMPLE 3

**Sketch $y = 2 \tan \pi x$.**

Period $= \dfrac{\pi}{\pi} = 1$

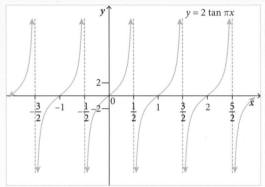

Because $\pi$ is included in the equation, the values on the $x$-axis do not include $\pi$.

→ **PRACTICE**

1  Sketch the graph of $y = 2 \sin 4x$.

2  Sketch the graph of $y = 3 \cos 2x$.

3  Sketch the graph of $y = 3 \tan \dfrac{x}{2}$ for $-2\pi \leq x \leq 2\pi$.

4*  Sketch the graph of $y = -\sin\left(\dfrac{x}{2}\right)$ for $-2\pi \leq x \leq 2\pi$.

Answers ⊃ p. 88

## 5 The length of an arc

➔ An **arc of a sector** of a circle is a **fraction of the circumference**. The particular fraction is determined by the angle at the centre of the circle.

➔ An angle of $\theta$ (measured in radians) will mean that the length of the arc is $\dfrac{\theta}{2\pi}$ of the circumference. Now $\dfrac{\theta}{2\pi}$ of $2\pi r$ is $r\theta$.

➔ **The formula for the length**, $l$ units, of an arc is $l = r\theta$ where $r$ is the radius of the circle and $\theta$ the angle at the centre measured in radians.

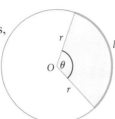

### EXAMPLE 1

An angle of $\dfrac{\pi}{5}$ radians is at the centre of a sector of a circle of radius 85 mm. Find the exact length of the arc of the sector.

$$l = r\theta$$
$$= 85 \times \frac{\pi}{5}$$
$$= 17\pi$$

*The exact length is required, so leave the answer in terms of $\pi$.*

∴ the length of the arc is $17\pi$ mm.

### EXAMPLE 2

The diagram shows a sector of a circle. Find the perimeter of the sector. Give the answer correct to one decimal place.

$$l = r\theta$$
$$= 7 \times \frac{5\pi}{9}$$
$$= 12.217\,3047\ldots$$
$$P = 2r + l$$
$$= 2 \times 7 + 12.217\,3047\ldots$$
$$= 26.217\,3047\ldots$$
$$= 26.2 \quad (1\ \text{d.p.})$$

*The perimeter of a sector is made up of two radii and the arc length.*

∴ the perimeter of the sector is 26.2 cm, correct to one decimal place.

### EXAMPLE 3

A sector has radius 15.8 m. Find the length of the arc, if the angle at the centre of the circle is 135°. Give the answer correct to two decimal places.

$$l = r\theta$$
$$= 15.8 \times 135° \times \frac{\pi}{180°}$$
$$= 37.227\,8729\ldots$$
$$= 37.23 \quad (2\ \text{d.p.})$$

*If the size of the angle is given in degrees, it must be converted to radians in order to find the arc length.*

∴ the length of the arc is 37.23 m, correct to two decimal places.

### EXAMPLE 4

An angle of $\dfrac{5\pi}{3}$ radians is subtended by an arc of length $12\pi$ m. Find the radius.

$$l = r\theta$$
$$12\pi = r \times \frac{5\pi}{3}$$
$$r = 12\pi \div \frac{5\pi}{3}$$
$$= 12\pi \times \frac{3}{5\pi}$$
$$= 7.2$$

*'Subtend' means to extend under or be opposite to. The radii drawn to the ends of the arc form the angle where they meet.*

∴ the length of the radius is 7.2 m.

### EXAMPLE 5

A sector of a circle of radius 8 cm has an arc of length 5 cm. Find, to the nearest degree, the size of the angle subtended by the arc.

$$l = r\theta$$
$$5 = 8\theta$$
$$\theta = \frac{5}{8}$$
$$= \frac{5}{8} \times \frac{180°}{\pi}$$
$$= 35.809\,862\ldots°$$
$$= 36° \quad (\text{nearest degree})$$

*The angle found using the formula is in radians. It must be converted if the answer in degrees is required.*

∴ the size of the angle is 36°, to the nearest degree.

### ➔ PRACTICE

1   An angle of $\dfrac{\pi}{8}$ radians is at the centre of a sector of a circle of radius 72 cm. Find the exact length of the arc of the sector.

2   The diagram shows a sector of a circle. Find the perimeter of the sector. Give the answer correct to one decimal place.

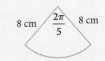

3  A sector has radius 7.8 cm. Find the length of the arc if it subtends an angle of 120°. Give the answer correct to two decimal places.

4  An angle of $\frac{7\pi}{6}$ radians subtends an arc of length 14π m. Find the radius.

5  A sector of a circle of radius 6 cm has an arc length of 4 cm. Find, to the nearest degree, the size of the angle subtended by the arc.

6*  Find the exact length of the arc of a sector of a circle of radius 12 cm if the arc subtends an angle at the centre of 50°.

Answers ➲ p. 88

## 6 The area of a sector

➜ The area of a sector of a circle is a **fraction of the area of the circle**. The particular fraction is determined by the angle at the centre of the circle.

➜ An angle of θ (measured in radians) will mean that the **area of the sector** is $\frac{\theta}{2\pi}$ of the area of the circle.
Now $\frac{\theta}{2\pi}$ of $\pi r^2$ is $\frac{1}{2}r^2\theta$.

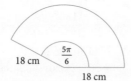

➜ The formula for the area, A units², of a sector is $A = \frac{1}{2}r^2\theta$ where r is the radius of the circle and θ the angle at the centre measured in radians.

### EXAMPLE 1

**The diagram shows a sector. Find its exact area.**

18 cm    $\frac{5\pi}{6}$

18 cm

$A = \frac{1}{2}r^2\theta$

$= \frac{1}{2} \times 18^2 \times \frac{5\pi}{6}$

Because we want the exact area we leave the answer in terms of π.

$= 135\pi$

∴ the area of the sector is 135π cm².

### EXAMPLE 2

A sector of a circle of radius 87 cm has angle at the centre of $\frac{11\pi}{8}$ radians. Find the area of the sector to the nearest square centimetre.

$A = \frac{1}{2}r^2\theta$

$= \frac{1}{2} \times 87^2 \times \frac{11\pi}{8}$

Because the angle is greater than π, this sector is larger than a semicircle.

$= 16\,347.8664\ldots$

$= 16\,348$    (nearest whole number)

∴ the area of the sector is 16 348 cm², to the nearest square centimetre.

### EXAMPLE 3

A sector of a circle of radius 4 m has its angle at the centre 75°. Find its area correct to one decimal place.

$A = \frac{1}{2}r^2\theta$

$= \frac{1}{2} \times 4^2 \times 75° \times \frac{\pi}{180°}$

The angle must be in radians. If it is in degrees it must be converted to radians. This can be done at the same time as finding the area.

$= 10.471\,9755\ldots$

$= 10.5$    (1 d.p.)

∴ the area of the sector is 10.5 m², to one decimal place.

### EXAMPLE 4

A sector of a circle has area 45π m². Find the radius if the angle subtended at the centre is $\frac{2\pi}{5}$.

$A = \frac{1}{2}r^2\theta$

$45\pi = \frac{1}{2} \times r^2 \times \frac{2\pi}{5}$

$45 = \frac{r^2}{5}$

$r^2 = 225$

$r = 15$   (r > 0)

The radius is a length so cannot be negative.

∴ the radius of the sector is 15 m.

### EXAMPLE 5

Find the size, in degrees, of the angle at the centre of a sector of radius 6 cm, if the area is 8π cm².

$A = \frac{1}{2}r^2\theta$

$8\pi = \frac{1}{2} \times 6^2 \times \theta$

$8\pi = 18\theta$

$\therefore \theta = \frac{8\pi}{18} \times \frac{180°}{\pi}$

There is no need to simplify the fraction before converting from radians to degrees.

$= 80°$

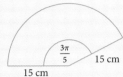

## → PRACTICE

1. The diagram shows a sector.

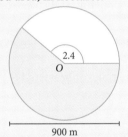

Find its exact area.

2. A sector of a circle of radius 57 cm has angle at the centre of $\frac{10\pi}{9}$ radians. Find the area of the sector to the nearest square centimetre.

3. A sector of a circle of radius 13 m has its angle at the centre 70°. Find its area correct to one decimal place.

4. Find the radius of a sector of a circle of area $28\pi$ m² if the angle subtended at the centre is $\frac{2\pi}{7}$.

5. Find the size, in degrees, of the angle at the centre of a sector of radius 12 m, if the area is $60\pi$ m².

6* Find the shaded area, in hectares.

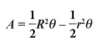

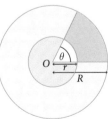

Answers ⊃ p. 89

## 7 Composite areas and problems

→ It might be necessary to first find the **angle or the radius** when solving problems involving parts of a circle.

→ A required area might be a **combination** of a sector and some other regular figure. The area can be found by adding the areas together.

→ The **area between two sectors** can be found by subtracting the smaller area from the larger one:

$$A = \frac{1}{2}R^2\theta - \frac{1}{2}r^2\theta$$

$$A = \frac{1}{2}\theta(R^2 - r^2)$$

→ The **area of a segment** can be found by subtracting the area of a triangle from the area of a sector:

$$A = \frac{1}{2}r^2\theta - \frac{1}{2}r^2\sin\theta$$

$$A = \frac{1}{2}r^2(\theta - \sin\theta)$$

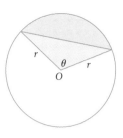

### EXAMPLE 1

The arc length of a sector is $9\pi$ cm. Find the area of the sector if the radius is 6 cm.

$$l = r\theta$$
$$9\pi = 6\theta$$
$$\theta = \frac{9\pi}{6}$$
$$= \frac{3\pi}{2}$$
$$A = \frac{1}{2}r^2\theta$$
$$= \frac{1}{2} \times 6^2 \times \frac{3\pi}{2}$$
$$= 27\pi$$

An angle of $\frac{3\pi}{2}$ is 270° and so the sector is $\frac{3}{4}$ of a circle of radius 6 cm.

∴ the area of the sector is $27\pi$ cm².

### EXAMPLE 2

Find the shaded area.

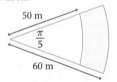

$$A = \frac{1}{2}R^2\theta - \frac{1}{2}r^2\theta$$
$$= \frac{1}{2} \times 60^2 \times \frac{\pi}{5} - \frac{1}{2} \times 50^2 \times \frac{\pi}{5}$$
$$= 110\pi$$

The shaded area is $110\pi$ m².

Or factorise first: $\frac{1}{2} \times \frac{\pi}{5} \times (60^2 - 50^2)$.

### EXAMPLE 3

The diagram shows a figure made up of a semicircle and a sector. Find its exact area.

The shape comprises a sector of radius 12 cm and a semicircle with diameter 12 cm.

$A = \dfrac{1}{2}R^2\theta + \dfrac{1}{2}\pi r^2$

The diameter of the semicircle is equal to the radius of the sector. So the radius of the semicircle is 6 cm.

$= \dfrac{1}{2} \times 12^2 \times \dfrac{\pi}{3} + \dfrac{1}{2} \times \pi \times 6^2$

$= 24\pi + 18\pi$

$= 42\pi$

$\therefore$ the area of the figure is $42\pi$ cm$^2$.

## EXAMPLE 4

The shaded region is a segment of a circle. Find its exact area.

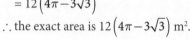

$A = \dfrac{1}{2}r^2(\theta - \sin\theta)$

$= \dfrac{1}{2} \times 12^2 \times \left(\dfrac{2\pi}{3} - \sin\dfrac{2\pi}{3}\right)$

$= 72\left(\dfrac{2\pi}{3} - \dfrac{\sqrt{3}}{2}\right)$

$= 72\left(\dfrac{4\pi - 3\sqrt{3}}{6}\right)$

$= 12\left(4\pi - 3\sqrt{3}\right)$

$\therefore$ the exact area is $12\left(4\pi - 3\sqrt{3}\right)$ m$^2$.

Extreme care must be taken when using this formula and a calculator. In the first part of the formula $\theta$ must be in radians. In the second part ($\sin\theta$), it doesn't matter whether $\theta$ is in degrees or radians provided the calculator is in the matching mode.

### → PRACTICE

1  The arc length of a sector is $8\pi$ cm. Find the area of the sector if the radius is 5 cm.

2  Find the exact shaded area.

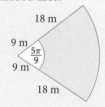

3  The diagram shows a figure made up of a semicircle and a sector. Find its exact area.

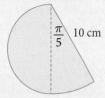

4  The shaded region is a segment of a circle. Find its exact area in square centimetres.

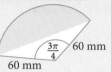

5*  Find the shaded area.

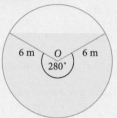

Answers ⊃ p. 89

## Trigonometric functions and identities

### 1 $y = \operatorname{cosec} x$

→ cosec is short for **cosecant**.

→ $y = \operatorname{cosec} x$ is the **reciprocal function** of $y = \sin x$.

→ $\operatorname{cosec} x = \dfrac{1}{\sin x}$    $(\sin x \neq 0)$

→ $y = \operatorname{cosec} x$ is **undefined** when $\sin x = 0$, i.e. $x = 0, \pm\pi, \pm 2\pi \ldots$

→ The **period** of the graph of $y = \operatorname{cosec} x$ is $2\pi$ and the **range** is $y \leq -1$ and $y \geq 1$.

→ $\operatorname{cosec} x$ is sometimes **abbreviated** to **csc $x$**.

## EXAMPLE 1

Find cosec 37° to four decimal places.

cosec 37° = 1.661 640 14…
           = 1.6616   (4 d.p.)

Either enter sin 37° and then the reciprocal button $\left(\dfrac{1}{x} \text{ or } x^{-1}\right)$ or use the fraction button $\left(\dfrac{1}{\sin 37°}\right)$.

## EXAMPLE 2

Find the exact value of $\operatorname{cosec} \dfrac{\pi}{3}$.

$$\operatorname{cosec} \frac{\pi}{3} = \frac{1}{\sin \frac{\pi}{3}}$$

$$= \frac{1}{\frac{\sqrt{3}}{2}}$$

$$= \frac{2}{\sqrt{3}}$$

There is no need to rationalise the denominator.

## EXAMPLE 3

Sketch $y = \operatorname{cosec} x$ for $0° < x < 360°$.

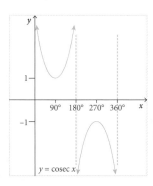

If $\sin x > 0$, $\operatorname{cosec} x > 0$; if $\sin x < 0$, $\operatorname{cosec} x < 0$; there are asymptotes at values of $x$ for which $\sin x = 0$.

## EXAMPLE 4

Sketch $y = 2 \operatorname{cosec} 3x$ for $-\pi < x < \pi$.

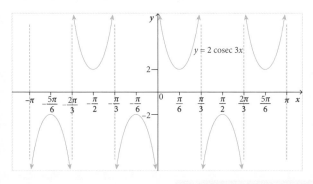

Period $= \dfrac{2\pi}{3}$; range is $y \le -2$ and $y \ge 2$.

## → PRACTICE

1  Find $\operatorname{cosec} 68°$ to four decimal places.

2  Find the exact value of $\operatorname{cosec} \dfrac{\pi}{4}$.

---

3  Sketch $y = \operatorname{cosec} x$ for $-180° < x < 720°$.

4  Sketch $y = 3 \operatorname{cosec} 2x$ for $0 < x < 2\pi$.

5*  Find the value(s) of $\theta$, $0° < \theta < 360°$, for which $\operatorname{cosec} \theta = 1.2345$.

Answers ⊃ p. 90

## 2 $y = \sec x$

→ sec is short for **secant**.

→ $y = \sec x$ is the **reciprocal function** of $y = \cos x$.

→ $\sec x = \dfrac{1}{\cos x}$  $(\cos x \ne 0)$

→ $y = \sec x$ is **undefined** when $\cos x = 0$,

  i.e. $x = \pm\dfrac{\pi}{2}, \pm\dfrac{3\pi}{2}, \pm\dfrac{5\pi}{2}\ldots$

→ The **period** of the graph of $y = \sec x$ is $2\pi$ and the **range** is $y \le -1$ and $y \ge 1$.

## EXAMPLE 1

Find $\sec 74°$ to four decimal places.

$\sec 74° = 3.627\,955\,27\ldots$
$\qquad = 3.6280$   (4 d.p.)

Either enter cos 74° and then the reciprocal button or use the fraction button.

## EXAMPLE 2

Find the exact value of $\sec \dfrac{5\pi}{6}$.

$$\sec \frac{5\pi}{6} = \frac{1}{\cos \frac{5\pi}{6}}$$

$$= \frac{1}{\cos\left(\pi - \frac{\pi}{6}\right)}$$

$$= \frac{1}{-\cos \frac{\pi}{6}}$$

$$= \frac{1}{-\frac{\sqrt{3}}{2}}$$

$$= -\frac{2}{\sqrt{3}}$$

An angle of $\dfrac{5\pi}{6}$ lies in the second quadrant, so $\cos \dfrac{5\pi}{6}$ (and hence $\sec \dfrac{5\pi}{6}$) is negative.

## EXAMPLE 3

Sketch $y = \sec x$ for $-270° \leq x \leq 270°$.

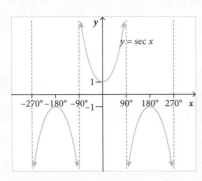

If $\cos x > 0$, $\sec x > 0$; if $\cos x < 0$, $\sec x < 0$; there are asymptotes at values of $x$ for which $\cos x = 0$.

## EXAMPLE 4

Sketch $y = 3 \sec 2x$ for $-2\pi \leq x \leq 2\pi$.

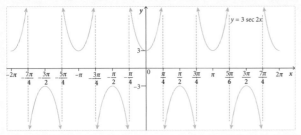

Period $= \dfrac{2\pi}{2} = \pi$ and range is $y \leq -3$ and $y \geq 3$.

### → PRACTICE

1   Find $\sec 19°$ to four decimal places.

2   Find the exact value of $\sec \dfrac{3\pi}{4}$.

3   Sketch $y = \sec x$ for $0° \leq x \leq 720°$.

4   Sketch $y = 2 \sec \dfrac{x}{2}$ for $-3\pi \leq x \leq 5\pi$.

5*  Find the values of $\theta$, $0 \leq \theta \leq 2\pi$, for which $\sec \theta = 2$.

Answers ⊃ p. 90

## 3  $y = \cot x$

→ cot is short for **cotangent**.

→ $y = \cot x$ is the **reciprocal function** of $y = \tan x$.

→ $\cot x = \dfrac{1}{\tan x}$  $(\tan x \neq 0)$

→ $y = \cot x$ is **undefined** when $\tan x = 0$,
   i.e. $x = 0, \pm\pi, \pm 2\pi \ldots$

→ The **period** of the graph of $y = \cot x$ is $\pi$ and the **range** is all real values of $y$.

## EXAMPLE 1

Find $\cot 52°$ to four decimal places.

$\cot 52° = 0.781\,285\,626\ldots$
$\qquad\quad = 0.7813$   (4 d.p.)

Either enter tan 52° and then the reciprocal button or use the fraction button.

## EXAMPLE 2

Find the exact value of $\cot \dfrac{4\pi}{3}$.

$$\tan \frac{4\pi}{3} = \tan\left(\pi + \frac{\pi}{3}\right)$$
$$= \tan \frac{\pi}{3}$$
$$= \sqrt{3}$$
$$\therefore \cot \frac{4\pi}{3} = \frac{1}{\sqrt{3}}$$

$\dfrac{4\pi}{3}$ is in the third quadrant, so $\tan \dfrac{4\pi}{3}$ and $\cot \dfrac{4\pi}{3}$ are both positive.

## EXAMPLE 3

Sketch $y = \cot x$ for $-360° \leq x \leq 360°$.

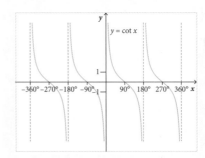

If $\tan x > 0$, $\cot x > 0$; if $\tan x < 0$, $\cot x < 0$; there are asymptotes at values of $x$ for which $\tan x = 0$; $\cot x = 0$ when $\tan x$ is undefined.

## EXAMPLE 4

Sketch $y = \dfrac{1}{2}\cot\dfrac{x}{2}$ for $0 < x < 2\pi$.

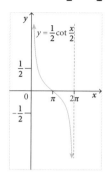

Period $= \dfrac{\pi}{\frac{1}{2}} = 2\pi$

---

→ **PRACTICE**

1  Find $\cot 39°$ to four decimal places.

2  Find the exact value of $\cot\dfrac{5\pi}{6}$.

3  Sketch $y = \cot x$ for $0° \le x \le 720°$.

4  Sketch $y = 2\cot 2x$ for $0 \le x \le \pi$.

5*  Find the size of the acute angle $\theta$ for which $\cot\theta = 5$. Give the answer to the nearest minute.

Answers ⊃ pp. 90–91

## 4 Expressions and identities

→  $\tan x = \dfrac{\sin x}{\cos x}$  $(\cos x \ne 0)$

→  $\cos^2 x$ means $(\cos x)^2$ and $\sin^2 x$ means $(\sin x)^2$. The $^2$ is written after the ratio so that we don't confuse, for example, $(\cos x)^2$ with $\cos(x^2)$.

→  From the unit circle we have $x^2 + y^2 = 1$. Substituting $\cos\theta = x$ and $\sin\theta = y$ gives the result $\cos^2\theta + \sin^2\theta = 1$.

→  An **identity** is something that is true for all values of the variable. The symbol $\equiv$ is sometimes used. It means 'is identically equal to'. The above result is an identity: $\cos^2 x + \sin^2 x \equiv 1$. Dividing by $\cos^2 x$ gives another identity: $1 + \tan^2 x \equiv \sec^2 x$. Dividing instead by $\sin^2 x$ gives the third of these **Pythagorean** identities: $\cot^2 x + 1 \equiv \operatorname{cosec}^2 x$.

→  **Co-ratios** are complementary ratios. As well as sine and **co**sine, tangent and **co**tangent (tan and cot) are co-ratios; $\tan\theta = \cot(90° - \theta)$ and $\cot\theta = \tan(90° - \theta)$, and secant and **co**secant are co-ratios; $\sec\theta = \operatorname{cosec}(90° - \theta)$ and $\operatorname{cosec}\theta = \sec(90° - \theta)$.

---

## EXAMPLE 1

Given that $\cos^2 x + \sin^2 x = 1$, show that $\sec^2 x - \tan^2 x = 1$.

$$\cos^2 x + \sin^2 x = 1$$
$$\frac{\cos^2 x}{\cos^2 x} + \frac{\sin^2 x}{\cos^2 x} = \frac{1}{\cos^2 x}$$
$$1 + \tan^2 x = \sec^2 x$$
$$1 = \sec^2 x - \tan^2 x$$

We begin by dividing each term by $\cos^2 x$.

## EXAMPLE 2

Show that $(\sin x + \cos x)(\sin x - \cos x) = 2\sin^2 x - 1$.

$$(\sin x + \cos x)(\sin x - \cos x) = \sin^2 x - \cos^2 x$$
$$= \sin^2 x - (1 - \sin^2 x)$$
$$= \sin^2 x - 1 + \sin^2 x$$
$$= 2\sin^2 x - 1$$

The sum of two terms multiplied by their difference produces the difference of two squares.

## EXAMPLE 3

Simplify $\dfrac{1}{\operatorname{cosec} x + \cot x} - \dfrac{1}{\operatorname{cosec} x - \cot x}$.

$$\frac{1}{\operatorname{cosec} x + \cot x} - \frac{1}{\operatorname{cosec} x - \cot x}$$
$$= \frac{(\operatorname{cosec} x - \cot x) - (\operatorname{cosec} x + \cot x)}{(\operatorname{cosec} x + \cot x)(\operatorname{cosec} x - \cot x)}$$
$$= \frac{\operatorname{cosec} x - \cot x - \operatorname{cosec} x - \cot x}{\operatorname{cosec}^2 x - \cot^2 x}$$
$$= \frac{-2\cot x}{\cot^2 x + 1 - \cot^2 x}$$
$$= -2\cot x$$

Use brackets when subtracting so that the signs are correct.

## EXAMPLE 4

Find the value of $x$, $0 < x < \dfrac{\pi}{2}$, if $\tan x = \cot\dfrac{3\pi}{10}$.

$$\tan x = \cot\frac{3\pi}{10}$$

Now $\cot\dfrac{3\pi}{10} = \tan\left(\dfrac{\pi}{2} - \dfrac{3\pi}{10}\right)$

$$= \tan\left(\frac{5\pi}{10} - \frac{3\pi}{10}\right)$$
$$= \tan\frac{2\pi}{10}$$
$$= \tan\frac{\pi}{5}$$

So $x = \dfrac{\pi}{5}$.

You could convert $\dfrac{3\pi}{10}$ into degrees to work out the answer, but the answer must be given in radians.

→ PRACTICE

1  Given that $\cos^2 x + \sin^2 x = 1$, show that $\text{cosec}^2 x - \cot^2 x = 1$.

2  Show that $(\sin x + \cos x)^2 + (\sin x - \cos x)^2 = 2$.

3  Simplify $\dfrac{1}{\sec x - \tan x} - \dfrac{1}{\sec x + \tan x}$.

4  Find the value of $x$, $0 \le x \le \dfrac{\pi}{2}$, if $\text{cosec } x = \sec \dfrac{2\pi}{9}$.

5*  Show that $\cot^2 x - \cos^2 x = \cos^2 x \cot^2 x$.

Answers ⊃ p. 91

## 5 Equations

→ **Trig equations** can be solved using all the rules that apply to ordinary equations.

→ When solving trig equations, it is necessary to find **all the solutions** in the specified domain.

→ The given **domain** will also determine whether the solution is required in **degrees** or in **radians**.

### EXAMPLE 1

Find all values of $x$, $0° \le x \le 360°$, for which $7 \sin x = 5 \sin x - 1$.

$7 \sin x = 5 \sin x - 1$
$2 \sin x = -1$
$\sin x = -\dfrac{1}{2}$
Now $\sin 30° = \dfrac{1}{2}$.

sin is negative in the 3rd and 4th quadrants.
$x = 180° + 30°$  or  $x = 360° - 30°$
$x = 210°$    or  $x = 330°$

Like all equations you can substitute the solutions into the original equation to check that it is correct.

### EXAMPLE 2

Solve $\tan^2 \theta = 3$ for $0 \le \theta \le 2\pi$.

$\tan^2 \theta = 3$
$\tan \theta = \pm\sqrt{3}$
Now $\tan \dfrac{\pi}{3} = \sqrt{3}$

$\therefore \theta = \dfrac{\pi}{3}$ or $\pi - \dfrac{\pi}{3}$ or $\pi + \dfrac{\pi}{3}$ or $2\pi - \dfrac{\pi}{3}$

$\therefore \theta = \dfrac{\pi}{3}, \dfrac{2\pi}{3}, \dfrac{4\pi}{3}$ or $\dfrac{5\pi}{3}$.

Both positive and negative values must be considered. So the angle can lie in any of the four quadrants.

### EXAMPLE 3

Find all values of $\theta$, for $-\pi \le \theta \le \pi$, for which $\sin \theta = \cos \theta$.

$\sin \theta = \cos \theta$
$\therefore \dfrac{\sin \theta}{\cos \theta} = 1$    $(\cos \theta \ne 0)$
$\therefore \tan \theta = 1$
Now $\tan \dfrac{\pi}{4} = 1$.

tan is positive in the first and third quadrants.
$-\pi \le \theta \le \pi$
$\therefore \theta = -\pi + \dfrac{\pi}{4}$  or  $\theta = \dfrac{\pi}{4}$

$\therefore \theta = \dfrac{\pi}{4}$    or  $\theta = -\dfrac{3\pi}{4}$

When $\cos \theta = 0$, $\sin \theta = 1$ ($\ne \cos \theta$), so $\cos \theta = 0$ is not a solution to the equation. Because $\cos \theta \ne 0$ we can divide by it.

### EXAMPLE 4

Solve $2 \sin 3x + \sqrt{3} = 0$ for $0 \le x \le \pi$.

$0 \le x \le \pi$
$\therefore 0 \le 3x \le 3\pi$

$2 \sin 3x + \sqrt{3} = 0$
$2 \sin 3x = -\sqrt{3}$
$\sin 3x = -\dfrac{\sqrt{3}}{2}$

Now $\sin \dfrac{\pi}{3} = \dfrac{\sqrt{3}}{2}$

Because we need to find the possible values of $3x$ we need to consider the domain for $3x$.

sin is negative in the third and fourth quadrants.
$\therefore 3x = \pi + \dfrac{\pi}{3}$ or $3x = 2\pi - \dfrac{\pi}{3}$

$3x = \dfrac{4\pi}{3}$  or  $3x = \dfrac{5\pi}{3}$

$\therefore x = \dfrac{4\pi}{9}$  or  $x = \dfrac{5\pi}{9}$

→ PRACTICE

1  Find all values of $x$, $0° \le x \le 360°$, for which $9 \cos x = \cos x - 4$.

2  Solve $\cos^2 \theta = \dfrac{1}{2}$ for $0 \le \theta \le 2\pi$.

3  Find all values of $\theta$, $-\pi \le \theta \le \pi$, for which $\sin \theta + \cos \theta = 0$.

4  Solve $\sqrt{3} \tan 2x = 1$ for $0 \le x \le \pi$.

**5\*** Find all values of $\theta$, $0 \leq \theta \leq 2\pi$, for which $3 \sin \theta - 1 = 0$. Give each answer correct to two decimal places.

Answers ⊃ pp. 91–92

## 6 Further equations

→ Trig equations can be solved **graphically**. If the graphs of two trigonometric functions are drawn, the **points of intersection** give the values that satisfy both equations at the same time. If drawing two or more graphs on the same axes, the **same scale** must be used.

→ **Quadratic equations** involved trig functions can also be solved. Trig equations might be able to be factorised or the quadratic equation could be used.

→ The **trig identities** may be needed to simplify an expression before an equation can be solved.

### EXAMPLE 1

a **On the same set of axes sketch the graphs of $y = \cos x$ and $y = -\sin x$ for $-2\pi \leq x \leq 2\pi$.**

b **For what values of $x$ ($-2\pi \leq x \leq 2\pi$) does $\cos x = -\sin x$?**

a
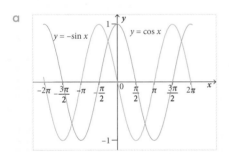

b From the graph $\cos x = -\sin x$ when
$$x = -\frac{5\pi}{4}, -\frac{\pi}{4}, \frac{3\pi}{4} \text{ and } \frac{7\pi}{4}$$

Sketch both $y = \cos x$ and $y = -\sin x$ on the same diagram and look for the points of intersection. It is immediately obvious from the graph that there are four solutions within the given domain.

### EXAMPLE 2

Solve $\operatorname{cosec}^2 x = 2$ for $0° \leq x \leq 360°$.

$\operatorname{cosec}^2 x = 2$
$\operatorname{cosec} x = \pm\sqrt{2}$

cosec is the reciprocal of sin.

$\therefore \quad \sin x = \pm\dfrac{1}{\sqrt{2}}$

$\quad x = 45°, 180° - 45°, 180° + 45° \text{ or } 360° - 45°$
$\quad x = 45°, 135°, 225° \text{ or } 315°$

### EXAMPLE 3

Show that the equation $\sin^2 x + 3 \sin x + 2 = 0$ has only one solution for $0 \leq x \leq 2\pi$ and find that solution.

$\sin^2 x + 3 \sin x + 2 = 0$
$(\sin x + 2)(\sin x + 1) = 0$
$\sin x + 2 = 0 \quad \text{or} \quad \sin x + 1 = 0$
$\quad \sin x = -2 \quad \text{or} \quad \sin x = -1$

No solution $\qquad\qquad x = \pi + \dfrac{\pi}{2}$

The range of $y = \sin x$ is $-1 \leq y \leq 1$ so there is no solution to $\sin x = -2$.

$$x = \frac{3\pi}{2}$$

$\therefore$ the equation has only one solution: $x = \dfrac{3\pi}{2}$.

### EXAMPLE 4

**Solve $\sec^2 x - \tan x = 7$ for $0° \leq x \leq 360°$. Give each answer to the nearest minute.**

$\sec^2 x - \tan x = 7$
$1 + \tan^2 x - \tan x = 7$
$\tan^2 x - \tan x - 6 = 0$

We need to find a link between $\sec^2 x$ and $\tan x$ so that is the identity $1 + \tan^2 x = \sec^2 x$.

$(\tan x - 3)(\tan x + 2) = 0$
$\therefore \tan x = 3 \quad \text{or} \quad \tan x = -2$
Now $\tan^{-1} 3 = 71°33'54.18''$
If $\tan x = 3$,
$x = 71°33'54.18'' \text{ or } 180° + 71°33'54.18''$
$x = 71° 34' \text{ or } 251° 34' \quad \text{(nearest minute)}$
Now $\tan^{-1} 2 = 63°26'5.82''$
If $\tan x = -2$,
$x = 180° - 63°26'5.82'' \text{ or } 360° - 63°26'5.82''$
$x = 116° 34' \text{ or } 296° 34' \quad \text{(nearest minute)}$
$\therefore x = 71° 34' \text{ or } 116° 34' \text{ or } 251° 34' \text{ or } 296° 34'$ to the nearest minute.

### → PRACTICE

1 a **On the same set of axes, for $0 \leq x \leq 2\pi$, sketch the graphs of $y = \cos x$ and $y = \sin x$.**

  b **For what values of $x$, $0 \leq x \leq 2\pi$, does $\cos x = \sin x$?**

2 **Solve $\cot^2 x = 3$ for $0° \leq x \leq 360°$.**

3 **Show that the equation $\sin^2 x + 2 \sin x - 3 = 0$ has only one solution for $0 \leq x \leq 2\pi$ and find that solution.**

4 **Solve $\sec^2 x = \tan x + 13$ for $0° \leq x \leq 360°$. Give each answer to the nearest minute.**

5\* **Solve $2 \sin x = \tan x$ for $0 \leq x \leq 2\pi$.**

Answers ⊃ p. 92

**Total marks: 50**

## PART A

(Suggested time: 15 minutes)

(1 mark each)

1  What is $\dfrac{5\pi}{6}$ in degrees?

   **A** 120°   **B** 135°   **C** 150°   **D** 160°

2  What is the exact value of tan 210°?

   **A** $\dfrac{1}{\sqrt{2}}$   **B** $\dfrac{1}{\sqrt{3}}$   **C** $\dfrac{\sqrt{3}}{2}$   **D** $\sqrt{3}$

3  In order to find the value of $x$ in each of these triangles, which rule should be used?

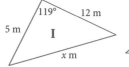 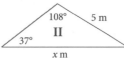

   **A** sine rule in both
   **B** sine rule in I, cosine rule in II
   **C** cosine rule in both
   **D** cosine rule in I, sine rule in II

4  $C$ is due west of $B$. $\angle ABC = 30°$ and $\angle ACB = 40°$. What is the bearing of $B$ from $A$?

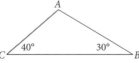

   **A** 110°   **B** 120°   **C** 130°   **D** 150°

5  What is the value of cos $\theta$?

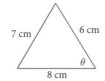

   **A** $\dfrac{1}{4}$   **B** $\dfrac{3}{4}$   **C** $\dfrac{11}{16}$   **D** $\dfrac{17}{32}$

6  Which is **not** correct if $0° \le \theta \le 90°$?

   **A** $\sin \theta = \operatorname{cosec}\left(\dfrac{1}{\theta}\right)$

   **B** $\tan \theta = \cot (90° - \theta)$
   **C** $\sec (360° - \theta) = \sec \theta$
   **D** $\cos (180° - \theta) = \cos (180° + \theta)$

7  What is the length of an arc of a sector of a circle of radius 24 cm if the angle at the centre is 75°?

   **A** 5 cm   **B** $5\pi$ cm   **C** 10 cm   **D** $10\pi$ cm

8  What is the area of this triangle?

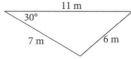

   **A** 19.25 m²   **B** 10.5 m²   **C** 16.5 m²   **D** 38.5 m²

9  Which is the graph of $y = \sec x$ for $-180° \le x \le 180°$?

   **A** 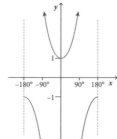   **B**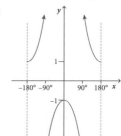

   **C** 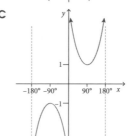   **D**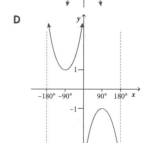

10  What are the solutions of $2 \cos x + \sqrt{3} = 0$ for $0 \le x \le 2\pi$?

   **A** $x = \dfrac{\pi}{6}$ and $x = \dfrac{11\pi}{6}$

   **B** $x = \dfrac{\pi}{3}$ and $x = \dfrac{5\pi}{3}$

   **C** $x = \dfrac{5\pi}{6}$ and $x = \dfrac{7\pi}{6}$

   **D** $x = \dfrac{2\pi}{3}$ and $x = \dfrac{4\pi}{3}$

11  To the nearest degree, what could be the size of $\angle PQR$?

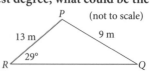

   **A** 44° only
   **B** 136° only
   **C** either 44° or 136°
   **D** neither 44° nor 136°

**12** Which is correct for the graph of $y = 2 \sin \frac{x}{2}$?

   **A** amplitude = 2; period = $\pi$

   **B** amplitude = 2; period = $4\pi$

   **C** amplitude = $\frac{1}{2}$; period = $\pi$

   **D** amplitude = $\frac{1}{2}$; period = $4\pi$

**PART B**          (Suggested time: 45 minutes)

Show all working.

**13** Express $\frac{4\pi}{5}$ in degrees.     (1 mark)

**14** Express 108° in radians in terms of $\pi$.   (1 mark)

**15** Find the value of cosec $\frac{2\pi}{5}$ to four decimal places. (1 mark)

**16** PQRS is a parallelogram. PQ = 7 m, QR = 4 m and $\angle PQR = 60°$.

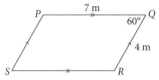

   Find the exact area of the parallelogram.   (2 marks)

**17** Find all solutions of $2 \sin^2 x = 1$ for $0 \leq x \leq 2\pi$.  (2 marks)

**18** A garden bed is bordered by two circular arcs (AB and CD) which subtend an angle of $\frac{3\pi}{8}$ at the centre O. OA = 5 m and AC = 9 m.

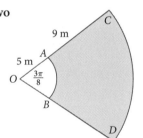

   **a** Find the perimeter of the garden bed. Give the correct answer to one decimal place.  (3 marks)

   **b** Topsoil needs to be added to the bed to a depth of 30 cm. Find the amount of topsoil needed in cubic metres, correct to one decimal place.  (2 marks)

**19** AB = 301 m, $\angle ACD = 147°$, $\angle BAD = 22°$ and $\angle CBD = 29°$

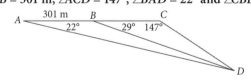

   **a** Find an expression for BD.  (2 marks)

   **b** Hence show that $CD = \dfrac{301 \sin 22° \sin 29°}{\sin 7° \sin 147°}$ and find the length of CD to the nearest metre.  (2 marks)

**20 a** Find the exact value of $3 \tan \frac{\pi}{6}$ and hence show that $3 \tan \frac{\pi}{6} = 2 \cos \frac{\pi}{6}$.  (2 marks)

   **b** On the same set of axes sketch the curves $y = 3 \tan x$ and $y = 2 \cos x$ for $-\frac{\pi}{2} \leq x \leq \frac{\pi}{2}$.  (2 marks)

   **c** Write down all solutions of $3 \tan x = 2 \cos x$ for $-\frac{\pi}{2} \leq x \leq \frac{\pi}{2}$. Justify your answer.  (1 mark)

**21** Three points, A, B and C, are such that B is 57 m from A and 94 m from C. The bearing of A from C is 312° and of B from C is 286°.

   **a** Show this information on a diagram.  (1 mark)

   **b** Find the size of $\angle BAC$.  (3 marks)

**22** Show that $\tan \alpha + \cot \alpha = \dfrac{1}{\sin \alpha \cos \alpha}$.  (2 marks)

**23** A and B are two positions at sea level, 1 km apart. From A the angle of elevation of the top of a tower, C, on a nearby hill is 38° and from B the angle of elevation of C is 29°. If A is due south of the tower and B is due east of the tower find the height of C above sea level.  (4 marks)

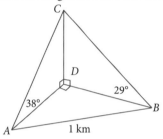

**24** $\triangle ABC$ is equilateral, of side length 1 unit. $\triangle ADC$ is isosceles, right-angled at C.

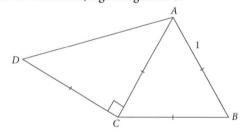

   **a** Use the cosine rule in $\triangle DAB$ to show that $BD^2 = 3 + 2\sqrt{2} \cos 75°$.  (3 marks)

   **b** Use the cosine rule in $\triangle BCD$ to show that $BD^2 = 2 + \sqrt{3}$.  (2 marks)

   **c** Hence show that $\cos 75° = \dfrac{\sqrt{6} - \sqrt{2}}{4}$.  (2 marks)

# ANSWERS

## 1 Trigonometry of right-angled triangles ⊃ p. 54

1  $\cos 26° = \dfrac{x}{9}$

$x = 9 \times \cos 26°$

$= 8.089\,146\,41...$

$= \mathbf{8.1}$  (1 d.p.)

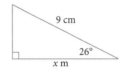

2  $\sin 53°25' = \dfrac{9.6}{x}$

$x \times \sin 53°25' = 9.6$

$x = \dfrac{9.6}{\sin 53°25'}$

$= 11.955\,3039...$

$= \mathbf{11.96}$  (2 d.p.)

**The length of the hypotenuse is 11.96 m, correct to two decimal places.**

3  $\cos \theta = \dfrac{16}{21}$

$\theta = \cos^{-1}\left(\dfrac{16}{21}\right)$

$= 40.367\,5935...°$

$= \mathbf{40°}$  (nearest degree)

4  $\tan B = \dfrac{82}{210}$

$B = \tan^{-1}\left(\dfrac{82}{210}\right)$

$= 21°19'46.06''$

$= \mathbf{21°20'}$  (nearest minute)

5  Let the distance of Sid from the tower be $x$ metres.

$\tan 15° = \dfrac{38}{x}$

$x = \dfrac{38}{\tan 15°}$

$= 141.817\,930...$

$= \mathbf{141.8}$  (1 d.p.)

$\therefore$ **Sid is 141.8 m, to one decimal place, from the base of the tower.**

6  Let the height of the tree be $h$ m.

$\tan 39° = \dfrac{h}{19}$

$h = 19 \times \tan 39°$

$= 15.385\,8966...$

$= \mathbf{15.4}$  (1 d.p.)

$\therefore$ **the tree is 15.4 m high.**

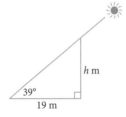

## 2 Complementary and supplementary angles ⊃ pp. 54–55

1  $\sin 49° = \cos (90° - 49°)$

$= \cos 41°$

So **$\cos 41° - \sin 49° = 0$.**

2  $\cos 156° = -0.913\,545\,457...$

$= \mathbf{-0.9135}$  (4 d.p.)

3  a  $\sin \theta = 0.2978$

$\theta = \sin^{-1}(0.2978)$

$= 17°19'31.85''$

$= \mathbf{17°20'}$  (nearest minute)

b  If $\theta$ is obtuse:

$\theta = 180° - 17°\,20'$

$= \mathbf{162°40'}$  (nearest minute)

4  $\cos \theta = -0.2194$

$\theta = \cos^{-1}(-0.2194)$

$= 102.673\,794...°$

$= \mathbf{103°}$  (nearest degree)

## 3 Sine rule—finding sides ⊃ p. 55

1  $\dfrac{a}{\sin A} = \dfrac{b}{\sin B}$

$\dfrac{a}{\sin 42°} = \dfrac{26.1}{\sin 63°}$

$a = \dfrac{26.1 \sin 42°}{\sin 63°}$

$= 19.600\,6520...$

$\therefore BC = \mathbf{19.6\ m}$  (1 d.p.)

2  $\angle R = 180° - (36 + 119)°$

$= 25°$

$\dfrac{r}{\sin R} = \dfrac{q}{\sin Q}$

$\dfrac{r}{\sin 25°} = \dfrac{57.2}{\sin 119°}$

$r = \dfrac{57.2 \sin 25°}{\sin 119°}$

$= 27.639\,1720...$

$= \mathbf{27.6}$  (1 d.p.)

$\therefore$ **PQ is 27.6 m to one decimal place.**

3  $\dfrac{d}{\sin D} = \dfrac{e}{\sin E}$

$\dfrac{d}{\sin 32°} = \dfrac{114}{\sin 67°}$

$d = \dfrac{114 \sin 32°}{\sin 67°}$

$= 65.627\,8952...$

$= \mathbf{65.63}$  (2 d.p.)

**The length of $EF$ is 65.63 m to the nearest centimetre.**

## 4 Sine rule—finding angles ⊃ p. 57

**1**

$$\frac{\sin A}{a} = \frac{\sin B}{b}$$

$$\frac{\sin A}{19} = \frac{\sin 71°}{26}$$

$$\sin A = \frac{19 \sin 71°}{26}$$

$$A = \sin^{-1}\left(\frac{19 \sin 71°}{26}\right)$$

$$= 43.705\,8229…°$$

∴ ∠*BAC* = **44° to the nearest degree.**

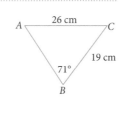

**2**

$$\frac{\sin P}{p} = \frac{\sin Q}{q}$$

$$\frac{\sin P}{9.1} = \frac{\sin 39°}{7.2}$$

$$\sin P = \frac{9.1 \sin 39°}{7.2}$$

$$P = \sin^{-1}\left(\frac{9.1 \sin 39°}{7.2}\right)$$

$$= 52.692\,206…° \text{ or } 180° - 52.692\,206…°$$

∴ ∠*QPR* = **53° or 127° to the nearest degree.**

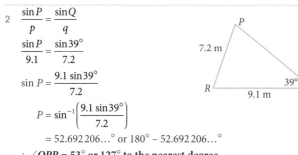

**3**

$$\frac{\sin A}{a} = \frac{\sin B}{b}$$

$$\frac{\sin \theta}{3.8} = \frac{\sin 74°}{5.2}$$

$$\sin \theta = \frac{3.8 \sin 74°}{5.2}$$

$$\theta = \sin^{-1}\left(\frac{3.8 \sin 74°}{5.2}\right)$$

$$= 44°37'29.07''$$

$$= 44°37' \quad \text{(nearest minute)}$$

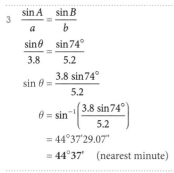

**4**

$$\frac{\sin G}{g} = \frac{\sin I}{i}$$

$$\frac{\sin G}{8.6} = \frac{\sin 112°}{17.3}$$

$$\sin G = \frac{8.6 \sin 112°}{17.3}$$

$$G = \sin^{-1}\left(\frac{8.6 \sin 112°}{17.3}\right)$$

$$= 27.445\,9861…°$$

$$= 27° \text{ to the nearest degree}$$

∴ ∠*GHI* = 180° − (112 + 27)°

$$= 41° \text{ to the nearest degree}$$

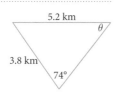

**5**

$$\frac{\sin X}{x} = \frac{\sin Y}{y}$$

$$\frac{\sin X}{13.5} = \frac{\sin 55°15'}{11.2}$$

$$\sin X = \frac{13.5 \sin 55°15'}{11.2}$$

$$X = \sin^{-1}\left(\frac{13.5 \sin 55°15'}{11.2}\right)$$

$$= 82°2'43.39'' \text{ or } 180° - 82°2'43.39''$$

∴ ∠*XYZ* = **82°3' or 97°57' to the nearest minute.**

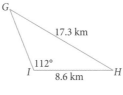

## 5 Cosine rule ⊃ p. 58

**1**

$$c^2 = a^2 + b^2 - 2ab \cos C$$

$$= 67^2 + 93^2 - 2 \times 67 \times 93 \times \cos 36°$$

$$= 3056.030\,21…$$

$$c = \sqrt{3056.030\,21…} \quad (c > 0)$$

$$= 55.281\,3731…$$

$$= 55.3 \quad \text{(1 d.p.)}$$

∴ **the length of *AB* is 55.3 m, correct to one decimal place.**

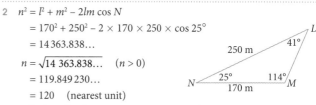

**2**

$$n^2 = l^2 + m^2 - 2lm \cos N$$

$$= 170^2 + 250^2 - 2 \times 170 \times 250 \times \cos 25°$$

$$= 14\,363.838…$$

$$n = \sqrt{14\,363.838…} \quad (n > 0)$$

$$= 119.849\,230…$$

$$= 120 \quad \text{(nearest unit)}$$

∴ **the length of *LM* is 120 m, correct to the nearest metre.**

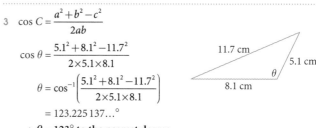

**3**

$$\cos C = \frac{a^2 + b^2 - c^2}{2ab}$$

$$\cos \theta = \frac{5.1^2 + 8.1^2 - 11.7^2}{2 \times 5.1 \times 8.1}$$

$$\theta = \cos^{-1}\left(\frac{5.1^2 + 8.1^2 - 11.7^2}{2 \times 5.1 \times 8.1}\right)$$

$$= 123.225\,137…°$$

∴ *θ* = **123° to the nearest degree**

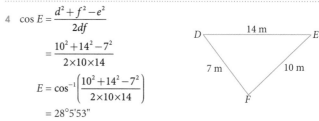

**4**

$$\cos E = \frac{d^2 + f^2 - e^2}{2df}$$

$$= \frac{10^2 + 14^2 - 7^2}{2 \times 10 \times 14}$$

$$E = \cos^{-1}\left(\frac{10^2 + 14^2 - 7^2}{2 \times 10 \times 14}\right)$$

$$= 28°5'53''$$

∴ **the smallest angle is 28°6' to the nearest minute.**

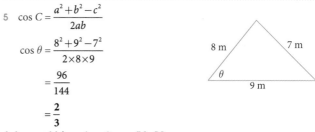

**5**

$$\cos C = \frac{a^2 + b^2 - c^2}{2ab}$$

$$\cos \theta = \frac{8^2 + 9^2 - 7^2}{2 \times 8 \times 9}$$

$$= \frac{96}{144}$$

$$= \frac{2}{3}$$

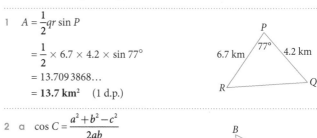

## 6 Area of triangles ⊃ pp. 58–59

**1**

$$A = \frac{1}{2}qr \sin P$$

$$= \frac{1}{2} \times 6.7 \times 4.2 \times \sin 77°$$

$$= 13.709\,3868…$$

$$= \mathbf{13.7\ km^2} \quad \text{(1 d.p.)}$$

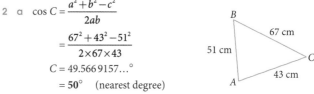

**2 a**

$$\cos C = \frac{a^2 + b^2 - c^2}{2ab}$$

$$= \frac{67^2 + 43^2 - 51^2}{2 \times 67 \times 43}$$

$$C = 49.566\,9157…°$$

$$= \mathbf{50°} \quad \text{(nearest degree)}$$

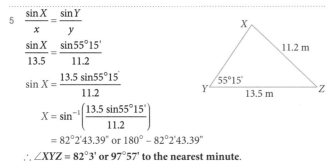

**b** $A = \dfrac{1}{2}ab \sin C$

$\qquad = \dfrac{1}{2} \times 67 \times 43 \times \sin 49.566\,157...°$

$\qquad = 1096.456\,65...$

$\qquad = \textbf{1096.5 cm}^2 \quad (\text{1 d.p.})$

3 $A = \dfrac{1}{2}ac \sin B$

$\qquad = \dfrac{1}{2} \times 740 \times 960 \times \sin 30°$

$\qquad = 177\,600 \text{ m}^2$

$\qquad = \textbf{17.76 ha}$

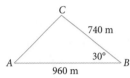

## 7 Bearings ⊃ p. 60

1 $\angle PQR = 90° - 72°$

$\qquad = 18°$

$\sin 18° = \dfrac{PR}{68}$

$\quad PR = 68 \sin 18°$

$\qquad = 21.013\,1556...$

$\qquad = 21 \text{ km} \quad (\text{nearest km})$

**It is 21 km, to the nearest kilometre, from $P$ to $R$.**

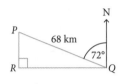

2 $\angle BAC = 360° - (45 + 205)°$

$\qquad = 110°$

$a^2 = b^2 + c^2 - 2bc \cos A$

$\qquad = 73^2 + 57^2 - 2 \times 73 \times 57 \times \cos 110°$

$\qquad = 11\,424.2916...$

$a = \sqrt{11\,424.2916...} \quad (a > 0)$

$\qquad = 106.884\,47...$

$\qquad = 107 \quad (\text{nearest unit})$

**The distance from $B$ to $C$ is 107 m to the nearest metre.**

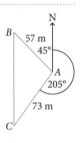

3 $\angle GFH = 180° - 163°$

$\qquad = 17°$

$\dfrac{\sin G}{g} = \dfrac{\sin F}{f}$

$\dfrac{\sin G}{16.4} = \dfrac{\sin 17°}{12.8}$

$\sin G = \dfrac{16.4 \sin 17°}{12.8}$

$\quad G = \sin^{-1}\left(\dfrac{16.4 \sin 17°}{12.8}\right)$

$G = 21.999\,669...°$ or $180° - 21.999\,669...°$

$\quad = 22°$ or $158° \quad (\text{nearest degree})$

**The bearing of $H$ from $G$ is 022° or 158°.**

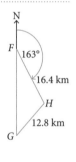

4 $\angle PAB = 180° - (57 + 45)°$

$\qquad = 78°$

The bearing of $A$ from $B$ is $360° - 45°$ or $315°$.

$\angle PBA = 348° - 315°$

$\qquad = 33°$

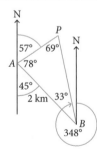

$\angle APB = 180° - (78 + 33)°$

$\qquad = 69°$

$\dfrac{b}{\sin B} = \dfrac{p}{\sin P}$

$\dfrac{b}{\sin 33°} = \dfrac{2}{\sin 69°}$

$\quad b = \dfrac{2 \sin 33°}{\sin 69°}$

$\qquad = 1.166\,774\,75$

$\qquad = 1.2 \quad (\text{1 d.p.})$

**The distance from $A$ to $P$ is 1.2 km, to the nearest 100 m.**

## 8 Problems ⊃ p. 61

1 **a** $\angle DAC + \angle ADC = \angle ACB \quad$ (exterior angle of $\triangle$)

$\qquad \angle DAC + 26° = 64°$

$\qquad \therefore \angle DAC = \mathbf{38°}$

**b** In $\triangle ACD$,

$\dfrac{d}{\sin D} = \dfrac{a}{\sin A}$

$\dfrac{d}{\sin 26°} = \dfrac{18}{\sin 38°}$

$\quad d = \dfrac{18 \sin 26°}{\sin 38°}$

$\qquad = 12.816\,5898...$

$\qquad = 12.8 \quad (\text{1 d.p.})$

$\therefore AC = \textbf{12.8 m}$ to one decimal place.

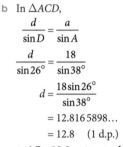

**c** In $\triangle ABC$,

$\sin 64° = \dfrac{AB}{AC}$

$\quad AB = AC \sin 64°$

$\qquad = 11.519\,4746...$

$\qquad = 11.5 \quad (\text{1 d.p.})$

**The height of the pole is 11.5 m to one decimal place.**

2 **a** In $\triangle LMN$,

$m^2 = l^2 + n^2 - 2ln \cos M$

$\qquad = 8^2 + 10^2 - 2 \times 8 \times 10 \times \cos 49°$

$\therefore LN^2 = \textbf{164} - \textbf{160} \cos \textbf{49°}$

**b** In $\triangle LKN$,

$\cos K = \dfrac{l^2 + n^2 - k^2}{2ln}$

$\qquad = \dfrac{7^2 + 6^2 - LN^2}{2 \times 7 \times 6}$

$\quad K = \cos^{-1}\left(\dfrac{7^2 + 6^2 - LN^2}{2 \times 7 \times 6}\right)$

$\qquad = 71.991\,3811...°$

$\therefore \angle LKN = \textbf{72°} \quad (\text{nearest degree})$

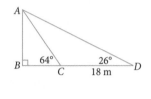

**c** Area = area of $\triangle LMN$ + area of $\triangle LKN$

$\qquad = \dfrac{1}{2} \times 10 \times 8 \times \sin 49° + \dfrac{1}{2} \times 6 \times 7 \times \sin 71.991\,3811...°$

$\qquad = 50.159\,5936...$

$\qquad = \textbf{50.16 m}^2 \quad (\text{2 d.p.})$

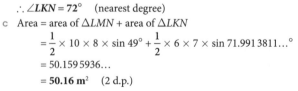

3 a In $\triangle PRS$,

$$\cos R = \frac{p^2 + s^2 - r^2}{2ps}$$

$$= \frac{7^2 + 12^2 - 7^2}{2 \times 7 \times 12}$$

$$= \frac{6}{7}$$

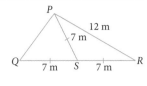

b In $\triangle PRQ$,

$$r^2 = p^2 + q^2 - 2pq \cos R$$

$$= 14^2 + 12^2 - 2 \times 14 \times 12 \times \frac{6}{7}$$

$$= 52$$

$$r = \sqrt{52} \quad (r > 0)$$

$$= 2\sqrt{13}$$

**The exact length of $PQ$ is $2\sqrt{13}$ m.**

c In $\triangle PRQ$,

$$\cos P = \frac{r^2 + q^2 - p^2}{2rq}$$

$$= \frac{52 + 12^2 - 14^2}{2 \times \sqrt{52} \times 12}$$

$$= 0$$

$$\therefore \angle QPR = 90°$$

**9 Exact ratios ⊃ p. 62**

1 In $\triangle BCD$,

$$\sin 30° = \frac{1}{BD}$$

$$BD = \frac{1}{\sin 30°}$$

$$= \frac{1}{\frac{1}{2}}$$

$$= 2$$

In $\triangle ABD$,

$$\cos 30° = \frac{BD}{AB}$$

$$AB = \frac{BD}{\cos 30°}$$

$$= \frac{2}{\frac{\sqrt{3}}{2}}$$

$$= \frac{4}{\sqrt{3}} \text{ units}$$

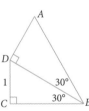

2 a In $\triangle BCD$,

$$\tan 60° = \frac{DC}{BC}$$

$$\sqrt{3} = \frac{DC}{1}$$

$$\therefore DC = \sqrt{3} \text{ units}$$

$$\cos 60° = \frac{BC}{BD}$$

$$\frac{1}{2} = \frac{1}{BD}$$

$$\therefore BD = 2 \text{ units}$$

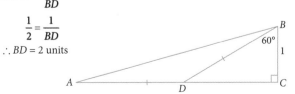

Now $BD = AD$

So $AD = 2$ units

$\therefore AC = (2 + \sqrt{3})$ **units**

b $\angle BDC = 180° - (90 + 60)°$

$$= 30°$$

$\angle BDC = \angle BAD + \angle ABD$ (ext. angle $\triangle$)

But $\angle BAD = \angle ABD$ ($\triangle ABD$ is isosceles)

So $\angle BAD = 15°$

In $\triangle ABC$,

$$\tan A = \frac{BC}{AC}$$

$$\tan 15° = \frac{1}{2 + \sqrt{3}}$$

$$= \frac{1}{2 + \sqrt{3}} \times \frac{2 - \sqrt{3}}{2 - \sqrt{3}}$$

$$= 2 - \sqrt{3}$$

3 Let $D$ be the point on $BC$ such that $AD \perp BC$.

In $\triangle ABD$,

$$\cos 45° = \frac{BD}{AB}$$

$$\frac{1}{\sqrt{2}} = \frac{BD}{5\sqrt{2}}$$

$$BD = 5 \text{ cm}$$

$$\sin 45° = \frac{AD}{AB}$$

$$\frac{1}{\sqrt{2}} = \frac{AD}{5\sqrt{2}}$$

$$AD = 5 \text{ cm}$$

In $\triangle ADC$,

$$\tan 30° = \frac{AD}{DC}$$

$$\frac{1}{\sqrt{3}} = \frac{5}{DC}$$

$$DC = 5\sqrt{3} \text{ cm}$$

**So $BC = (5 + 5\sqrt{3})$ cm.**

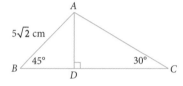

**10 Three-dimensional trigonometry ⊃ p. 64**

1 Let the midpoint of $BC$ be $E$ and the midpoint of $DC$ be $F$.

Let the required angle be $\theta$.

$OP = 16$ cm, $OF = EC = 10$ cm

$$\tan \theta = \frac{16}{10}$$

$$\theta = \tan^{-1}\left(\frac{16}{10}\right)$$

$$= 57.994\,6167\ldots°$$

$$= \mathbf{58°} \quad \text{(nearest degree)}$$

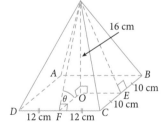

**2 a** In $\triangle ABC$,

$$\tan 19° = \frac{AB}{206}$$

$$AB = 206 \tan 19°$$
$$= 70.931\,4883\ldots$$
$$= 71 \text{ m} \quad \text{(nearest metre)}$$

**The height of the tower is 71 m to the nearest metre.**

**b** In $\triangle ABD$,

$$\tan 25° = \frac{AB}{BD}$$

$$BD = \frac{AB}{\tan 25°}$$
$$= 152.113\,067\ldots$$
$$= 152 \text{ m} \quad \text{(nearest metre)}$$

**Dan is 152 m from the base of the tower, to the nearest metre.**

**c** In $\triangle BCD$,

$$DC^2 = BC^2 + BD^2$$
$$= 206^2 + (152.113\,067\ldots)^2$$
$$= 65\,574.3853\ldots$$
$$DC = 256.074\,960\ldots$$
$$= 256 \text{ m} \quad \text{(nearest metre)}$$

**Chris and Dan are 256 m apart to the nearest metre.**

**3** In $\triangle PQS$,

$$\tan 41° = \frac{74}{SQ}$$

$$\therefore SQ = \frac{74}{\tan 41°}$$

In $\triangle PQR$,

$$\tan 33° = \frac{74}{QR}$$

$$\therefore QR = \frac{74}{\tan 33°}$$

In $\triangle SQR$,

$$q^2 = r^2 + s^2 - 2rs \cos 118°$$

$$SR^2 = \left(\frac{74}{\tan 41°}\right)^2 + \left(\frac{74}{\tan 33°}\right)^2 - 2 \times \frac{74}{\tan 41°} \times \frac{74}{\tan 33°} \times \cos 118°$$

$$= 29\,339.2399\ldots$$

$$SR = 171.287\,010\ldots$$

$$= 171 \text{ m} \quad \text{(nearest metre)}$$

**The distance from $S$ to $R$ is 171 m, to the nearest metre.**

**4** Let $h$ m be the height of the cliff.

In $\triangle APB$,

$$\tan 17° = \frac{h}{PB}$$

$$PB = \frac{h}{\tan 17°}$$

In $\triangle AQB$,

$$\tan 13° = \frac{h}{QB}$$

$$QB = \frac{h}{\tan 13°}$$

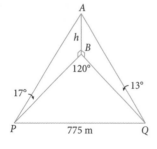

In $\triangle PQB$,

$$b^2 = p^2 + q^2 - 2pq \cos B$$

$$775^2 = \left(\frac{h}{\tan 13°}\right)^2 + \left(\frac{h}{\tan 17°}\right)^2 - 2 \times \frac{h}{\tan 13°} \times \frac{h}{\tan 17°} \times \cos 120°$$

$$775^2 = \frac{h^2}{(\tan 13°)^2} + \frac{h^2}{(\tan 17°)^2} - \frac{2h^2}{\tan 13° \tan 17°} \times -\frac{1}{2}$$

$$775^2 = \frac{h^2}{(\tan 13°)^2} + \frac{h^2}{(\tan 17°)^2} + \frac{h^2}{\tan 13° \tan 17°}$$

$$775^2 = h^2 \left( \frac{1}{(\tan 13°)^2} + \frac{1}{(\tan 17°)^2} + \frac{1}{\tan 13° \tan 17°} \right)$$

$$h^2 = 775^2 \div \left( \frac{1}{(\tan 13°)^2} + \frac{1}{(\tan 17°)^2} + \frac{1}{\tan 13° \tan 17°} \right)$$

$$= 13\,767.0312\ldots$$

$$h = 117.332\,992\ldots \quad (h > 0)$$

$$= 117 \quad \text{(nearest whole number)}$$

**The height of the cliff is 117 m, to the nearest metre.**

**5 a** In $\triangle PQB$,

$$\tan 30° = \frac{75}{QB}$$

$$QB = \frac{75}{\tan 30°}$$

$$= \frac{75}{\frac{1}{\sqrt{3}}}$$

$$= 75 \times \frac{\sqrt{3}}{1}$$

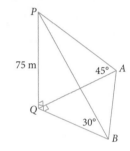

**So the exact length of $QB$ is $75\sqrt{3}$ m.**

**b** $\triangle PQA$ is a right-angled isosceles triangle so $AQ = 75$ m.

In $\triangle AQB$,

$$q^2 = a^2 + b^2$$
$$= (75\sqrt{3})^2 + 75^2$$
$$= 22\,500$$
$$q = 150 \quad (q > 0)$$

**The distance from $A$ to $B$ is 150 m.**

**c** In $\triangle AQB$,

$$\sin B = \frac{75}{150}$$

$$B = 30°$$

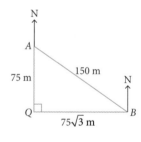

**The bearing of $A$ from $B$ is $(270 + 30)°$ or $300°$.**

11 Angles of any magnitude ⊃ p. 65

**1 a** $\cos 330° = \cos (360 - 30)°$

$$= \cos 30°$$

$$= \frac{\sqrt{3}}{2}$$

**b** $\tan 150° = \tan (180 - 30)°$

$$= -\tan 30°$$

$$= -\frac{1}{\sqrt{3}}$$

**2 a** $\cos \theta = 0.5299$

$\cos^{-1}(0.5299) = 58.0013015...°$

$\qquad = 58°$ (nearest degree)

cos is positive in the 1st and 4th quadrants

So $\theta = 58°$ or $360° - 58°$

**$\theta = 58°$ or $302°$ to the nearest degree.**

**b** $\tan \theta = -1.932$

$\tan^{-1}(1.932) = 62.6339909...°$

$\qquad = 63°$ (nearest degree)

tan is negative in the 2nd and 4th quadrants.

So $\theta = 180° - 63°$ or $360° - 63°$

**$\theta = 117°$ or $297°$ to the nearest degree.**

---

**3** $\sin \theta = 0.5$

$\sin^{-1}(0.5) = 30°$

sin is positive in the 1st and 2nd quadrants.

So $\theta = 30°$ or $180° - 30°$ or $360° + 30°$ or $540° - 30°$

**$\theta = 30°$ or $150°$ or $390°$ or $510°$**

---

**4** $\cos x = 0.375$

$\cos^{-1}(0.375) = 67.9756871...°$

$\qquad = 68°$ (nearest degree)

cos is positive in the 1st and 4th quadrants.

So $x = 68°$ or $0° - 68°$

**$x = 68°$ or $-68°$**

---

**5** $\sin \theta = -0.7503$

$\sin^{-1}(0.7503) = 48°36'\,58.94''$

$\qquad = 48°37'$ (nearest minute)

sin is negative in the 3rd and 4th quadrants.

$\theta = 180° + 48°37'$ or $\quad \theta = 360° - 48°37'$

**$\theta = 228°37'$ or $\quad \theta = 311°23'$**

---

**12 Graphs of trig ratios ⊃ p. 66**

**1**

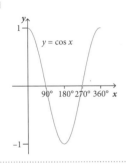

**2 a** The curve repeats every $360°$.

Now $1440 \div 360 = 4$

**So the curve repeats 4 times.**

**b** Whenever $y = 0$ the curve changes concavity.

**3** The graph of $y = \tan x$ has an asymptote at $x = 270°$. **As $x$ gets closer to $270°$ from below, the value of $y$ gets larger and larger. As $x$ gets closer and closer to $270°$ from above, the value of $y$ is negative but gets larger and larger negatively.**

**4** $y = \sin x$ and $y = \cos x$ have the same shape and size. They only differ by their position. The graph of $y = \sin x$ is the same as the graph of $y = \cos x$ moved $90°$ to the right.

---

**1 Introduction to radians ⊃ p. 67**

**1** $35° = 35° \times \dfrac{\pi}{180°}$

$\qquad = 0.610865238...$

$\qquad = \mathbf{0.61}$ (2 d.p.)

---

**2** $120° = 120° \times \dfrac{\pi}{180°}$

$\qquad = \dfrac{2\pi}{3}$

---

**3** $0.8 = 0.8 \times \dfrac{180°}{\pi}$

$\qquad = 45.8366236...°$

$\qquad = \mathbf{46°}$ (nearest degree)

---

**4** $\dfrac{3\pi}{5} = \dfrac{3 \times 180°}{5}$

$\qquad = \mathbf{108°}$

---

**5** $225° = 225° \times \dfrac{\pi}{180°}$

$\qquad = \dfrac{5\pi}{4}$

**2 The trig ratios with radians ⊃ p. 68**

**1** $\tan 0.6 = 0.684136808...$

$\qquad = \mathbf{0.6841}$ (4 d.p.)

---

**2** $\dfrac{9.2\sin(0.75)}{8.75} = 0.716694467...$

$\qquad = \mathbf{0.717}$ (3 d.p.)

---

**3** $\cos\left(\dfrac{5\pi}{3}\right) = 0.5$

---

**4** $\dfrac{3.7\sin\dfrac{\pi}{5}}{\sin\dfrac{\pi}{4}} = 3.0756393...$

$\qquad = \mathbf{3.08}$ (2 d.p.)

**3 Further values with radians ⊃ p. 69**

**1 a** $\tan\dfrac{2\pi}{3} = \tan\left(\pi - \dfrac{\pi}{3}\right)$

$\qquad = -\tan\dfrac{\pi}{3}$

$\qquad = \mathbf{-\sqrt{3}}$

**b** $\sin\dfrac{7\pi}{4} = \sin\left(2\pi - \dfrac{\pi}{4}\right)$

$\qquad = -\sin\dfrac{\pi}{4}$

$\qquad = \mathbf{-\dfrac{1}{\sqrt{2}}}$

---

**2** $\tan \theta = \dfrac{5}{6}$

Now $\tan^{-1}\left(\dfrac{5}{6}\right) = 0.694738276...$

tan is positive in the 1st and 3rd quadrants.

---

$\therefore \theta = 0.694738276...$    or    $\theta = \pi + 0.694738276...$
$= 3.8363309...$
$\therefore \boldsymbol{\theta = 0.6947}$    **or**    $\boldsymbol{\theta = 3.8363}$    (4 d.p.)

3   $\sin \theta = -0.8$

Now $\sin^{-1} 0.8 = 0.92729521...$

$\sin$ is negative in the 3rd and 4th quadrants.

$\therefore \theta = \pi + 0.92729521...$   or   $\theta = 2\pi - 0.92729521...$
$\theta = 4.06888787...$    or    $\theta = 5.35589008...$
$\boldsymbol{\theta = 4.069}$      **or**      $\boldsymbol{\theta = 5.356}$    (3 d.p.)

4   $\cos \theta = -0.8765$

Now $\cos^{-1}(0.8765) = 0.502253394...$

$\cos$ is negative in the 2nd and 3rd quadrants.

So $\theta = \pi - 0.502253394...$ or   $\theta = -\pi + 0.502253394..$
$\theta = 2.63933925...$   or   $\theta = -2.63933925...$
$\boldsymbol{\theta = 2.6393}$      **or**      $\boldsymbol{\theta = -2.6393}$    (4 d.p.)

## 4 The graphs of $y = \sin x$, $y = \cos x$ and $y = \tan x$ ⊃ p. 70

1   $y = 2 \sin 4x$

Amplitude = 2

$\text{Period} = \dfrac{2\pi}{4}$
$= \dfrac{\pi}{2}$

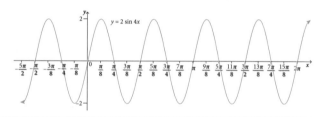

2   $y = 3 \cos 2x$

Amplitude = 3

$\text{Period} = \dfrac{2\pi}{2}$
$= \pi$

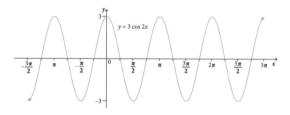

3   $y = 3 \tan \dfrac{x}{2}, -2\pi \leq x \leq 2\pi$

$\text{Period} = \dfrac{\pi}{\frac{1}{2}}$
$= 2\pi$

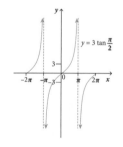

4   $y = -\sin\left(\dfrac{x}{2}\right), -2\pi \leq x \leq 2\pi$

Amplitude = 1

$\text{Period} = \dfrac{2\pi}{\frac{1}{2}}$
$= 4\pi$

## 5 The length of an arc ⊃ pp. 71–72

1   $l = r\theta$
$= 72 \times \dfrac{\pi}{8}$
$= 9\pi$

$\therefore$ **the length of the arc is $9\pi$ cm.**

2   $l = r\theta$
$= 8 \times \dfrac{2\pi}{5}$
$= 10.0530964...$
$P = 2r + l$
$= 2 \times 8 + 10.0530964...$
$= 26.0530964...$
$= 26.1$    (1 d.p.)

$\therefore$ **the perimeter of the sector is 26.1 cm, correct to one decimal place.**

3   $l = r\theta$
$= 7.8 \times 120° \times \dfrac{\pi}{180°}$
$= 16.336281...$
$= 16.34$    (2 d.p.)

$\therefore$ **the length of the arc is 16.34 cm, correct to two decimal places.**

4     $l = r\theta$
$14\pi = r \times \dfrac{7\pi}{6}$
$r = 14\pi \div \dfrac{7\pi}{6}$
$= 14\pi \times \dfrac{6}{7\pi}$
$= 12$

$\therefore$ **the length of the radius is 12 m.**

5   $l = r\theta$
$4 = 6\theta$
$\theta = \dfrac{4}{6}$
$= \dfrac{2}{3} \times \dfrac{180°}{\pi}$
$= 38.1971863...°$
$= 38°$   (nearest degree)

$\therefore$ **the size of the angle is 38°, to the nearest degree.**

6   $l = r\theta$
$= 12 \times 50° \times \dfrac{\pi}{180°}$
$= \dfrac{10\pi}{3}$

$\therefore$ **the length of the arc is $\dfrac{10\pi}{3}$ cm.**

## 6 The area of a sector ⊃ p. 73

**1** $A = \frac{1}{2}r^2\theta$

$= \frac{1}{2} \times 15^2 \times \frac{3\pi}{5}$

$= \frac{135\pi}{2}$

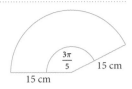

∴ the area of the sector is $\frac{135\pi}{2}$ cm².

**2** $A = \frac{1}{2}r^2\theta$

$= \frac{1}{2} \times 57^2 \times \frac{10\pi}{9}$

$= 5670.5747\ldots$

$= 5671$ (nearest whole number)

∴ the area of the sector is **5671 cm², to the nearest square centimetre.**

**3** $A = \frac{1}{2}r^2\theta$

$= \frac{1}{2} \times 13^2 \times 70° \times \frac{\pi}{180°}$

$= 103.236\,225\ldots$

$= 103.2$ (1 d.p.)

∴ the area of the sector is **103.2 m², to one decimal place.**

**4** $A = \frac{1}{2}r^2\theta$

$28\pi = \frac{1}{2} \times r^2 \times \frac{2\pi}{7}$

$28 = \frac{r^2}{7}$

$r^2 = 196$

$r = 14$ $(r > 0)$

∴ the radius of the sector is **14 m.**

**5** $A = \frac{1}{2}r^2\theta$

$60\pi = \frac{1}{2} \times 12^2 \times \theta$

$60\pi = 72\theta$

$\therefore \theta = \frac{60\pi}{72} \times \frac{180°}{\pi}$

$= 150°$

**6** $r = 900 \div 2$

$= 450$

$\theta = 2\pi - 2.4$

Shaded area $= \frac{1}{2}r^2\theta$

$= \frac{1}{2} \times 450^2 \times (2\pi - 2.4)$

$= 393\,172.512\ldots$ m²

$= \textbf{39.32 ha}$ (2 d.p.)

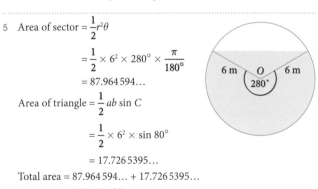

## 7 Composite areas and problems ⊃ p. 74

**1** $l = r\theta$

$8\pi = 5\theta$

$\theta = \frac{8\pi}{5}$

$A = \frac{1}{2}r^2\theta$

$= \frac{1}{2} \times 5^2 \times \frac{8\pi}{5}$

$= 20\pi$

∴ the area of the sector is **20π cm².**

**2** $A = \frac{1}{2}R^2\theta - \frac{1}{2}r^2\theta$

$= \frac{1}{2} \times 27^2 \times \frac{5\pi}{9} - \frac{1}{2} \times 9^2 \times \frac{5\pi}{9}$

$= 180\pi$

The shaded area is **180π m².**

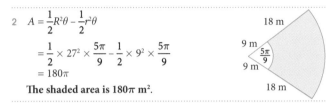

**3** The shape comprises a sector of radius 10 cm and a semicircle with diameter 10 cm.

$A = \frac{1}{2}R^2\theta + \frac{1}{2}\pi r^2$

$= \frac{1}{2} \times 10^2 \times \frac{\pi}{5} + \frac{1}{2} \times \pi \times 5^2$

$= 10\pi + \frac{25\pi}{2}$

$= \frac{45\pi}{2}$

∴ the area of the figure is $\frac{45\pi}{2}$ cm².

**4** Radius = 60 mm = 6 cm

$A = \frac{1}{2}r^2(\theta - \sin\theta)$

$= \frac{1}{2} \times 6^2 \times \left(\frac{3\pi}{4} - \sin\frac{3\pi}{4}\right)$

$= 18\left(\frac{3\pi}{4} - \frac{1}{\sqrt{2}}\right)$

$= 18\left(\frac{3\pi - 2\sqrt{2}}{4}\right)$

$= 9\left(\frac{3\pi - 2\sqrt{2}}{2}\right)$

∴ the exact area is $9\left(\dfrac{3\pi - 2\sqrt{2}}{2}\right)$ cm².

**5** Area of sector $= \frac{1}{2}r^2\theta$

$= \frac{1}{2} \times 6^2 \times 280° \times \frac{\pi}{180°}$

$= 87.964\,594\ldots$

Area of triangle $= \frac{1}{2}ab\sin C$

$= \frac{1}{2} \times 6^2 \times \sin 80°$

$= 17.726\,5395\ldots$

Total area $= 87.964\,594\ldots + 17.726\,5395\ldots$

$= 105.691\,133\ldots$

$= \textbf{105.7 m}^2$ (1 d.p.)

## TRIGONOMETRIC FUNCTIONS AND IDENTITIES

### 1 $y = \operatorname{cosec} x$ ⊃ p. 75

1  $\operatorname{cosec} 68° = 1.078\,534\,74\ldots$
$\qquad = \mathbf{1.0785}$  (4 d.p.)

2  $\operatorname{cosec} \dfrac{\pi}{4} = \dfrac{1}{\sin \dfrac{\pi}{4}}$

$\qquad = \dfrac{1}{\dfrac{1}{\sqrt{2}}}$

$\qquad = \sqrt{2}$

3
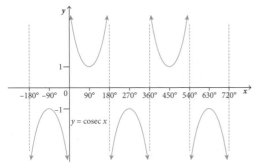

4  $y = 3\operatorname{cosec} 2x, \quad 0 < x < 2\pi$
Period $= \dfrac{2\pi}{2} = \pi$

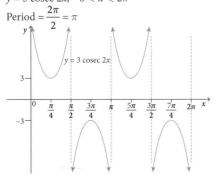

5  $\operatorname{cosec} \theta = 1.2345$

$\qquad \sin \theta = \dfrac{1}{1.2345}$

$\qquad \theta = \sin^{-1}\left(\dfrac{1}{1.2345}\right)$

$\qquad = 54.100\,2845\ldots°$

$\qquad = 54°$  (nearest degree)

sin is positive in 1st and 2nd quadrants.
So $\theta = 54°$ or $\theta = 180° - 54°$
$\qquad \boldsymbol{\theta = 54° \text{ or } 126°}$

### 2 $y = \sec x$ ⊃ p. 76

1  $\sec 19° = 1.057\,620\,68\ldots$
$\qquad = \mathbf{1.0576}$  (4 d.p.)

2  $\sec \dfrac{3\pi}{4} = \dfrac{1}{\cos \dfrac{3\pi}{4}}$

$\qquad = \dfrac{1}{\cos\left(\pi - \dfrac{\pi}{4}\right)}$

$\qquad = \dfrac{1}{-\cos \dfrac{\pi}{4}}$

$\qquad = \dfrac{1}{-\dfrac{1}{\sqrt{2}}}$

$\qquad = -\sqrt{2}$

3
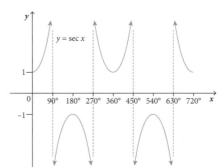

4  $y = 2 \sec \dfrac{x}{2}, \quad -3\pi \le x \le 5\pi$

Period $= \dfrac{2\pi}{\dfrac{1}{2}}$

$\qquad = 4\pi$

5  $\sec \theta = 2, \quad 0 \le \theta \le 2\pi$

$\qquad \therefore \cos \theta = \dfrac{1}{2}$

Now $\cos \dfrac{\pi}{3} = \dfrac{1}{2}$

cos is positive in the first and fourth quadrants.
So $\theta = \dfrac{\pi}{3}$ or $\theta = 2\pi - \dfrac{\pi}{3}$

$\qquad \boldsymbol{\theta = \dfrac{\pi}{3} \text{ or } \dfrac{5\pi}{3}}$.

### 3 $y = \cot x$ ⊃ p. 77

1  $\cot 39° = 1.234\,897\,15\ldots$
$\qquad = \mathbf{1.2349}$  (4 d.p.)

**2**    $\tan \dfrac{5\pi}{6} = \tan\left(2\pi - \dfrac{\pi}{6}\right)$

$= -\tan\dfrac{\pi}{6}$

$= -\dfrac{1}{\sqrt{3}}$

$\therefore \cot \dfrac{5\pi}{6} = -\sqrt{3}$

**3**

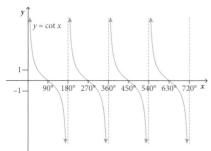

**4**    $y = 2\cot 2x$

Period $= \dfrac{\pi}{2}$

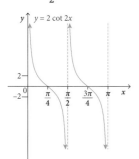

**5**    $\cot\theta = 5$

$\therefore \tan\theta = \dfrac{1}{5}$

$\theta = \tan^{-1}\left(\dfrac{1}{5}\right)$

$= 11°18'\,35.76''$

$= \mathbf{11°\,19'}$    (nearest minute)

### 4 Expressions and identities ➲ p. 78

**1**    $\cos^2 x + \sin^2 x = 1$

$\dfrac{\cos^2 x}{\sin^2 x} + \dfrac{\sin^2 x}{\sin^2 x} = \dfrac{1}{\sin^2 x}$

$\cot^2 x + 1 = \operatorname{cosec}^2 x$

$1 = \operatorname{cosec}^2 x - \cot^2 x$

$\therefore \mathbf{cosec^2\,x - cot^2\,x = 1}$

**2**    $(\sin x + \cos x)^2 + (\sin x - \cos x)^2$

$= \sin^2 x + 2\sin x \cos x + \cos^2 x + \sin^2 x - 2\sin x \cos x + \cos^2 x$

$= 2\sin^2 x + 2\cos^2 x$

$= 2(\sin^2 x + \cos^2 x)$

$= \mathbf{2}$

**3**    $\dfrac{1}{\sec x - \tan x} - \dfrac{1}{\sec x + \tan x}$

$= \dfrac{(\sec x + \tan x) - (\sec x - \tan x)}{(\sec x - \tan x)(\sec x + \tan x)}$

$= \dfrac{\sec x + \tan x - \sec x + \tan x}{\sec^2 x - \tan^2 x}$

$= \dfrac{2\tan x}{1 + \tan^2 x - \tan^2 x}$

$= \mathbf{2\tan x}$

**4**    $\operatorname{cosec} x = \sec \dfrac{2\pi}{9}$

Now $\sec \dfrac{2\pi}{9} = \operatorname{cosec}\left(\dfrac{\pi}{2} - \dfrac{2\pi}{9}\right)$

$= \operatorname{cosec}\left(\dfrac{9\pi}{18} - \dfrac{4\pi}{18}\right)$

$= \operatorname{cosec} \dfrac{5\pi}{18}$

So $\mathbf{x = \dfrac{5\pi}{18}}$.

**5**    $\cot^2 x - \cos^2 x$

$= \dfrac{\cos^2 x}{\sin^2 x} - \cos^2 x$

$= \cos^2 x\left(\dfrac{1}{\sin^2 x} - 1\right)$

$= \cos^2 x\left(\dfrac{1 - \sin^2 x}{\sin^2 x}\right)$

$= \cos^2 x\left(\dfrac{\cos^2 x}{\sin^2 x}\right)$

$= \mathbf{cos^2\,x\,cot^2\,x}$

### 5 Equations ➲ pp. 78–79

**1**    $9\cos x = \cos x - 4$

$8\cos x = -4$

$\cos x = -\dfrac{1}{2}$

Now $\cos 60° = \dfrac{1}{2}$

cos is negative in the 2nd and 3rd quadrants.

$x = 180° - 60°$   or   $x = 180° + 60°$

$\mathbf{x = 120°}$     **or**     $\mathbf{x = 240°}$

**2**    $\cos^2\theta = \dfrac{1}{2}$

$\therefore \cos\theta = \pm\dfrac{1}{\sqrt{2}}$

Now $\cos \dfrac{\pi}{4} = \dfrac{1}{\sqrt{2}}$

$\therefore \theta = \dfrac{\pi}{4}$   or   $\pi - \dfrac{\pi}{4}$   or   $\pi + \dfrac{\pi}{4}$   or   $2\pi - \dfrac{\pi}{4}$

$\therefore \boldsymbol{\theta = \dfrac{\pi}{4}, \dfrac{3\pi}{4}, \dfrac{5\pi}{4}}$ **or** $\boldsymbol{\dfrac{7\pi}{4}}$.

**3**    $\sin\theta + \cos\theta = 0$

$\sin\theta = -\cos\theta$

$\therefore \dfrac{\sin\theta}{\cos\theta} = -1$    $(\cos\theta \neq 0)$

$\therefore \tan\theta = -1$

Now $\tan \dfrac{\pi}{4} = 1$

tan is negative in the second and fourth quadrants.

$-\pi \le \theta \le \pi$

$\therefore \theta = -\dfrac{\pi}{4}$ or $\theta = \pi - \dfrac{\pi}{4}$

$\therefore \theta = -\dfrac{\pi}{4}$ or $\theta = \dfrac{3\pi}{4}$

4  $0 \le x \le \pi$

$\therefore 0 \le 2x \le 2\pi$

$\sqrt{3}\tan 2x = 1$

$\tan 2x = \dfrac{1}{\sqrt{3}}$

Now $\tan \dfrac{\pi}{6} = \dfrac{1}{\sqrt{3}}$

tan is positive in the first and third quadrants.

$\therefore 2x = \dfrac{\pi}{6}$ or $2x = \pi + \dfrac{\pi}{6}$

$2x = \dfrac{\pi}{6}$ or $2x = \dfrac{7\pi}{6}$

$x = \dfrac{\pi}{12}$ or $x = \dfrac{7\pi}{12}$

5  $3\sin\theta - 1 = 0$

$3\sin\theta = 1$

$\sin\theta = \dfrac{1}{3}$

Now $\sin^{-1}\left(\dfrac{1}{3}\right) = 0.339\,836\,909\ldots$

sin is positive in the 1st and 2nd quadrants.

So $\theta = 0.339\,836\,909\ldots$ or $\theta = \pi - 0.339\,836\,909\ldots$

$\theta = 0.339\,836\,909$ or $\theta = 2.801\,755\,74\ldots$

$\theta = 0.34$ or $\theta = 2.80$ (2 d.p.)

## 6 Further equations ⊃ p. 79

1  a

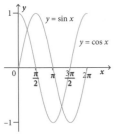

b  From the graph $\cos x = \sin x$ when $x = \dfrac{\pi}{4}$, and $\dfrac{5\pi}{4}$.

2  $\cot^2 x = 3$

$\cot x = \pm\sqrt{3}$

$\therefore \tan x = \pm\dfrac{1}{\sqrt{3}}$

$x = 30°, 180° - 30°, 180° + 30°$ or $360° - 30°$

$x = 30°, 150°, 210°$ or $330°$

3  $\sin^2 x + 2\sin x - 3 = 0$

$(\sin x + 3)(\sin x - 1) = 0$

$\sin x + 3 = 0$ or $\sin x - 1 = 0$

$\sin x = -3$ or $\sin x = 1$

No solution $\qquad x = \dfrac{\pi}{2}$

$\therefore$ **the equation has only one solution $x = \dfrac{\pi}{2}$.**

4  $\qquad\qquad \sec^2 x = \tan x + 13$

$\qquad\qquad 1 + \tan^2 x = \tan x + 13$

$\tan^2 x - \tan x - 12 = 0$

$(\tan x - 4)(\tan x + 3) = 0$

$\therefore \tan x = 4$ or $\tan x = -3$

Now $\tan^{-1}(4) = 75°57'49.52''$

If $\tan x = 4$,

$x = 75°57'49.52''$ or $180° + 75°57'49.52''$

$x = 75°58'$ or $255°58'$ (nearest minute)

$\tan^{-1}(3) = 71°33'54.18''$

If $\tan x = -3$,

$x = 180° - 71°33'54.18''$ or $360° - 71°33'54.18''$

$x = 108°26'$ or $288°26'$ (nearest minute)

$\therefore x = 75°58'$ or $108°26'$ or $255°58'$ or $288°26'$ **to the nearest minute.**

5  $\qquad\qquad 2\sin x = \tan x$

$\qquad 2\sin x - \tan x = 0$

$\qquad 2\sin x - \dfrac{\sin x}{\cos x} = 0$

$\sin x\left(2 - \dfrac{1}{\cos x}\right) = 0$

$\sin x = 0$ or $2 = \dfrac{1}{\cos x}$

$\sin x = 0$ or $\cos x = \dfrac{1}{2}$

$x = 0, \pi,$ or $2\pi$ or $x = \dfrac{\pi}{3}$ or $2\pi - \dfrac{\pi}{3}$

$\therefore x = 0, \dfrac{\pi}{3}, \pi, \dfrac{5\pi}{3}$ or $2\pi$

**Part A**

**1  C**  $\dfrac{5\pi}{6} = \dfrac{5 \times 180°}{6}$

$= 150°$

**2  B**  $\tan 210° = \tan (180 + 30)°$

$= \tan 30°$

$= \dfrac{1}{\sqrt{3}}$

**3  D**  cosine rule in I, sine rule in II

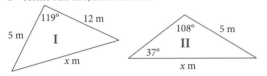

**4  B**  The bearing of $B$ from $A$ is $120°$.

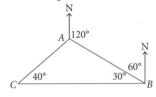

**5  D**  $\cos\theta = \dfrac{6^2 + 8^2 - 7^2}{2 \times 6 \times 8}$

$= \dfrac{17}{32}$

**6  A**  $\sin\theta = \dfrac{1}{\operatorname{cosec}\theta}$  $\left(\text{not } \operatorname{cosec}\!\left(\dfrac{1}{\theta}\right)\right)$

**7  D**  $l = r\theta$

$= 24 \times 75° \times \dfrac{\pi}{180°}$

$= 10\pi$ cm

**8  A**  $A = \dfrac{1}{2}ab\sin C$

$= \dfrac{1}{2} \times 7 \times 11 \times \sin 30°$

$= 19.25$ m$^2$

**9  A**

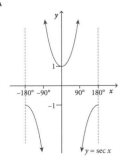

**10  C**  $2\cos x + \sqrt{3} = 0$

$2\cos x = -\sqrt{3}$

$\cos x = -\dfrac{\sqrt{3}}{2}$

Now $\cos\dfrac{\pi}{6} = \dfrac{\sqrt{3}}{2}$

cos is negative in the 2nd and 3rd quadrants.

So $x = \pi - \dfrac{\pi}{6}$  or  $\pi + \dfrac{\pi}{6}$

$x = \dfrac{5\pi}{6}$ or $x = \dfrac{7\pi}{6}$

**11  C**  $\dfrac{\sin Q}{13} = \dfrac{\sin 29°}{9}$

$Q = \sin^{-1}\!\left(\dfrac{13\sin 29°}{9}\right)$

$= 44°$  (nearest degree)

$\angle PQR = 44°$ or $180° - 44°$

$= 44°$ or $136°$

**12  B**  $y = 2\sin\dfrac{x}{2}$

Amplitude $= 2$

Period $= \dfrac{2\pi}{\dfrac{1}{2}}$

$= 4\pi$

**Part B**

**13**  $\dfrac{4\pi}{5} = \dfrac{4\pi}{5} \times \dfrac{180°}{\pi}$

$= \mathbf{144°}$  ✓

**14**  $108° = 108° \times \dfrac{\pi}{180°}$

$= \dfrac{\mathbf{3\pi}}{\mathbf{5}}$  ✓

**15**  $\operatorname{cosec}\dfrac{2\pi}{5} = 1.051\,462\,22\ldots$

$= \mathbf{1.0515}$  (4 d.p.)  ✓

**16**  $A = \dfrac{1}{2}ab\sin C$

Area of parallelogram

$= 2 \times \dfrac{1}{2} \times 7 \times 4 \times \sin 60°$  ✓

$= 28 \times \dfrac{\sqrt{3}}{2}$

$= \mathbf{14\sqrt{3}}$ **m**$^2$  ✓

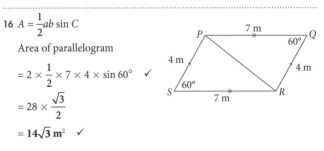

**17** $2\sin^2 x = 1$

$$\sin^2 x = \frac{1}{2}$$

$$\sin x = \pm\frac{1}{\sqrt{2}}$$

Now $\sin\dfrac{\pi}{4} = \dfrac{1}{\sqrt{2}}$ ✓

So $x = \dfrac{\pi}{4},\ \pi - \dfrac{\pi}{4},\ \pi + \dfrac{\pi}{4}$ or $2\pi - \dfrac{\pi}{4}$

$x = \dfrac{\pi}{4}, \dfrac{3\pi}{4}, \dfrac{5\pi}{4}$ or $\dfrac{7\pi}{4}$ ✓

**18 a**           $l = r\theta$

$$AB = 5 \times \frac{3\pi}{8}$$

$$= \frac{15\pi}{8}\ ✓$$

$$CD = 14 \times \frac{3\pi}{8}$$

$$= \frac{21\pi}{4}\ ✓$$

$$\text{Perimeter} = \frac{15\pi}{8} + \frac{21\pi}{4} + 2 \times 9$$

$$= 40.383\,8476\ldots$$

$$= \textbf{40.4 m}\quad (1\text{ d.p.})\ ✓$$

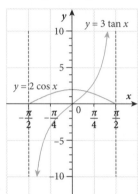

**b**  $A = \dfrac{1}{2}R^2\theta - \dfrac{1}{2}r^2\theta$

$$= \frac{1}{2} \times 14^2 \times \frac{3\pi}{8} - \frac{1}{2} \times 5^2 \times \frac{3\pi}{8}$$

$$= 100.727\,314\ldots\ \text{m}^2\ ✓$$

Depth of soil $= 0.3$ m

$$\text{Volume} = 100.727\,314\ldots \times 0.3$$

$$= 30.218\,1943\ldots$$

$$= \textbf{30.2 m}^3\quad (1\text{ d.p.})\ ✓$$

**19 a**      $\angle CBD = \angle BAC + \angle ADB$  (ext. angle of $\triangle$)

$\therefore \angle ADB = 29° - 22°$

$\qquad\qquad = 7°$ ✓

In $\triangle ABD$,

$$\frac{a}{\sin A} = \frac{d}{\sin D}$$

$$\frac{BD}{\sin 22°} = \frac{301}{\sin 7°}$$

$$\therefore BD = \frac{301\sin 22°}{\sin 7°}\ ✓$$

**b**  In $\triangle BCD$,

$$\frac{b}{\sin B} = \frac{c}{\sin C}$$

$$\frac{CD}{\sin 29°} = \frac{BD}{\sin 147°}$$

$$\therefore CD = \frac{301\sin 22°\sin 29°}{\sin 7°\sin 147°}\ ✓$$

$$= 823.587\,802\ldots$$

$$= \textbf{824 m}\quad (\text{nearest metre})\ ✓$$

**20 a**  $3\tan\dfrac{\pi}{6} = 3 \times \dfrac{1}{\sqrt{3}}$

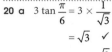

$$= \sqrt{3}\ ✓$$

$2\cos\dfrac{\pi}{6} = 2 \times \dfrac{\sqrt{3}}{2}$

$$= \sqrt{3}\ ✓$$

$$\therefore \textbf{3} \tan\frac{\pi}{6} = \textbf{2}\cos\frac{\pi}{6}$$

**b**

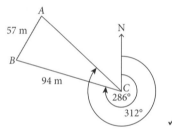

✓✓

**c**  The only solution of $3\tan x = 2\cos x$ for $-\dfrac{\pi}{2} \le x \le \dfrac{\pi}{2}$ is $x = \dfrac{\pi}{6}$.
From the graph there is only one point of intersection and from part **a** that solution is $x = \dfrac{\pi}{6}$. ✓

**21 a**

$$A = \sin^{-1}\left(\frac{94\sin 26°}{57}\right)$$

(diagram: 57 m, B, 94 m, N, C, 286°, 312°) ✓

**b**  $\angle ACB = 312° - 286°$

$$= 26°\ ✓$$

$$\frac{\sin A}{a} = \frac{\sin C}{c}$$

$$\frac{\sin A}{94} = \frac{\sin 26°}{57}$$

$$A = \sin^{-1}\left(\frac{94\sin 26°}{57}\right)$$

$$= 46.296\,7417\ldots°$$

$$= 46°\quad (\text{nearest degree})\ ✓$$

So $\angle BAC = 46°$ or $180° - 46°$

$$= \textbf{46° or 134°}\ \textbf{to the nearest degree}\ ✓$$

**22**  $\tan\alpha + \cot\alpha = \dfrac{\sin\alpha}{\cos\alpha} + \dfrac{\cos\alpha}{\sin\alpha}$ ✓

$$= \frac{\sin^2\alpha + \cos^2\alpha}{\cos\alpha\sin\alpha}$$

$$= \frac{\textbf{1}}{\sin\alpha\,\cos\alpha}\ ✓$$

**23** Let $h$ m be the height of $C$ above sea level.

In $\triangle CBD$,

$$\tan 29° = \frac{h}{BD}$$

$$\therefore BD = \frac{h}{\tan 29°} \quad \checkmark$$

In $\triangle ACD$,

$$\tan 38° = \frac{h}{AD}$$

$$\therefore AD = \frac{h}{\tan 38°} \quad \checkmark$$

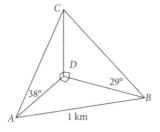

In $\triangle ABD$,

$$AB^2 = BD^2 + AD^2$$

$$1000^2 = \left(\frac{h}{\tan 29°}\right)^2 + \left(\frac{h}{\tan 38°}\right)^2$$

$$= h^2\left(\left(\frac{1}{\tan 29°}\right)^2 + \left(\frac{1}{\tan 38°}\right)^2\right)$$

$$h^2 = 1000^2 \div \left(\left(\frac{1}{\tan 29°}\right)^2 + \left(\frac{1}{\tan 38°}\right)^2\right) \quad \checkmark$$

$$= 204\,380.324\ldots$$

$$h = 452.084\,422\ldots \quad (h > 0)$$

$$= 450 \quad (2 \text{ sig. fig.})$$

**The height of $C$ above sea level is approximately 450 m.** $\checkmark$

**24 a** In $\triangle DAB$,

$$\angle DAB = 45° + 60°$$

$$= 105°$$

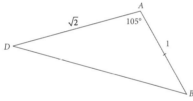

$$AD = \sqrt{2} \quad \text{(by Pythagoras' theorem)} \quad \checkmark$$

$$a^2 = b^2 + d^2 - 2bd \cos A$$

$$BD^2 = \left(\sqrt{2}\right)^2 + 1^2 - 2 \times \sqrt{2} \times 1 \times \cos 105°$$

$$= 3 - 2\sqrt{2} \cos 105° \quad \checkmark$$

But $\cos 105° = \cos (180 - 75)°$

$$= -\cos 75°$$

$$\therefore BD^2 = 3 + 2\sqrt{2} \cos 75° \quad \checkmark$$

**b** $\angle BCD = 90° + 60°$

$$= 150°$$

In $\triangle BCD$,

$$c^2 = b^2 + d^2 - 2bd \cos C$$

$$BD^2 = 1^2 + 1^2 - 2 \times 1 \times 1 \times \cos 150° \quad \checkmark$$

$$= 2 - 2 \cos 150°$$

But $\cos 150° = \cos (180 - 30)°$

$$= -\cos 30°$$

$$= -\frac{\sqrt{3}}{2}$$

So $BD^2 = 2 - 2 \times -\dfrac{\sqrt{3}}{2}$

$$= 2 + \sqrt{3} \quad \checkmark$$

**c** $3 + 2\sqrt{2} \cos 75° = 2 + \sqrt{3}$

$$2\sqrt{2} \cos 75° = -1 + \sqrt{3}$$

$$\cos 75° = \frac{-1+\sqrt{3}}{2\sqrt{2}} \quad \checkmark$$

$$= \frac{-1+\sqrt{3}}{2\sqrt{2}} \times \frac{\sqrt{2}}{\sqrt{2}}$$

$$= \frac{-\sqrt{2}+\sqrt{6}}{4}$$

$$= \frac{\sqrt{6}-\sqrt{2}}{4} \quad \checkmark$$

# CHAPTER 3
# INTRODUCTION TO DIFFERENTIATION

## Gradients of tangents

### 1 Continuity

→ Informally, a curve is **continuous** if it is unbroken, with no gaps or jumps.

→ If there are gaps or jumps in a curve then it is **discontinuous**.

→ Informally, a curve is **smooth** if it is continuous with no sharp corners.

### EXAMPLE 1

State whether the following curves are continuous or discontinuous.

a
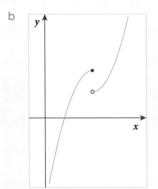

b

a continuous

b discontinuous

The open circle shows the position of the curve but that point is not included. The solid circle shows the point that does lie on the curve.

### EXAMPLE 2

a Sketch the function $f(x) = \begin{cases} x^2 & \text{for} \quad x > 1 \\ 3 - 2x & \text{for} \quad x \le 1 \end{cases}$

b Is the curve continuous?

c Is the curve smooth?

a
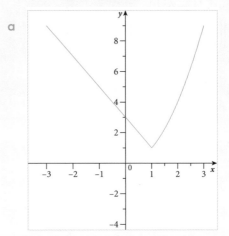

b Yes, the curve is continuous.

c No, the curve is not smooth.

There are no gaps or jumps in the curve so it is continuous but it is not smooth because of the sharp corner.

### EXAMPLE 3

Determine whether the curve $y = f(x)$ is continuous where $f(x) = \begin{cases} x^2 - 5 & \text{if} \quad x \ge 0 \\ 5 - x^2 & \text{if} \quad x < 0 \end{cases}$.

$y = \begin{cases} x^2 - 5 & \text{if} \quad x \ge 0 \\ 5 - x^2 & \text{if} \quad x < 0 \end{cases}$

When $x = 0$,
$\begin{aligned} x^2 - 5 &= 0^2 - 5 \\ &= -5 \end{aligned}$

When $x = 0$,
$\begin{aligned} 5 - x^2 &= 5 - 0^2 \\ &= 5 \end{aligned}$

As these two values are not equal the curve is not continuous.

Although the bottom part of the definition is not used when $x = 0$, as $x$ gets closer to 0 from below, the curve would get closer to 5 not −5 and there would be a jump.

1   State whether the following curves are continuous or discontinuous.

a

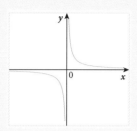

b

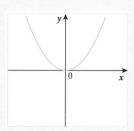

2   a   Sketch the function $f(x) = \begin{cases} 4-x^2 & \text{for} \quad x \geq -1 \\ -4x-1 & \text{for} \quad x < -1 \end{cases}$

    b   Is the curve continuous?
    c   Is the curve smooth?

3   Determine whether the curve $y = f(x)$ is continuous

    where $f(x) = \begin{cases} 2x^2 -1 & \text{if} \quad x > 1 \\ 2x+1 & \text{if} \quad x \leq 1 \end{cases}$

4*  $f(x) = \begin{cases} x^2 + 3x & \text{if} \quad x \geq 1 \\ ax+6 & \text{if} \quad x < 1 \end{cases}$

    If $y = f(x)$ is continuous, find the value of $a$.

Answers ⊃ p. 120

## 2 Gradients

→   The gradient of a line is its **slope**. If the line leans to the right (/) the gradient is **positive** and if it leans to the left (\\), the gradient is **negative**.

→   The gradient, $m$, of the line through the points $(x_1, y_1)$

    and $(x_2, y_2)$ is given by the **gradient formula** $m = \dfrac{y_2 - y_1}{x_2 - x_1}$.

→   If a line makes an angle of $\theta$ with the positive direction of the $x$-axis then $m = \tan \theta$.

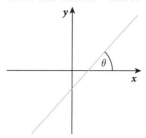

### EXAMPLE 1

**Find the gradient of the line that passes through the points (–2, 7) and (–3, –4).**

$(-2, 7), (-3, -4)$

$m = \dfrac{y_2 - y_1}{x_2 - x_1}$

$= \dfrac{-4-7}{-3-(-2)}$

$= 11$

*Refer to the section on linear functions to see more examples on gradients.*

### EXAMPLE 2

**The gradient of a line is $\dfrac{3}{5}$. Find, to the nearest degree, the angle the line makes with the positive direction of the $x$-axis.**

$\tan \theta = m$

$= \dfrac{3}{5}$

$\therefore \theta = \tan^{-1}\left(\dfrac{3}{5}\right)$

$= 30.963\,7565\ldots°$

$= 31°$   (nearest degree)

*$\tan \theta = \dfrac{\text{opposite}}{\text{adjacent}} = \dfrac{\text{rise}}{\text{run}}$*

### EXAMPLE 3

**Find the size of the angle the line $y = -2x + 3$ makes with the positive direction of the $x$-axis.**

$y = -2x + 3$

  Gradient: $m = -2$

    $\therefore \tan \theta = -2$

Now $\tan^{-1}(2) = 63.434\,9488\ldots°$

            $= 63°$ to the nearest degree

$\therefore \theta = 180° - 63°$

    $= 117°$

$\therefore$ the line $y = -2x + 3$ makes an angle of $117°$, to the nearest degree, with the positive direction of the $x$-axis.

*The gradient is the coefficient of $x$ in the equation $y = mx + c$.*

## EXAMPLE 4

A line crosses the $y$-axis at $y = -1$ and makes an angle of $45°$ with the positive direction of the $x$-axis. What is the equation of the line?

$y$-intercept $= -1$
Now $m = \tan \theta$
$\quad = \tan 45°$
$\quad = 1$

The $y$-intercept is the value $c$ in the equation $y = mx + c$.

The equation of the line is $y = x - 1$.

### → PRACTICE

1  Find the gradient of the line that passes through the points $(5, -1)$ and $(-1, -4)$.

2  The gradient of a line is $\dfrac{2}{3}$. Find, to the nearest degree, the angle the line makes with the positive direction of the $x$-axis.

3  Find the size of the angle the line $y = -3x - 11$ makes with the positive $x$-axis.

4  A line crosses the $y$-axis at $y = 7$ and makes an angle of $135°$ with the positive direction of the $x$-axis. What is the equation of the line?

5*  What is the equation of the line that passes through the point $(8, -3)$ and meets the positive direction of the $x$-axis at an angle of $45°$?

Answers ⊃ p. 120

## 3 The gradient of a secant

→ A **secant** is a straight line passing through two points on a curve.

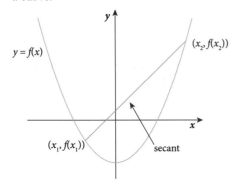

→ The gradient of a secant can be found by simply using the **gradient formula**.

→ The **gradient of the secant** to the curve $y = f(x)$ through the points $(x_1, f(x_1))$ and $(x_2, f(x_2))$ is given by $m = \dfrac{f(x_2) - f(x_1)}{x_2 - x_1}$.

## EXAMPLE 1

Find the gradient of the secant to the curve $y = f(x)$ through the points $(1, 2)$ and $(2, 16)$.

$(1, 2), \quad (2, 16)$

$m = \dfrac{y_2 - y_1}{x_2 - x_1}$

$\quad = \dfrac{16 - 2}{2 - 1}$

$\quad = 14$

It doesn't matter what the equation of the curve is.

The gradient of the secant is 14.

## EXAMPLE 2

Find the gradient of the secant to $y = x^2$ that cuts the curve at $x = 1$ and $x = 5$.

$y = x^2, \quad x_1 = 1, \quad x_2 = 5$

$m = \dfrac{f(x_2) - f(x_1)}{x_2 - x_1}$

$\quad = \dfrac{5^2 - 1^2}{5 - 1}$

$\quad = 6$

We could find the $y$-values of the coordinates of the points and use the usual gradient formula but it is quicker and easier to do it all at once.

∴ the gradient of the secant is 6.

## EXAMPLE 3

A secant to the curve $y = \dfrac{1}{x}$ passes through the points on the curve where $x = 2$ and $x = 6$. Find its gradient.

$y = \dfrac{1}{x}, \quad x_1 = 2, \quad x_2 = 6$

$m = \dfrac{f(x_2) - f(x_1)}{x_2 - x_1}$

$\quad = \dfrac{\dfrac{1}{6} - \dfrac{1}{2}}{6 - 2}$

$\quad = -\dfrac{1}{12}$

We should recognise the equation $y = \dfrac{1}{x}$ as that of a hyperbola and expect that the gradient of the secant will be negative because the secant will lean to the left (\).

∴ the gradient of the secant is $-\dfrac{1}{12}$.

1   Find the gradient of the secant to the curve $y = f(x)$ through the points $(2, 5)$ and $(5, 11)$.

2   Find the gradient of the secant to $y = x^3$ that cuts the curve at $x = 1$ and $x = 2$.

3   A secant to the curve $y = x^2 - x$ passes through the points on the curve where $x = -1$ and $x = 3$. Find its gradient.

4*  A secant to the curve $y = 2x^2 - 1$ has gradient 4. If it meets the curve at $x = -1$ and $x = a$, find the value of $a$.

Answers ⊃ pp. 120–121

## 4 The gradient of a tangent

→ A **tangent** is a line that touches a curve at a point.

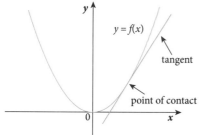

→ The **gradient of a tangent** can be **approximated** by finding the gradient of a secant drawn through two nearby points on the curve.

→ As the **distance between the two points** gets smaller and smaller, the gradient of the secant gets **closer and closer** to the gradient of the tangent.

### EXAMPLE 1

a   Find the gradient of the secant to $y = x^3$ through the points on the curve where $x = 0$ and $x = 2$.

b   Find the gradient of the secant through the points $x = 0.5$ and $x = 1.5$ on the curve $y = x^3$ and also the gradient of the secant through $x = 0.75$ and $x = 1.25$. Give an approximation of the gradient of the tangent at $x = 1$.

a   $y = x^3$, $x_1 = 0$, $x_2 = 2$

$$m = \frac{f(x_2) - f(x_1)}{x_2 - x_1}$$
$$= \frac{2^3 - 0^3}{2 - 0}$$
$$= 4$$

∴ the gradient of the secant is 4.

b   $y = x^3$, $x_1 = 0.5$, $x_2 = 1.5$

$$m = \frac{f(x_2) - f(x_1)}{x_2 - x_1}$$
$$= \frac{1.5^3 - 0.5^3}{1.5 - 0.5}$$
$$= 3.25$$

$y = x^3$, $x_1 = 0.75$, $x_2 = 1.25$

$$m = \frac{f(x_2) - f(x_1)}{x_2 - x_1}$$
$$= \frac{1.25^3 - 0.75^3}{1.25 - 0.75}$$
$$= 3.0625$$

> We could continue this process choosing points closer and closer to 1 and show that the gradient gets closer and closer to 3.

∴ an approximation for the gradient of the tangent is 3.

### EXAMPLE 2

a   Show that $y = x^2 - 3$ and $y = 4x - 7$ meet at just one point and find the coordinates of that point.

b   Briefly explain why it follows that the gradient of the tangent to the curve $y = x^2 - 3$ at $x = 2$ is equal to 4.

c   Show that the gradient of the secant through the points at $x = 1$ and $x = 3$ on the curve $y = x^2 - 3$ is equal to the gradient of the tangent at $x = 2$.

a   $y = x^2 - 3$, $y = 4x - 7$

At any point of intersection
$$x^2 - 3 = 4x - 7$$
$$x^2 - 4x + 4 = 0$$
$$(x - 2)^2 = 0$$
$$x = 2$$

When $x = 2$, $y = 4 \times 2 - 7$
$$= 1$$

∴ there is only one point of intersection, at $(2, 1)$.

b   The line $y = 4x - 7$ is a tangent to the curve $y = x^2 - 3$ because it touches it at one point. The gradient of the line $y = 4x - 7$ is 4, so the gradient of the tangent is 4.

> A tangent might touch a curve in one place and intersect it at another.

c   $y = x^2 - 3$, $x_1 = 1$, $x_2 = 3$

$$m = \frac{f(x_2) - f(x_1)}{x_2 - x_1}$$
$$= \frac{(3^2 - 3) - (1^2 - 3)}{3 - 1}$$
$$= 4$$

∴ the gradient of the secant is 4.

∴ the gradient of the secant is equal to the gradient of the tangent at $x = 2$.

→ PRACTICE

1  a  Find the gradient of the secant to the curve $y = x^4$ through the points where $x = 0.5$ and $x = 1.5$.

   b  Find the gradient of the secant through the points $x = 0.75$ and $x = 1.25$ on the curve $y = x^4$ and also the gradient of the secant through $x = 0.9$ and $x = 1.1$. Give an approximation of the gradient of the tangent at $x = 1$.

2  a  Show that $y = 4 - x^2$ and $y = 8 - 4x$ meet at just one point and find the coordinates of that point.

   b  Briefly explain why it follows that the gradient of the tangent to the curve $y = 4 - x^2$ at $x = 2$ is equal to $-4$.

   c  Show that the gradient of the secant through the points at $x = 1$ and $x = 3$ on the curve $y = 4 - x^2$ is equal to the gradient of the tangent at $x = 2$.

3*  Sketch the curve $y = \sqrt{16 - x^2}$ showing the tangent at $x = 0$. What is the gradient of the tangent?

Answers ⊃ p. 121

## Difference quotients

### 1 The behaviour of functions and tangents

→ A curve is **increasing** if it leans to the right. If it is increasing, the **gradient** of the tangent will be **positive**. A curve is **decreasing** if it leans to the left. If it is decreasing, the **gradient** of the tangent will be **negative**.

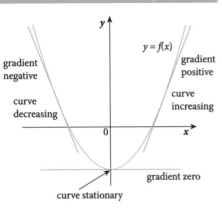

→ A curve is **stationary** if it is neither increasing nor decreasing. The tangent is **horizontal** at a stationary point and the gradient of the tangent is **zero**.

→ If a function is a straight line the gradient of the tangent is **constant** (it does not change).

→ If the gradient of the tangent of a curve that is increasing is also increasing, the curve is **increasing at an increasing rate**. If the gradient of the tangent of a curve that is increasing is decreasing, then the curve is **increasing at a decreasing rate**. If the gradient of the tangent of a curve that is decreasing is increasing, the curve is **decreasing at a decreasing rate**. If a negative gradient is increasing, the absolute value of the gradient will be decreasing. If the gradient of the tangent of a curve that is decreasing is also decreasing, then the curve is **decreasing at an increasing rate**.

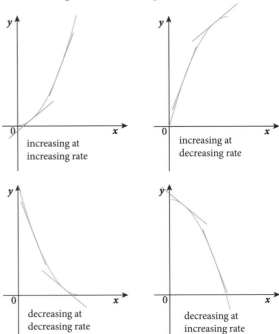

**EXAMPLE 1**

Describe the behaviour of the curve $y = f(x)$ at:

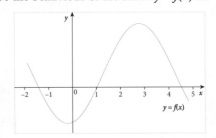

a  $x = -1$

b  $x = 2$

c  $x = 4$

We can also see that the curve has a point of inflexion, where the curve changes concavity, at about $x = 1\frac{1}{2}$.

a  At $x = -1$, the curve is decreasing at a decreasing rate.

b  At $x = 2$, the curve is increasing at a decreasing rate.

c  At $x = 4$, the curve is decreasing at an increasing rate.

## EXAMPLE 2

A company produced this graph of the level of gases emitted over the last few years.

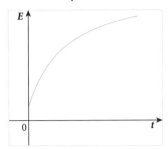

They claim that it shows that their policies to reduce emissions are working. Do you agree? Justify your answer.

Yes, although the amount of emissions is increasing, the rate of increase is decreasing.

The gradient of the tangent is positive but is decreasing.

→ PRACTICE

1 Describe the behaviour of the curve $y = f(x)$ at:

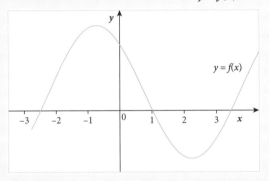

a $x = -2$
b $x = 2$
c $x = 3$

2 An advertising company showed the following graph of sales figures for a product.

The company claims that the graph shows that their campaign to significantly increase sales is working. Do you agree? Justify your answer.

3* Determine whether the gradient will be positive, negative or zero at each of the points $a$, $b$, $c$, $d$, $e$ and $f$.

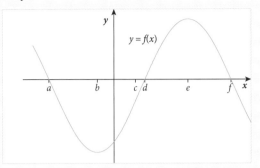

Answers ➲ pp. 121–122

## 2 Average rates of change

→ The **gradient of a secant** to a curve through the points $(a, f(a))$ and $((a + h), f(a + h))$ is given by $\dfrac{f(a+h)-f(a)}{h}$.

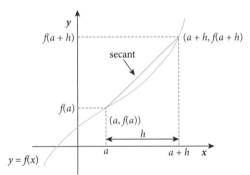

→ If $y = f(x)$, then $\dfrac{f(a+h)-f(a)}{h}$ gives the rate at which the function is changing. It is the **average rate of change**.

## EXAMPLE 1

The volume of a cone of fixed height 8.6 cm is given by $V = 9r^2$ where $r$ is the radius.

a Find the volume of such a cone of radius 2 cm.
b Find the volume of such a cone with radius 7 cm.
c Find the average change in volume for these radii.

a $V = 9r^2$
  When $r = 2$,
  $V = 9 \times 2^2$
  $= 36$ cm$^3$

b  $V = 9r^2$
   When $r = 7$,
   $V = 9 \times 7^2$
      $= 441$ cm$^3$

c  Average change $= \dfrac{441 - 36}{7 - 2}$

                 $= 81$ cm$^3$ per cm of radius

> The average rate of change will not always be the same. It will be different for different values of $r$.

$I = 80t + \dfrac{60}{t+1}$

Rate $= \dfrac{I(9) - I(0)}{9 - 0}$

> Never just assume that $f(0) = 0$. In this case $I(0) = 60$.

$= \dfrac{80 \times 9 + \dfrac{60}{9+1} - \left(80 \times 0 + \dfrac{60}{0+1}\right)}{9}$

$= 74$ tonnes per hour

## EXAMPLE 2

Sebastian, a runner on a charity run, states that each day the distance, $d$ km, that he covers is given by $d = 5.4t - 0.3t^2$ where $t$ is the time in hours ($0 \le t \le 9$) from the beginning of the day's run.

a  How far has Sebastian gone after 2 hours?

b  How far has Sebastian gone after 6 hours?

c  What is Sebastian's average speed over those 4 hours?

a  $d = 5.4t - 0.3t^2$
   When $t = 2$,
   $d = 5.4 \times 2 - 0.3 \times 2^2$
      $= 9.6$
   After 2 hours Sebastian has gone 9.6 km.

b  $d = 5.4t - 0.3t^2$
   When $t = 6$,
   $d = 5.4 \times 6 - 0.3 \times 6^2$
      $= 21.6$
   After 6 hours Sebastian has gone 21.6 km.

c  Average speed $= \dfrac{21.6 - 9.6}{4}$

                   $= 3$ km/h
   Sebastian's average speed is 3 km/h.

> Speed is the average rate of change of distance in this case.

## EXAMPLE 3

The amount of input resources in tonnes used in a factory is given by $I = 80t + \dfrac{60}{t+1}$ where $t$ is the time in hours that the factory has been operating. Find the average rate of resource use in the first 9 hours of operation.

### → PRACTICE

1  The volume of a cylinder of fixed height 14 cm is given by $V = 44r^2$ where $r$ is the radius.

   a  Find the volume of such a cylinder of radius 3 cm.

   b  Find the volume of such a cylinder with radius 9 cm.

   c  Find the average change in volume for these radii.

2  Phoebe, a walker on a charity walk, states that each day the distance, $d$ km, that she covers is given by $d = 5t - 0.3125t^2$ where $t$ is the time in hours ($0 \le t \le 8$) from the beginning of the day's walk.

   a  How far has Phoebe gone after 2 hours?

   b  How far has Phoebe gone after 6 hours?

   c  What is Phoebe's average speed over those 4 hours?

3  The amount of product in tonnes of output by a factory is given by $P = 180t + \dfrac{180}{t+1}$ where $t$ is the time in hours that the factory has been operating. Find the average use of product in the first 8 hours of operation.

4*  A ball dropped from a tower falls so that its height, $h$ m, at time $t$ seconds is given by $h = 320 - 5t^2$. What is the average rate of change of its height in the first 7 seconds?

Answers ⊃ p. 122

## The derivative function and its graph

### 1 The derivative from first principles

→ The notation $\lim\limits_{h\to 0}$ means the **limit** as $h$ approaches 0. It is the value of the expression (that follows that notation) as $h$ gets closer and closer to 0.

→ The notation $f'(x)$ or $y'$ means the **derivative** of the function $y = f(x)$.

→ The **derivative is the gradient of the tangent** to the graph of $y = f(x)$ at a point $x$.

→ The derivative from **first principles** is given by

$$f'(x) = \lim_{h\to 0}\frac{f(x+h)-f(x)}{h}.$$

### EXAMPLE 1

Find the derivative from first principles of $f(x) = 4x^2$.

$$f(x) = 4x^2$$
$$f'(x) = \lim_{h\to 0}\frac{f(x+h)-f(x)}{h}$$
$$= \lim_{h\to 0}\frac{4(x+h)^2 - 4x^2}{h}$$
$$= \lim_{h\to 0}\frac{4x^2 + 8xh + 4h^2 - 4x^2}{h}$$
$$= \lim_{h\to 0}\frac{h(8x+4h)}{h}$$
$$= \lim_{h\to 0}(8x+4h)$$
$$= 8x$$

We can't just substitute $h = 0$ into the expression because the denominator cannot be zero. We simplify the expression and get rid of the $h$ in the denominator, by factorising and then cancelling, and then we can let $h = 0$.

### EXAMPLE 2

If $f(x) = x^3$, find $f'(x)$, from first principles.

$$f(x) = x^3$$
$$f'(x) = \lim_{h\to 0}\frac{f(x+h)-f(x)}{h}$$
$$= \lim_{h\to 0}\frac{(x+h)^3 - x^3}{h}$$
$$= \lim_{h\to 0}\frac{x^3 + 3x^2h + 3xh^2 + h^3 - x^3}{h}$$
$$= \lim_{h\to 0}\frac{h(3x^2 + 3xh + h^2)}{h}$$
$$= \lim_{h\to 0}(3x^2 + 3xh + h^2)$$
$$= 3x^2$$

As $h \to 0$, $3xh \to 0$ and $h^2 \to 0$, so the limit is equal to $3x^2$.

### EXAMPLE 3

Find, by first principles, the gradient of the tangent to $f(x) = x - x^2$ at $x = 3$.

$$f(x) = x - x^2$$
$$f'(x) = \lim_{h\to 0}\frac{f(x+h)-f(x)}{h}$$
$$= \lim_{h\to 0}\frac{(x+h)-(x+h)^2 - (x-x^2)}{h}$$
$$= \lim_{h\to 0}\frac{x+h-x^2-2xh-h^2-x+x^2}{h}$$
$$= \lim_{h\to 0}\frac{h-2xh-h^2}{h}$$
$$= \lim_{h\to 0}\frac{h(1-2x-h)}{h}$$
$$= \lim_{h\to 0}(1-2x-h)$$
$$= 1 - 2x$$
$$f'(3) = 1 - 2 \times 3 = -5$$

Just as $f(3)$ is the value of $f(x)$ when $x = 3$, $f'(3)$ is the value of $f'(x)$ when $x = 3$.

### → PRACTICE

1   Find the derivative from first principles of $f(x) = x^2$.

2   If $f(x) = 3x^2 + 2x$, find $f'(x)$, from first principles.

3   Find, by first principles, the gradient of the tangent to $f(x) = 1 - x^2$ at $x = 2$.

4*  Find, from first principles, the derivative of $f(x) = 7x$.

Answers ⊃ pp. 122–123

### 2 The gradient function

→ Differentiating from first principles allows us to find the gradient at any point. This means we are finding the **gradient function**.

→ $f'(x)$ and $\dfrac{dy}{dx}$ are both **notations** used for the **derivative**.

→ $\dfrac{dy}{dx}$ (spoken as 'd y d x') is the **derivative of $y$ with respect to $x$**, meaning we are differentiating the function $y$ and the variable is $x$.

### EXAMPLE 1

a   Find the gradient function for the curve $y = 5x^2 - 3x + 4$.

b **Hence find the gradient of the tangent to the curve**
$y = 5x^2 - 3x + 4$ **at the point where:**

  i   $x = 2$

  ii   $x = 0$

  iii   $x = -1$

a   $y = 5x^2 - 3x + 4$

$$\frac{dy}{dx} = \lim_{h \to 0} \frac{f(x+h) - f(x)}{h}$$

$$= \lim_{h \to 0} \frac{5(x+h)^2 - 3(x+h) + 4 - (5x^2 - 3x + 4)}{h}$$

$$= \lim_{h \to 0} \frac{5x^2 + 10xh + 5h^2 - 3x - 3h + 4 - 5x^2 + 3x - 4}{h}$$

$$= \lim_{h \to 0} \frac{10xh + 5h^2 - 3h}{h}$$

$$= \lim_{h \to 0} \frac{h(10x + 5h - 3)}{h}$$

$$= \lim_{h \to 0} (10x + 5h - 3)$$

$$= 10x - 3$$

b  i   $\dfrac{dy}{dx} = 10x - 3$

      When $x = 2$,

      $\dfrac{dy}{dx} = 10 \times 2 - 3$

        $= 17$

  ii   When $x = 0$,

      $\dfrac{dy}{dx} = 10 \times 0 - 3$

        $= -3$

  iii   When $x = -1$,

      $\dfrac{dy}{dx} = 10 \times -1 - 3$

> Once we have the gradient function we can find the gradient of the tangent at any point on the curve.

        $= -13$

## EXAMPLE 2

a   **Find the gradient function for the function**
$f(x) = x^2 - 1$.

b   **Draw sketches, on separate diagrams, of $y = f(x)$ and $y = f'(x)$.**

c   **Explain the geometrical significance of these results.**

a   $f(x) = x^2 - 1$

$$f'(x) = \lim_{h \to 0} \frac{f(x+h) - f(x)}{h}$$

$$= \lim_{h \to 0} \frac{(x+h)^2 - 1 - (x^2 - 1)}{h}$$

$$= \lim_{h \to 0} \frac{x^2 + 2xh + h^2 - 1 - x^2 + 1}{h}$$

$$= \lim_{h \to 0} \frac{h(2x + h)}{h}$$

$$= \lim_{h \to 0} (2x + h)$$

$$= 2x$$

b

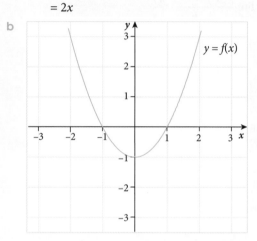

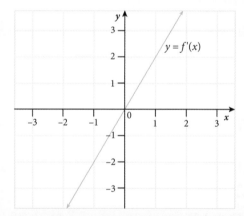

c   The graph of $y = f'(x)$ shows the gradient of the curve at every point. From the graph of the gradient function we can immediately see certain things about the relationship between the curve $y = x^2 + 1$ and its gradient at any point. For example, the gradient is positive when $x > 0$, where the curve is increasing. The gradient is negative when $x < 0$, when the curve is decreasing and the gradient is zero at $x = 0$, when the curve is at its minimum value.

> Don't confuse the graph of the gradient function with a tangent to the curve. It is the gradient of the tangent to the curve for different values of $x$. The equation of the tangent at each point is not the same as the gradient function.

→ PRACTICE

1  a  Find the gradient function for the curve
      $y = 6x^2 - 5x$.

   b  Hence find the gradient of the tangent to the
      curve $y = 6x^2 - 5x$ at the point where:

      i   $x = 3$

      ii  $x = 0$

      iii $x = -2$

2  a  Find the gradient function for the function
      $f(x) = 3 - 2x^2$.

   b  Draw sketches, on separate diagrams, of
      $y = f(x)$ and $y = f'(x)$.

   c  Explain the geometrical significance of these
      results.

3*  a  Find the derivative of $5x - 8$.

   b  What do you notice about the gradient of the
      tangent for different values of $x$? Discuss.

Answers ⊃ p. 123

## Calculating with derivatives

### 1 The derivative of $x^n$

→ To **differentiate** means to find the derivative.

→ From the **derivative from first principles** we find that:

if $y = x^2$, $\dfrac{dy}{dx} = 2x$;  if $y = x^3$, $\dfrac{dy}{dx} = 3x^2$;  if $y = x^4$, $\dfrac{dy}{dx} = 4x^3$;

if $y = x^5$, $\dfrac{dy}{dx} = 5x^4$.

→ From this pattern we develop a **rule** which can be shown
   to be correct for all **real values** of $n$.

→ If $y = x^n$, $\dfrac{dy}{dx} = nx^{n-1}$.

#### EXAMPLE 1

Differentiate $x^6$.

$y = x^6$

$\dfrac{dy}{dx} = 6x^5$

*You only need to use first principles if
specifically asked to do a question that
way. Otherwise use this simple rule.*

#### EXAMPLE 2

Find $f'(x)$ if $f(x) = x^9$.

$f(x) = x^9$
$f'(x) = 9x^8$

*In the answer use the same notation
that is used in the question.*

#### EXAMPLE 3

Find $\dfrac{d}{dx}(x^{13})$.

$\dfrac{d}{dx}(x^{13}) = 13x^{12}$

*This is a similar notation to $\dfrac{dy}{dx}$. You are
looking for the derivative of the function
$y = x^{13}$ with respect to $x$.*

#### EXAMPLE 4

Find $\dfrac{dy}{dx}$ if $y = x^{-5}$.

$y = x^{-5}$

$\dfrac{dy}{dx} = -5x^{-6}$

*Often simple mistakes are made with negative
integers so take care: $-5 - 1 = -6$ not $-4$.*

#### EXAMPLE 5

Differentiate $x^{\frac{1}{4}}$.

$y = x^{\frac{1}{4}}$

$\dfrac{dy}{dx} = \dfrac{1}{4}x^{-\frac{3}{4}}$

*Whenever $n$ is a rational number, follow
the rule to differentiate $x^n$.
If $n = \dfrac{1}{4}$, $n - 1 = \dfrac{1}{4} - 1 = -\dfrac{3}{4}$.*

→ PRACTICE

1  Differentiate $x^4$.

2  Find $f'(x)$ if $f(x) = x^8$.

3  Find $\dfrac{d}{dx}(x^{11})$.

4  Find $\dfrac{dy}{dx}$ if $y = x^{-3}$.

5  Differentiate $x^{\frac{1}{2}}$.

6* Find the derivative of $x^{2.4}$.

Answers ⊃ pp. 123–124

### 2 Further rules for differentiation

→ The **derivative** of any **constant** is 0.

→ If a term is **multiplied by a constant**, the derivative will
   also be multiplied by that constant.

→ The derivative of the **sum (or difference)** of terms is the
   sum (or difference) of the derivative of each term.

## EXAMPLE 1

Find $\dfrac{dy}{dx}$ if $y = 6$.

$y = 6$

$\dfrac{dy}{dx} = 0$

> The rule for differentiation still works: $6 = 6x^0$ so the derivative is $0x^{-1} = 0$.

## EXAMPLE 2

Find $f'(x)$ if $f(x) = x^5 - x^2 - x$.

$f(x) = x^5 - x^2 - x$
$f'(x) = 5x^4 - 2x - 1$

> $x = x^1$ so the derivative of $x$ is $1x^0 = 1 \times 1 = 1$.

## EXAMPLE 3

Find the derivative, with respect to $x$, of $7x^2$.

$y = 7x^2$
$y' = 7 \times 2x$
$\quad = 14x$

> $y'$ is another way of writing the derivative of $y$. It doesn't matter which notation is used when none is given in the question, but a function is not usually equal to its derivative, so never write something like, for this question, $7x^2 = 14x$.

## EXAMPLE 4

Differentiate $9 - 4x^5 - 3x^4 + 6x^3 - 9x^2$.

$y = 9 - 4x^5 - 3x^4 + 6x^3 - 9x^2$

$\dfrac{dy}{dx} = -20x^4 - 12x^3 + 18x^2 - 18x$

> We understand from the question that the variable is $x$ and so we need to differentiate with respect to $x$.

## EXAMPLE 5

Find the derivative of $1 - x^{-6}$.

$y = 1 - x^{-6}$

$\dfrac{dy}{dx} = 6x^{-7}$

> The derivative of 1 is 0.

### → PRACTICE

1. Find $\dfrac{dy}{dx}$ if $y = 17$.

2. Find $f'(x)$ if $f(x) = x^4 - x^3 + x$.

3. Find the derivative, with respect to $x$, of $12x^9$.

4. Differentiate $3x^6 - 2x^5 + 5x^3 - 4x^2 - 3$.

---

5. Find the derivative of $2 - 3x^{-4}$.

6* If $y = \dfrac{x^2}{2}$ find $y'$.

Answers ⊃ p. 124

## 3 Notations

→ The **notations** $\dfrac{dy}{dx}$, $f'(x)$, $y'$ and $\dfrac{d}{dx}$ are all used for the derivative.

→ Different **variables** may be used in expressions that need to be differentiated and so the notations must reflect this.

## EXAMPLE 1

Differentiate with respect to $t$: $\;x = -5t^2 + 2t - 8$.

$x = -5t^2 + 2t - 8$
$\dfrac{dx}{dt} = -10t + 2$

> The notation for the derivative must change to match the question. We are looking for the derivative of $x$ with respect to $t$.

## EXAMPLE 2

Differentiate $a = y^3 - y^2 + y - 1$.

$a = y^3 - y^2 + y - 1$
$\dfrac{da}{dy} = 3y^2 - 2y + 1$

> From the question we can see that we need to differentiate $a$ with respect to $y$.

## EXAMPLE 3

Find $h'(t)$ if $h(t) = 1 - t - 2t^2$.

$h(t) = 1 - t - 2t^2$
$h'(t) = -1 - 4t$

> Although $f$ is usually used for functions, any variable can be used. This is a function of $t$.

## EXAMPLE 4

Find $\dfrac{d}{dv}\left(-v^6 - 5v^4\right)$.

$\dfrac{d}{dv}\left(-v^6 - 5v^4\right) = -6v^5 - 20v^3$

> The question asks us to differentiate the given function with respect to $v$.

## EXAMPLE 5

Differentiate $f(n) = \dfrac{n^4}{2}$.

$$f(n) = \frac{n^4}{2}$$

$$f'(n) = \frac{4n^3}{2}$$

$$= 2n^3$$

Or the derivative of $\frac{1}{2}n^4$ is $\frac{1}{2} \times 4n^3 = 2n^3$.

$$f(x) = \frac{4}{x} - \frac{1}{x^3}$$

$$= 4x^{-1} - x^{-3}$$

$$f'(x) = -4x^{-2} + 3x^{-4}$$

$$= -\frac{4}{x^2} + \frac{3}{x^4}$$

In general, when differentiating we should give the answer in the same form as the question. If the question is in index form, leave the answer in index form. If the question is in fractional form, change the answer back to fractional form.

## → PRACTICE

1  Differentiate with respect to $t$:  $s = 9t^3 + 6t^2 - t$.

2  Differentiate $h = -m^4 + 5m^3 - 2m - 3$.

3  Find $g'(a)$ if $g(a) = -4a^5 - 7a^3 + 9a - 1$.

4  Find $\dfrac{d}{du}\left(u^3 + 5u^2 - 7u\right)$.

5  Differentiate $\dfrac{p^6}{3}$.

6*  Find the derivative of $\dfrac{1}{2}y^2 - \dfrac{2}{3}y^3$.

Answers ⊃ p. 124

## 4 Derivatives of rational expressions

→ An expression can be differentiated if it can be **expressed in the form** $x^n$.

→ The **index laws** are applied to change expressions involving, for example, fractions or square roots into the form $x^n$.

→ $\dfrac{1}{a} = a^{-1}$    $\dfrac{1}{a^m} = a^{-m}$    $\sqrt{a} = a^{\frac{1}{2}}$    $\sqrt[n]{a^m} = a^{\frac{m}{n}}$

### EXAMPLE 1

Find $\dfrac{dy}{dx}$ if $y = \dfrac{1}{x^2}$.

$$y = \frac{1}{x^2}$$

$$= x^{-2}$$

$$\frac{dy}{dx} = -2x^{-3}$$

$$= -\frac{2}{x^3}$$

Change the expression into index form so that it can be differentiated.

### EXAMPLE 2

If $f(x) = \dfrac{4}{x} - \dfrac{1}{x^3}$ find $f'(x)$.

### EXAMPLE 3

Find the derivative of $6\sqrt{x}$.

$$y = 6\sqrt{x}$$

$$= 6x^{\frac{1}{2}}$$

$$\frac{dy}{dx} = 3x^{-\frac{1}{2}}$$

$$= \frac{3}{\sqrt{x}}$$

$6 \times \frac{1}{2}x^{\frac{1}{2}-1} = 3x^{-\frac{1}{2}}$

### EXAMPLE 4

Differentiate $y = \sqrt[3]{x^2}$.

$$y = \sqrt[3]{x^2}$$

$$= x^{\frac{2}{3}}$$

$$y' = \frac{2}{3}x^{-\frac{1}{3}}$$

$$= \frac{2}{3\sqrt[3]{x}}$$

Make sure that you understand and can work quickly and easily with negative and fractional indices.

### EXAMPLE 5

Find $f'(x)$ if $f(x) = x\sqrt{x}$.

$$f(x) = x\sqrt{x}$$

$$= x \times x^{\frac{1}{2}}$$

$$= x^{\frac{3}{2}}$$

$$f'(x) = \frac{3}{2}x^{\frac{1}{2}}$$

$$= \frac{3\sqrt{x}}{2}$$

We must express the function as a single power of $x$ before attempting to differentiate.

1 Find $\dfrac{dy}{dx}$ if $y = \dfrac{1}{x^7}$.

2 If $f(x) = \dfrac{1}{x} - \dfrac{3}{x^2}$ find $f'(x)$.

3 Find the derivative of $4\sqrt{x}$.

4 Differentiate $y = \sqrt[4]{x^3}$.

5 Find $f'(x)$ if $f(x) = x^2\sqrt{x}$.

6* Find $\dfrac{dy}{dx}$ if $y = \dfrac{1}{\sqrt[5]{x}}$.

Answers ⊃ p. 124

## 5 The product rule

→ When differentiating a function that is the **product of two other functions**, the result is not the same as the product of the derivatives.

→ One way to differentiate products is to first **expand** so that the expression involves just the sum or difference of terms.

→ There is a **rule for differentiating products**:

  if $y = uv$, where $u$ and $v$ are functions of $x$,

  then $\dfrac{dy}{dx} = u\dfrac{dv}{dx} + v\dfrac{du}{dx}$.

### EXAMPLE 1

Differentiate after expanding $x(x^2 + 3)$.

$y = x(x^2 + 3)$
$\quad = x^3 + 3x$
$\dfrac{dy}{dx} = 3x^2 + 3$

> Note the derivative is not $2x$ which is the product of the derivatives of the two parts. The product rule could be used but in this case it is simpler to expand and then differentiate.

### EXAMPLE 2

Use the product rule to differentiate $y = (x + 4)(x + 3)$.

$y = (x + 4)(x + 3)$
$u = x + 4 \qquad\qquad v = x + 3$
$\dfrac{du}{dx} = 1 \qquad\qquad \dfrac{dv}{dx} = 1$

$\dfrac{dy}{dx} = u\dfrac{dv}{dx} + v\dfrac{du}{dx}$

$\quad = (x + 4) \times 1 + (x + 3) \times 1$
$\quad = x + 4 + x + 3$
$\quad = 2x + 7$

> In this question it would be easier to expand first and get $y = x^2 + 7x + 12$. We can see that the derivative is correct.

### EXAMPLE 3

Use the product rule to differentiate $y = (3x^2 + 7x - 5)(8x - 1)$.

$y = (3x^2 + 7x - 5)(8x - 1)$
$u = 3x^2 + 7x - 5$
$v = 8x - 1$
$\dfrac{du}{dx} = 6x + 7 \qquad \dfrac{dv}{dx} = 8$

$\dfrac{dy}{dx} = u\dfrac{dv}{dx} + v\dfrac{du}{dx}$

> You do not need to write out the values of $u$ and $v$ and their derivatives at the start, but if you prefer to do so it is okay.

$\quad = (3x^2 + 7x - 5) \times 8 + (8x - 1) \times (6x + 7)$
$\quad = 24x^2 + 56x - 40 + 48x^2 + 56x - 6x - 7$
$\quad = 72x^2 + 106x - 47$

### EXAMPLE 4

Use the product rule to differentiate $y = (x^2 + x - 1)(x^2 + 1)$.

$y = (x^2 + x - 1)(x^2 + 1)$
$\dfrac{dy}{dx} = u\dfrac{dv}{dx} + v\dfrac{du}{dx}$

$\quad = (x^2 + x - 1) \times \dfrac{d}{dx}(x^2 + 1) + (x^2 + 1) \times \dfrac{d}{dx}(x^2 + x - 1)$
$\quad = (x^2 + x - 1) \times 2x + (x^2 + 1) \times (2x + 1)$
$\quad = 2x^3 + 2x^2 - 2x + 2x^3 + x^2 + 2x + 1$
$\quad = 4x^3 + 3x^2 + 1$

> The product rule should only be used where the expression to be differentiated is the product of two or more functions. It is not necessary to use the product rule when the product involves a constant and a function. The product rule will give the correct answer but is longer and more involved than straight differentiation.

1 Differentiate after expanding $x(x^2 - 3x + 4)$.

2 Use the product rule to differentiate $y = (x - 2)(x + 7)$.

3 Use the product rule to differentiate $y = (x - 3)(x^2 + x - 3)$.

4 Use the product rule to differentiate $y = (x^2 - x + 1)(x^3 - 1)$.

5* Use the product rule to differentiate $y = (x^4 - 2)(5 - 3x - x^2)$.

Answers ⊃ pp. 124–125

## 6 The quotient rule

→ Whenever one function is divided by another we can use the **quotient rule** to find the derivative.

→ The quotient rule states, if $y = \dfrac{u}{v}$, where $u$ and $v$ are functions of $x$, then $\dfrac{dy}{dx} = \dfrac{v\dfrac{du}{dx} - u\dfrac{dv}{dx}}{v^2}$.

### EXAMPLE 1

**Use the quotient rule to differentiate $\dfrac{x+1}{x+2}$.**

$y = \dfrac{x+1}{x+2}$

$u = x + 1 \qquad v = x + 2$

$\dfrac{du}{dx} = 1 \qquad \dfrac{dv}{dx} = 1$

$\dfrac{dy}{dx} = \dfrac{v\dfrac{du}{dx} - u\dfrac{dv}{dx}}{v^2}$

$= \dfrac{(x+2)\times 1 - (x+1)\times 1}{(x+2)^2}$

$= \dfrac{x+2-x-1}{(x+2)^2}$

$= \dfrac{1}{(x+2)^2}$

*u must be the function in the numerator and v the function in the denominator.*

### EXAMPLE 2

**Differentiate $\dfrac{x}{x^2+1}$.**

$y = \dfrac{x}{x^2+1}$

$u = x \qquad v = x^2 + 1$

$\dfrac{du}{dx} = 1 \qquad \dfrac{dv}{dx} = 2x$

$\dfrac{dy}{dx} = \dfrac{v\dfrac{du}{dx} - u\dfrac{dv}{dx}}{v^2}$

$= \dfrac{(x^2+1)\times 1 - x\times 2x}{(x^2+1)^2}$

$= \dfrac{x^2+1-2x^2}{(x^2+1)^2}$

$= \dfrac{1-x^2}{(x^2+1)^2}$

*The denominator is generally left in factorised form unless the expression can be simplified.*

### EXAMPLE 3

**Find $f'(x)$ if $f(x) = \dfrac{x^3+2}{3x}$.**

$f(x) = \dfrac{x^3+2}{3x}$

$u = x^3 + 2 \qquad v = 3x$

$\dfrac{du}{dx} = 3x^2 \qquad \dfrac{dv}{dx} = 3$

$f'(x) = \dfrac{v\dfrac{du}{dx} - u\dfrac{dv}{dx}}{v^2}$

$= \dfrac{3x\times 3x^2 - \left(x^3+2\right)\times 3}{(3x)^2}$

$= \dfrac{9x^3 - 3x^3 - 6}{9x^2}$

$= \dfrac{6x^3 - 6}{9x^2}$

$= \dfrac{6\left(x^3-1\right)}{9x^2}$

$= \dfrac{2\left(x^3-1\right)}{3x^2}$

*You do not need to write out the values of u and v and their derivatives at the start, but if you prefer to do so it is okay.*

### EXAMPLE 4

**Use the quotient rule to find the derivative, with respect to $x$, of $\dfrac{2}{x^4-3}$.**

$y = \dfrac{2}{x^4-3}$

$\dfrac{dy}{dx} = \dfrac{v\dfrac{du}{dx} - u\dfrac{dv}{dx}}{v^2}$

$= \dfrac{\left(x^4-3\right)\times\dfrac{d}{dx}(2) - 2\times\dfrac{d}{dx}\left(x^4-3\right)}{\left(x^4-3\right)^2}$

$= \dfrac{\left(x^4-3\right)\times 0 - 2\times 4x^3}{\left(x^4-3\right)^2}$

$= \dfrac{-8x^3}{\left(x^4-3\right)^2}$

*This derivative can also be found by expressing the function in index form, $2(x^4 - 3)^{-1}$, and using the chain rule.*

→ **PRACTICE**

1 Use the quotient rule to differentiate $\dfrac{x-1}{x+3}$.

2 Differentiate $\dfrac{2x}{x^3-5}$.

**CHAPTER 3: INTRODUCTION TO DIFFERENTIATION**  109

3  Find $f'(x)$ if $f(x) = \dfrac{x^2-3x-1}{x}$.

4  Use the quotient rule to find the derivative, with respect to $x$, of $\dfrac{5}{x^2-2}$.

5*  Find the derivative of $\dfrac{x^2+5x-7}{x^2-4x+3}$.

Answers ⊃ p. 125

## 7 The chain rule

→ The derivative of a **composite function** is not the composite function of the individual derivatives.

→ If $y$ is a function of $u$, where $u$ is a function of $x$,

then $\dfrac{dy}{dx} = \dfrac{dy}{du} \times \dfrac{du}{dx}$.

→ This rule is commonly called the **chain rule** but it is also known as the composite function rule or as finding the derivative of a function of a function.

### EXAMPLE 1

**Differentiate** $y = (x^2 - 2)^2$.

$y = (x^2 - 2)^2$

$\dfrac{dy}{dx} = \dfrac{dy}{du} \times \dfrac{du}{dx}$

$= 2(x^2 - 2) \times \dfrac{d}{dx}(x^2 - 2)$

$= 2(x^2 - 2) \times 2x$

$= 4x(x^2 - 2)$

$y = u^2$  where  $u = x^2 - 2$.

### EXAMPLE 2

**Find the derivative of** $(2x - 1)^5$.

$y = (2x - 1)^5$

$\dfrac{dy}{dx} = \dfrac{dy}{du} \times \dfrac{du}{dx}$

$= 5(2x - 1)^4 \times \dfrac{d}{dx}(2x - 1)$

$= 5(2x - 1)^4 \times 2$

$= 10(2x - 1)^4$

$y = u^5$  where  $u = 2x - 1$.

### EXAMPLE 3

If $f(x) = (x^2 - 2x + 3)^9$, find $f'(x)$.

$f(x) = (x^2 - 2x + 3)^9$

$f'(x) = 9(x^2 - 2x + 3)^8 \times \dfrac{d}{dx}(x^2 - 2x + 3)$

$= 9(x^2 - 2x + 3)^8 \times (2x - 2)$

$= 18(x - 1)(x^2 - 2x + 3)^8$

We leave the answer in factorised form.

### EXAMPLE 4

Use the chain rule to find the derivative of $\dfrac{1}{7-3x}$.

$y = \dfrac{1}{7-3x}$

$= (7 - 3x)^{-1}$

$\dfrac{dy}{dx} = -(7 - 3x)^{-2} \times \dfrac{d}{dx}(7 - 3x)$

$= -(7 - 3x)^{-2} \times -3$

$= \dfrac{3}{(7-3x)^2}$

Alternatively, this could have been differentiated using the quotient rule.

### EXAMPLE 5

Differentiate $y = \sqrt{x^2 - 9}$.

$y = \sqrt{x^2 - 9}$

$= \left(x^2 - 9\right)^{\frac{1}{2}}$

$\dfrac{dy}{dx} = \dfrac{1}{2}\left(x^2 - 9\right)^{-\frac{1}{2}} \times \dfrac{d}{dx}\left(x^2 - 9\right)$

$= \dfrac{1}{2} \times \dfrac{1}{\sqrt{x^2-9}} \times 2x$

$= \dfrac{x}{\sqrt{x^2-9}}$

Many mistakes in differentiating result from failure to properly use the chain rule. Take care whenever you are differentiating a function of a function.

### → PRACTICE

1  Differentiate $y = (4x + 3)^3$.

2  Find the derivative of $(x^3 - 5)^7$.

3  If $f(x) = (x^2 + 7x - 6)^4$, find $f'(x)$.

4  Use the chain rule to find the derivative of $\dfrac{1}{5x-9}$.

5  Differentiate $\sqrt{16-x^2}$.

6*  Find the derivative of $\dfrac{1}{(2x+3)^5}$ using the chain rule.

Answers ⊃ pp. 125–126

## 8 Combinations of the rules

→ In some more cumbersome differentiations it is necessary to use **the chain rule with** either the **product** or **quotient rule**.

→ Chain rule: $\dfrac{dy}{dx} = \dfrac{dy}{du} \times \dfrac{du}{dx}$

Product rule: $\dfrac{dy}{dx} = u\dfrac{dv}{dx} + v\dfrac{du}{dx}$

Quotient rule: $\dfrac{dy}{dx} = \dfrac{v\dfrac{du}{dx} - u\dfrac{dv}{dx}}{v^2}$

### EXAMPLE 1

Differentiate $x(x^2 + 5)^4$.

$y = x(x^2 + 5)^4$

$\dfrac{dy}{dx} = x \times \dfrac{d}{dx}(x^2 + 5)^4 + (x^2 + 5)^4 \times \dfrac{d}{dx}(x)$

$\quad = x \times 4(x^2 + 5)^3 \times 2x + (x^2 + 5)^4 \times 1$

$\quad = 8x^2(x^2 + 5)^3 + (x^2 + 5)^4$

$\quad = (x^2 + 5)^3[8x^2 + (x^2 + 5)]$

$\quad = (x^2 + 5)^3(9x^2 + 5)$

The product of two functions ($x$ and $(x^2 + 5)^4$), but the second function is a function (the $4^{th}$ power) of another function ($x^2 + 5$).

### EXAMPLE 2

Find the derivative of $x^2(3x - 1)^7$.

$y = x^2(3x - 1)^7$

$\dfrac{dy}{dx} = x^2 \times \dfrac{d}{dx}((3x - 1)^7) + (3x - 1)^7 \times \dfrac{d}{dx}(x^2)$

$\quad = x^2 \times 7(3x - 1)^6 \times 3 + (3x - 1)^7 \times 2x$

$\quad = 21x^2(3x - 1)^6 + 2x(3x - 1)^7$

$\quad = x(3x - 1)^6[21x + 2(3x - 1)]$

$\quad = x(3x - 1)^6(21x + 6x - 2)$

$\quad = x(27x - 2)(3x - 1)^6$

We factorise to get the answer in simplest form.

### EXAMPLE 3

Find the derivative of $\dfrac{(2x+3)^4}{x}$.

$y = \dfrac{(2x+3)^4}{x}$

$\dfrac{dy}{dx} = \dfrac{x \times \dfrac{d}{dx}\left((2x+3)^4\right) - (2x+3)^4 \times \dfrac{d}{dx}(x)}{x^2}$

$\quad = \dfrac{x \times 4(2x+3)^3 \times 2 - (2x+3)^4 \times 1}{x^2}$

$\quad = \dfrac{8x(2x+3)^3 - (2x+3)^4}{x^2}$

$\quad = \dfrac{(2x+3)^3\left(8x - (2x+3)\right)}{x^2}$

$\quad = \dfrac{(6x-3)(2x+3)^3}{x^2}$

$\quad = \dfrac{3(2x-1)(2x+3)^3}{x^2}$

Alternatively, the function could be written as $y = x^{-1}(2x + 3)^4$ and the product rule used.

### EXAMPLE 4

Differentiate $y = \dfrac{x-1}{(3x-1)^2}$.

$y = \dfrac{x-1}{(3x-1)^2}$

$\dfrac{dy}{dx} = \dfrac{(3x-1)^2 \times 1 - (x-1) \times 2(3x-1) \times 3}{\left((3x-1)^2\right)^2}$

$\quad = \dfrac{(3x-1)^2 - 6(x-1)(3x-1)}{(3x-1)^4}$

$\quad = \dfrac{(3x-1)\left((3x-1) - 6(x-1)\right)}{(3x-1)^4}$

$\quad = \dfrac{3x - 1 - 6x + 6}{(3x-1)^3}$

$\quad = \dfrac{-3x + 5}{(3x-1)^3}$

Always look out for common factors in these type of questions.

### EXAMPLE 5

Differentiate $f(x) = 2x\sqrt{x+1}$.

$f(x) = 2x\sqrt{x+1}$

$\quad = 2x(x+1)^{\frac{1}{2}}$

$f'(x) = 2x \times \dfrac{1}{2}(x+1)^{-\frac{1}{2}} \times 1 + (x+1)^{\frac{1}{2}} \times 2$

$\quad = \dfrac{x}{\sqrt{x+1}} + 2\sqrt{x+1}$

$\quad = \dfrac{x}{\sqrt{x+1}} + \dfrac{2(x+1)}{\sqrt{x+1}}$

$\quad = \dfrac{3x+2}{\sqrt{x+1}}$

The question is not wrong if the answer is left as $\dfrac{x}{\sqrt{x+1}} + 2\sqrt{x+1}$ but it is better to express the answer as a single fraction.

### → PRACTICE

1 Differentiate $x(x^2 - 1)^5$.

2 Find the derivative of $x^3(5 - 4x)^4$.

3 Find the derivative of $\dfrac{(5x+3)^5}{x}$.

4  Differentiate $y = \dfrac{2x-1}{(x+1)^3}$.

5  Differentiate $f(x) = 4x\sqrt{1-x}$.

6*  Find $\dfrac{dy}{dx}$ if $y = (7x-1)^2(5x+2)^3$.

Answers ⊃ p. 126

## 9 Equations of tangents

→ The **tangent line** is the limiting position of the secant. The limiting value of the gradient of the secant at $P$ is defined to be the gradient of the tangent at $P$ or simply the **gradient of the curve** at $P$.

→ Using the **derivative**, we can find the **gradient of the tangent** to a curve at any point (provided it exists).

→ To find the **equation of the tangent** we must simply find the equation of a straight line. We use the formula $y - y_1 = m(x - x_1)$.

### EXAMPLE 1

**Find the equation of the tangent to the curve $y = x^2 + 3x$ at (1, 4).**

$y = x^2 + 3x$

$\dfrac{dy}{dx} = 2x + 3$

When $x = 1$,

$\dfrac{dy}{dx} = 2 \times 1 + 3 = 5$

∴ $m = 5$

$y - y_1 = m(x - x_1)$

$y - 4 = 5(x - 1)$

$y - 4 = 5x - 5$

$y = 5x - 1$

∴ the equation of the tangent is $y = 5x - 1$.

> The derivative gives the gradient function. Substituting the $x$-value of the point of contact gives the gradient at that point.

### EXAMPLE 2

**Find the equation of the tangent to the curve $y = x^3 - 2x^2 + x + 4$ at the point where $x = -1$.**

$y = x^3 - 2x^2 + x + 4$

$\dfrac{dy}{dx} = 3x^2 - 4x + 1$

When $x = -1$,

$\dfrac{dy}{dx} = 3(-1)^2 - 4(-1) + 1$

$= 8$

∴ $m = 8$

When $x = -1$,

$y = (-1)^3 - 2(-1)^2 + (-1) + 4$

$= 0$

$m = 8, \ (-1, 0)$

$y - y_1 = m(x - x_1)$

$y - 0 = 8(x - (-1))$

$y = 8(x + 1)$

$y = 8x + 8$

The equation of the tangent is $y = 8x + 8$.

> We use the equation of the curve to find the $y$-value of the point of contact.

### EXAMPLE 3

**The tangent to the curve $y = x^3 - 5x^2 + 6$ at the point $P$ has equation $y = -7x + 9$. Find the coordinates of $P$.**

$y = -7x + 9$ is the equation of the tangent at $P$.

∴ the gradient of the tangent at $P$ is $-7$.

$y = x^3 - 5x^2 + 6$

$\dfrac{dy}{dx} = 3x^2 - 10x$

At $P$, $\dfrac{dy}{dx} = -7$

∴ $3x^2 - 10x = -7$

$3x^2 - 10x + 7 = 0$

$(3x - 7)(x - 1) = 0$

$3x - 7 = 0$  or  $x - 1 = 0$

$x = 2\dfrac{1}{3}$ or  $x = 1$

When $x = 2\dfrac{1}{3}$,

$y = \left(2\dfrac{1}{3}\right)^3 - 5 \times \left(2\dfrac{1}{3}\right)^2 + 6$

$= -8\dfrac{14}{27}$

When $x = 1$,

$y = 1^3 - 5 \times 1^2 + 6$

$= 2$

Now $P$ lies on the line $y = -7x + 9$.

When $x = 2\dfrac{1}{3}$,

$y = -7 \times 2\dfrac{1}{3} + 9$

$= -7\dfrac{1}{3} \quad \left(\neq -8\dfrac{14}{27}\right)$

When $x = 1$,

$y = -7 \times 1 + 9$

$= 2$

∴ $P$ is the point (1, 2).

> There are two values of $x$ on the curve for which the gradient is $-7$ but only one of the points has the tangent $y = -7x + 9$.

1 Find the equation of the tangent to the curve $y = x^2 + 6x - 7$ at the point $(2, 9)$.

2 Find the equation of the tangent to the curve $y = x^3 - 4x^2 + 9x - 11$ at the point where $x = 3$.

3 The tangent to the curve $y = x^3 + 2x^2 - 5x + 7$ at the point $P$ has equation $y = 15 - x$. Find the coordinates of $P$.

4* Find the equation of the tangent to the curve $y = \dfrac{1}{x}$ at the point where $x = -1$.

Answers ⊃ pp. 126–127

## 10 The equation of a normal to a curve

→ A **normal** to a curve at a particular point, $P$, is perpendicular to the tangent at that point.

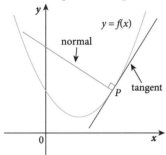

→ To find the **gradient of the normal**, first find the gradient of the tangent and then use the fact that if two lines are perpendicular, their gradients $m_1$ and $m_2$ are such that $m_1 m_2 = -1$.

### EXAMPLE 1

**Find the equation of the normal to the curve $y = x^3 + 1$ at the point $(1, 2)$.**

$y = x^3 + 1$

$\dfrac{dy}{dx} = 3x^2$

When $x = 1$,

$\dfrac{dy}{dx} = 3 \times 1^2$

$= 3$

∴ the gradient of the tangent is 3.

∴ the gradient of the normal is $-\dfrac{1}{3}$.

$m = -\dfrac{1}{3}, \quad (1, 2)$

$y - y_1 = m(x - x_1)$

$y - 2 = -\dfrac{1}{3}(x - 1)$

$y - 2 = -\dfrac{1}{3}x + \dfrac{1}{3}$

$y = -\dfrac{1}{3}x + 2\dfrac{1}{3}$

*Or the equation in general form is $x + 3y - 7 = 0$.*

∴ the equation of the normal is $y = -\dfrac{1}{3}x + 2\dfrac{1}{3}$.

### EXAMPLE 2

**Find the equation of the normal to the curve $y = \dfrac{4}{x}$ at the point where $x = 4$.**

$y = \dfrac{4}{x}$

$= 4x^{-1}$

$\dfrac{dy}{dx} = -4x^{-2}$

$= -\dfrac{4}{x^2}$

*$\dfrac{4}{x}$ is expressed in index form so that it can be easily differentiated.*

When $x = 4$,

$\dfrac{dy}{dx} = -\dfrac{4}{4^2}$

$= -\dfrac{1}{4}$

∴ the gradient of the tangent is $-\dfrac{1}{4}$.

∴ the gradient of the normal is 4.

When $x = 4$,

$y = \dfrac{4}{4}$

$= 1$

$m = 4, \quad (4, 1)$

$y - y_1 = m(x - x_1)$

$y - 1 = 4(x - 4)$

$y - 1 = 4x - 16$

$y = 4x - 15$

∴ the equation of the normal is $y = 4x - 15$.

## EXAMPLE 3

a Find the equation of the normal to the curve
$y = \frac{1}{4}x^2$ at the point $P(2, 1)$.

b Find the coordinates of the point $Q$ where this normal meets the curve again.

a $\quad y = \frac{1}{4}x^2$

$\frac{dy}{dx} = \frac{1}{2}x$

When $x = 2$,

$\frac{dy}{dx} = \frac{1}{2} \times 2$

$\qquad = 1$

∴ the gradient of the tangent is 1.

The gradient of the normal is –1.

$m = -1, \quad (2, 1)$

$y - y_1 = m(x - x_1)$

$y - 1 = -1(x - 2)$

$y - 1 = -x + 2$

$\qquad y = -x + 3$

The equation of the normal is $y = -x + 3$.

b The points of intersection of the parabola and the normal occur when:

$\frac{1}{4}x^2 = -x + 3$

$\qquad x^2 = -4x + 12$

$x^2 + 4x - 12 = 0$

$(x + 6)(x - 2) = 0$

$x = -6 \quad \text{or} \quad x = 2$

Now $P$ is the point where $x = 2$.

∴ $Q$ is the point where $x = -6$.

When $x = -6$, $\quad y = -(-6) + 3$

$\qquad\qquad\qquad = 9$

So $Q$ is the point $(-6, 9)$.

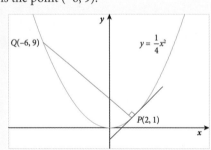

When solving questions of this type, remember that you already know one point that satisfies the simultaneous solution of the equation of the curve and of the normal. You can use this point to help you find the factors of the equation you are trying to solve.

→ PRACTICE

1 Find the equation of the normal to the curve $y = x - x^2$ at the point $(1, 0)$.

2 Find the equation of the normal to the curve $y = \frac{3}{x}$ at the point where $x = 6$.

3 a Find the equation of the normal to the curve $y = \frac{x^2}{8}$ at the point $P(4, 2)$.

   b Find the coordinates of the point $Q$ where this normal meets the curve again.

4* Find the equation of the normal to the curve $y = (2x - 1)^4$ at $x = 1$.

Answers ⊃ pp. 127–128

## 11 Rates of change

→ $\frac{f(a+h)-f(a)}{h}$ gives the **average rate** of change of the function $f(x)$.

→ If we want to find the **instantaneous rate** of change then we need to consider the change in the function over a very small value of $h$. The instantaneous rate of change is given by $\lim\limits_{h \to 0} \frac{f(a+h)-f(a)}{h}$.

→ This is the formula for the derivative from first principles, so $f'(x)$ is the **rate of change** of the function.

## EXAMPLE 1

The volume of water in a container, $V$ litres at time $t$ seconds, is given by $V = 3t^2 + 8t + 4$. Find the rate at which $V$ is changing when $t = 5$.

$V = 3t^2 + 8t + 4$

$\frac{dV}{dt} = 6t + 8$

When $t = 5$,

$\frac{dV}{dt} = 6 \times 5 + 8$

$\qquad = 38$

The volume is changing at the rate of 38 L per second.

Because the answer is a rate the units are amount (litres) per period of time (seconds).

## EXAMPLE 2

A tank is being emptied. The volume of water remaining in the tank $t$ minutes after it started emptying is given by: $V = t^2 - 300t + 22\,500$.

a   If the tank was initially full, what is its capacity?

b   Show that the tank is empty after $2\frac{1}{2}$ hours.

c   At what rate is the water flowing out of the tank when just 2500 L remain?

a   $V = t^2 - 300t + 22\,500$
When $t = 0$,
$V = 0^2 - 300 \times 0 + 22\,500$
$\quad = 22\,500$
The capacity of the tank is 22 500 L.

b   $2\frac{1}{2}$ hours $= 2\frac{1}{2} \times 60$ minutes
$\qquad\qquad = 150$ minutes
When $t = 150$,
$V = 150^2 - 300 \times 150 + 22\,500$
$\quad = 0$
∴ the tank is empty after $2\frac{1}{2}$ hours

c   When $V = 2500$,
$t^2 - 300t + 22\,500 = 2500$
$t^2 - 300t + 20\,000 = 0$
$(t - 100)(t - 200) = 0$
$\quad t = 100 \quad$ or $\quad t = 200$
But the tank is empty when $t = 150$.
∴ $t = 100$
$V = t^2 - 300t + 22\,500$
$\dfrac{dV}{dt} = 2t - 300$
When $t = 100$,

> The original expression gives the volume of water in the tank. The fact that the derivative is negative means that the volume is decreasing.

$\dfrac{dV}{dt} = 2 \times 100 - 300$
$\quad = -100$
∴ the water is flowing out of the tank at the rate of 100 L per minute.

## EXAMPLE 3

The number of people in a shopping centre is approximated by the formula $N = 729 + 72t^2 - t^4$ where $t$ is the time in hours after 10 am $(0 \leq t \leq 9)$.

a   Approximately how many people are in the shopping centre at 10 am?

b   How many people are in the shopping centre after 9 hours?

c   Find the rate at which the number of people in the centre is changing when $t = 2$ and when $t = 8$. Briefly comment on the significance of the answers.

a   $N = 729 + 72t^2 - t^4$
When $t = 0$,
$N = 729 + 72 \times 0^2 - 0^4$
$\quad = 729$

> The formula is an approximation. It gives a rough idea of the numbers of people at different times of the day.

There are approximately 729 people in the shopping centre at 10 am.

b   When $t = 9$,
$N = 729 + 72 \times 9^2 - 9^4$
$\quad = 0$
There are no people left in the shopping centre after 9 hours.

c   $N = 729 + 72t^2 - t^4$
$\dfrac{dN}{dt} = 144t - 4t^3$
When $t = 2$,
$\dfrac{dN}{dt} = 144 \times 2 - 4 \times 2^3$
$\quad = 256$
When $t = 8$,
$\dfrac{dN}{dt} = 144 \times 8 - 4 \times 8^3$
$\quad = -896$
After 2 hours the number of people is increasing by 256 people per hour but after 8 hours the number of people is decreasing by 896 people per hour.

## EXAMPLE 4

A vase is being filled by water flowing into it at a constant rate. The vase is 20 cm high and has straight sides at the bottom and top, with a curved middle section, as shown in the diagram.

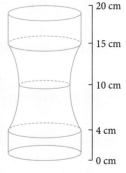

$h(t)$ is the depth of water in the vase as a function of time.

a   What can you say about $\dfrac{dh}{dt}$ while the water is filling the bottom 4 cm of the vase?

b   What can you say about $\dfrac{dh}{dt}$ when the vase is filled to a height of 10 cm?

c   Comment on the essential features of the graph of $h$ as a function of time.

a   While filling the bottom 4 cm, the depth of the water will be increasing constantly. $\dfrac{dh}{dt}$ will be a positive constant.

> $\frac{dh}{dt}$ is the rate at which the height is changing.

b The depth of water in the vase will be increasing at its fastest rate at the narrowest part of the vase. $\frac{dh}{dt}$ will be a maximum.

c The graph will be an increasing curve. It will be a straight line, with positive gradient, for $0 \le h \le 4$. The height is then increasing at an increasing rate so the curve will be concave up until $h = 10$, where it will change concavity. The height will be increasing at a decreasing rate for $10 \le h \le 15$ and then the graph will be a straight (increasing) line for $15 \le h \le 20$.

→ **PRACTICE**

1 The volume of water in a container, $V$ litres at time $t$ seconds, is given by $V = 7t^2 + 4t + 6$. Find the rate at which $V$ is changing when $t = 3$.

2 A vat is being emptied. The volume of fluid remaining in the vat $t$ minutes after it started emptying, $V$ litres, is given by $V = t^2 - 420t + 8000$.
  a If the vat is initially full, what is its capacity?
  b Show that the vat is empty after 20 minutes.
  c At what rate is the fluid flowing out of the vat when 1925 L remain?

3 The number of people attending a concert is approximated by the formula $N = 833 + 32t^2 - t^4$ where $t$ is the time in hours after 6 pm ($0 \le t \le 7$).
  a Approximately how many people are at the concert at 6 pm?
  b How many people are at the concert at the end of 7 hours?
  c Find the rate at which the number of people at the concert is changing when $t = 1$ and when $t = 6$. Briefly comment on the significance of the answers.

4 A bottle is being filled with water flowing into it at a constant rate. The bottle (as seen in the diagram) can be filled to a height of 25 cm.

Let $h$ be the depth of water in the bottle as a function of time.

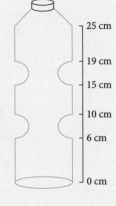
25 cm
19 cm
15 cm
10 cm
6 cm
0 cm

  a What can you say about $\frac{dh}{dt}$ while the water is filling the bottom 6 cm of the bottle?

b What can you say about $\frac{dh}{dt}$ when the bottle is filled to a height of 8 cm?

c Comment on the essential features of the graph of $h$ as a function of $t$.

5* The volume of fuel flowing through a hose ($V$ litres at time $t$ seconds) is given by $V = 6t - \frac{t^2}{90}$.
  a At what rate is the fuel initially flowing?
  b How long does it take for the fuel to stop flowing?
  c How much fuel flows through the hose in that time?

Answers ⊃ pp. 128–129

## 12 Displacement, velocity and acceleration

→ **Displacement** is the **position** of an object from a central position, $O$, the origin. For a particle moving in a straight line a negative displacement means that the particle is to the left of the origin and a positive displacement means the particle is to the right of the origin. $x$ is usually used for the displacement.

→ **Velocity** is defined as the **rate of change of displacement**. The velocity gives both the speed and direction of the particle. A negative velocity means that the particle is moving to the left. A positive velocity means that the particle is moving to the right. $v$ is often used for the velocity.

→ **Acceleration** is defined as the **rate of change of velocity**. A positive acceleration means that the acceleration is acting to the right. A negative acceleration means that it is acting to the left. $a$ is often used for the acceleration.

### EXAMPLE 1

A particle is moving in a straight line so that at time $t$ seconds its displacement, $x$ metres, is given by $x = 12t - t^2$.
  a Find an expression for the velocity.
  b Find the velocity of the particle when $t = 8$.
  c Find the velocity of the particle when $x = 36$.

a $x = 12t - t^2$

$\frac{dx}{dt} = 12 - 2t$

So an expression for the velocity is $v = 12 - 2t$.

b   When $t = 8$,

$v = 12 - 2 \times 8$

$\phantom{v} = -4$

When $t = 8$, the velocity is $-4$ ms$^{-1}$.

c   When $x = 36$,

$36 = 12t - t^2$

$t^2 - 12t + 36 = 0$

$(t - 6)^2 = 0$

$t = 6$

When $t = 6$,

$v = 12 - 2 \times 6$

$\phantom{v} = 0$

If the velocity is zero, the particle is not moving. We say it is at rest. If a particle is at rest, $v = 0$.

The velocity is 0 when $x = 36$.

## EXAMPLE 2

The displacement of a moving particle is given by $x = t^2 - 9t + 14$. Show that the acceleration is constant.

$x = t^2 - 9t + 14$

$v = \dfrac{dx}{dt}$

$\phantom{v} = 2t - 9$

$a = \dfrac{dv}{dt}$

The acceleration does not change. It is always the same irrespective of the time or position.

$\phantom{a} = 2$

$\therefore$ the acceleration is constant.

## EXAMPLE 3

A particle moving in a straight line has its displacement, $x$ m, from a fixed point $O$ given by:

$x = 8 + 12t - 3t^2$, where $t$ is the time in seconds.

a   When and where is the particle at rest?

b   In what direction will it then move? Justify your answer.

a   $x = 8 + 12t - 3t^2$

$v = 12 - 6t$

The particle is at rest when $v = 0$

i.e. $12 - 6t = 0$

$6t = 12$

$t = 2$

When $t = 2$,

$x = 8 + 12 \times 2 - 3 \times 2^2$

$\phantom{x} = 20$

$\therefore$ the particle is at rest after 2 seconds at a position 20 m to the right of $O$.

b   $v = 12 - 6t$

$a = -6$

Because the particle is at rest the direction of the force applied to it is the direction it will go.

$\therefore$ the particle will move to the left because the acceleration is negative.

### → PRACTICE

1   A particle is moving in a straight line so that at time $t$ seconds its displacement, $x$ m, is: $x = 18t - t^2$.

a   Find an expression for the velocity.

b   Find the velocity of the particle when $t = 6$.

c   Find the velocity of the particle when $x = 81$.

2   The displacement of a moving particle is given by $x = 2t^2 - 7t + 8$. Show that the acceleration is constant.

3   A particle moving in a straight line has its displacement, $x$ m, from a fixed point $O$ given by $x = 11 + 20t - 2t^2$ where $t$ is the time in seconds.

a   When and where is the particle at rest?

b   In what direction will it then move? Justify your answer.

4*  A particle moves with displacement $x$ metres at time $t$ seconds given by $x = 1 + 4t + 15t^2 - t^3$. Find the velocity at the time when the acceleration is zero.

Answers ⊃ p. 129

**Total marks: 50**

## PART A
(Suggested time: 15 minutes)

(1 mark each)

1  Which of these functions is continuous?

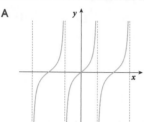
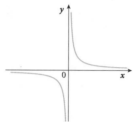
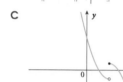
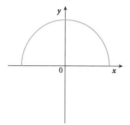

2  At what angle, to the nearest degree, will the line $y = 3x - 5$ meet the positive direction of the $x$-axis?

A  $72°$       B  $79°$
C  $63°$       D  $18°$

3  What is the gradient of the secant through the points where $x = 1$ and $x = 2$ on the curve $y = x^2 + 3$?

A  1       B  2
C  3       D  4

4  Which is **not** a correct notation for the derivative of $y = f(x)$?

A  $\dfrac{dy}{dx}$       B  $f'(x)$

C  $f(x')$       D  $y'$

5  The equation of the tangent to a curve at $P$ is $y = \dfrac{1}{2}x - 7$. What is the gradient of the normal at $P$?

A  $\dfrac{1}{2}$       B  $-\dfrac{1}{2}$

C  2       D  $-2$

6  What is the derivative, with respect to $x$, of $\dfrac{1}{x^2}$?

A  $\dfrac{1}{2x}$       B  $\dfrac{1}{x^3}$

C  $-\dfrac{2}{x^3}$       D  $-\dfrac{1}{2x^3}$

7  Which rule would be best to use to find the derivative of $(x^3 + 1)(x^2 + x + 1)$?

A  chain rule       B  product rule
C  quotient rule       D  first principles

8  If the velocity of a moving particle at time $t$ is given by $v = 5 - 3t$, what is the acceleration at time $t$?

A  5       B  $-3$
C  2       D  depends on $t$

9  If $V = 8t^2 - 6t + 7$ what is an expression for the rate of change of $V$?

A  $16t - 6$       B  $10t$
C  $16t + 1$       D  $10t - 6$

10  What is $f'(2)$ if $f(x) = 9 - 3x^2$?

A  $-3$       B  $-12$
C  6       D  12

11  A curve is increasing at point $P$. Which of the following must be true about the gradient of the tangent at $P$?

A  positive       B  negative
C  zero       D  increasing

12  What is the derivative with respect to $x$ of $(5x^2 - 2)^7$?

A  $7(5x^2 - 2)^6$       B  $35(5x^2 - 2)^6$
C  $70(5x^2 - 2)^6$       D  $70x(5x^2 - 2)^6$

## PART B
(Suggested time: 45 minutes)

Show all working.

13  If $f(x) = x^6 - 2x^3 + 7x$, find $f'(x)$.    (1 mark)

14  Find $\dfrac{d}{du}\left(\dfrac{u}{2}\right)$.    (1 mark)

15  a  Differentiate $f(x) = x^2 - 6x + 5$.    (1 mark)

     b  Hence find the point on the curve $y = f(x)$ where the gradient of the tangent is 0.    (2 marks)

     c  What will be special about the curve at the point found in part b?    (1 mark)

16  Differentiate $\dfrac{1}{1-x}$ using the chain rule.    (2 marks)

17 Differentiate, with respect to $x$:

   a   $\dfrac{3}{x^5}$        (2 marks)

   b   $\sqrt[3]{x}$        (2 marks)

   c   $x(7 - 4x)^9$        (2 marks)

   d   $\dfrac{2x+1}{2x-1}$        (2 marks)

18 For what values of $x$ is the function $f(x) = x^2 + 12x - 5$ increasing? (2 marks)

19 Find the gradient of the normal to the curve $y = \sqrt{x}$ at the point where $x = 4$. (3 marks)

20 Find the equation of the tangent to $y = (x - 2)^2$ at the point where $x = 3$. (2 marks)

21 Consider the function $f(x) = x^3$.

   a   Find $f'(x)$. (1 mark)

   b   Sketch $y = f(x)$ and $y = f'(x)$ on the same diagram. (2 marks)

   c   Discuss the relationship between the two curves shown in part b. (1 mark)

22 Find the derivative of $x^2 + 6x$ from first principles. (2 marks)

23 The displacement, $x$ m at $t$ seconds, of a particle moving in a straight line is given by $x = t^2 - 8t - 7$ $(t \geq 0)$.

   a   Find the initial position of the particle. (1 mark)

   b   Find an expression for the velocity. (1 mark)

   c   Find the time when the particle is at rest. (1 mark)

   d   Find an expression for the acceleration. (1 mark)

24 The volume $V$ litres of water remaining in a tank as it is being emptied is given by $V = t^2 - 200t + 10\,000$ where $t$ is the time in minutes $(t \geq 0)$.

   a   How much water was in the tank before it began to be emptied? (1 mark)

   b   What is the average rate of change in volume in the first 10 minutes? (2 marks)

   c   At what rate is the water flowing from the tank after one hour? (2 marks)

# ANSWERS

**GRADIENTS OF TANGENTS**

## 1 Continuity ⊃ p. 97

1  a  **discontinuous**
   b  **continuous**

2  a  $f(x) = \begin{cases} 4-x^2 & \text{for } x \geq -1 \\ -4x-1 & \text{for } x < -1 \end{cases}$

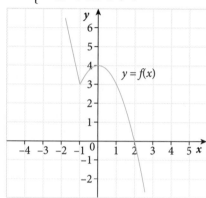

$y = f(x)$

   b  **Yes, the curve is continuous.**
   c  **No, the curve is not smooth.**

3  $y = \begin{cases} 2x^2 - 1 & \text{if } x > 1 \\ 2x + 1 & \text{if } x \leq 1 \end{cases}$

   When $x = 1$,
   $2x^2 - 1 = 2 \times 1^2 - 1$
   $\qquad = 1$
   When $x = 1$,
   $2x + 1 = 2 \times 1 + 1$
   $\qquad = 3$
   **As these two values are not equal the curve is not continuous.**

4  $f(x) = \begin{cases} x^2 + 3x & \text{if } x \geq 1 \\ ax + 6 & \text{if } x < 1 \end{cases}$

   When $x = 1$,
   $x^2 + 3x = 1^2 + 3 \times 1$
   $\qquad = 4$
   When $x = 1$,
   $ax + 6 = a + 6$
   If $y = f(x)$ is continuous these two values must be equal.
   $\therefore a + 6 = 4$
   $\qquad \boldsymbol{a = -2}$

## 2 Gradients ⊃ p. 98

1  $(5, -1), \quad (-1, -4)$
   $m = \dfrac{y_2 - y_1}{x_2 - x_1}$
   $\quad = \dfrac{-4 - (-1)}{-1 - 5}$
   $\quad = \dfrac{-3}{-6}$
   $\quad = \dfrac{1}{2}$

2  $\tan \theta = m$
   $\qquad = \dfrac{2}{3}$
   $\therefore \theta = \tan^{-1}\left(\dfrac{2}{3}\right)$
   $\qquad = 33.690\,0675\ldots°$
   $\qquad = \mathbf{34°} \quad \text{(nearest degree)}$

3  $y = -3x - 11$
   Gradient: $m = -3$
   $\qquad \therefore \tan \theta = -3$
   Now $\tan^{-1}(3) = 71.565\,0511\ldots°$
   $\qquad\qquad\qquad = 72°$ to the nearest degree
   $\therefore \theta = 180° - 72°$
   $\qquad = 108°$
   **∴ the line $y = -3x - 11$ makes an angle of 108°, to the nearest degree, with the positive direction of the $x$-axis.**

4  $y$-intercept $= 7$
   Now $m = \tan \theta$
   $\qquad = \tan 135°$
   $\qquad = -1$
   **The equation of the line is $y = -x + 7$.**

5  $m = \tan \theta$
   $\quad = \tan 45°$
   $\quad = 1$
   $m = 1, \quad (8, -3)$
   $y - y_1 = m(x - x_1)$
   $y - (-3) = 1(x - 8)$
   $y + 3 = x - 8$
   $\qquad \boldsymbol{y = x - 11}$

## 3 The gradient of a secant ⊃ p. 99

1  $(2, 5), \quad (5, 11)$
   $m = \dfrac{y_2 - y_1}{x_2 - x_1}$
   $\quad = \dfrac{11 - 5}{5 - 2}$
   $\quad = 2$
   **The gradient of the secant is 2.**

120    *EXCEL* YEAR 11 MATHEMATICS ADVANCED

2  $y = x^3$,  $x_1 = 1$,  $x_2 = 2$

$$m = \frac{f(x_2) - f(x_1)}{x_2 - x_1}$$

$$= \frac{2^3 - 1^3}{2 - 1}$$

$$= 7$$

∴ the gradient of the secant is 7.

3  $y = x^2 - x$,  $x_1 = -1$,  $x_2 = 3$

$$m = \frac{f(x_2) - f(x_1)}{x_2 - x_1}$$

$$= \frac{(3^2 - 3) - ((-1)^2 - (-1))}{3 - (-1)}$$

$$= 1$$

∴ the gradient of the secant is 1.

4  $y = 2x^2 - 1$,  $m = 4$,  $x_1 = -1$,  $x_2 = a$

$$m = \frac{f(x_2) - f(x_1)}{x_2 - x_1}$$

$$4 = \frac{(2a^2 - 1) - (2(-1)^2 - 1)}{a - (-1)}$$

$$4 = \frac{2a^2 - 2}{a + 1}$$

$$4 = \frac{2(a + 1)(a - 1)}{a + 1}$$

$$4 = 2(a - 1)$$

So  $a - 1 = 2$

$$a = 3$$

## 4 The gradient of a tangent ⊃ p. 100

1  a  $y = x^4$,  $x_1 = 0.5$,  $x_2 = 1.5$

$$m = \frac{f(x_2) - f(x_1)}{x_2 - x_1}$$

$$= \frac{1.5^4 - 0.5^4}{1.5 - 0.5}$$

$$= 5$$

∴ the gradient of the secant is 5.

b  $y = x^4$,  $x_1 = 0.75$,  $x_2 = 1.25$

$$m = \frac{f(x_2) - f(x_1)}{x_2 - x_1}$$

$$= \frac{1.25^4 - 0.75^4}{1.25 - 0.75}$$

$$= 4.25$$

$y = x^4$,  $x_1 = 0.9$,  $x_2 = 1.1$

$$m = \frac{f(x_2) - f(x_1)}{x_2 - x_1}$$

$$= \frac{1.1^4 - 0.9^4}{1.1 - 0.9}$$

$$= 4.04$$

∴ an approximation for the gradient of the tangent is 4.

2  a  $y = 4 - x^2$,  $y = 8 - 4x$

At any point of intersection

$$8 - 4x = 4 - x^2$$

$$x^2 - 4x + 4 = 0$$

$$(x - 2)^2 = 0$$

$$x = 2$$

When  $x = 2$,

$$y = 4 - 2^2$$

$$= 0$$

∴ there is only one point of intersection, at (2, 0).

b  The line  $y = 8 - 4x$  is a tangent to the curve  $y = 4 - x^2$  because it touches it at one point. The gradient of the line  $y = 8 - 4x$  is –4, so the gradient of the tangent is –4.

c  $y = 4 - x^2$,  $x_1 = 1$,  $x_2 = 3$

$$m = \frac{f(x_2) - f(x_1)}{x_2 - x_1}$$

$$= \frac{(4 - 3^2) - (4 - 1^2)}{3 - 1}$$

$$= -4$$

∴ the gradient of the secant is –4

∴ the gradient of the secant is equal to the gradient of the tangent at  $x = 2$.

3  The equation of the tangent is  $y = 4$.

**The gradient is 0.**

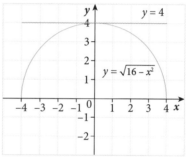

## DIFFERENCE QUOTIENTS

### 1 The behaviour of functions and tangents ⊃ p. 101

1  a  At  $x = -2$, the curve is increasing at a decreasing rate.

b  At  $x = 2$, the curve is decreasing at a decreasing rate.

c  At  $x = 3$, the curve is increasing at an increasing rate.

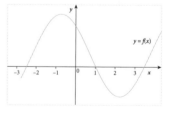

**2** Yes, the graph shows that sales are increasing at an increasing rate.

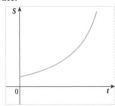

**3** The gradient is negative at $x = a$, zero at $x = b$ and positive at $c$ and at $d$. The gradient is zero again at $x = e$ and negative at $x = f$.

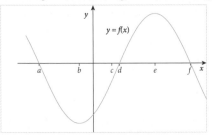

## 2 Average rates of change ⇒ p. 102

**1 a** $V = 44r^2$

When $r = 3$,

$V = 44 \times 3^2$

$= 396$ cm$^3$

**b** $V = 44r^2$

When $r = 9$,

$V = 44 \times 9^2$

$= 3564$ cm$^3$

**c** Average change $= \dfrac{3564 - 396}{9 - 3}$

$= 528$ cm$^3$ per cm of radius

**2 a** $d = 5t - 0.3125t^2$

When $t = 2$,

$d = 5 \times 2 - 0.3125 \times 2^2$

$= 8.75$

**After 2 hours Phoebe has gone 8.75 km.**

**b** $d = 5t - 0.3125t^2$

When $t = 6$,

$d = 5 \times 6 - 0.3125 \times 6^2$

$= 18.75$

**After 6 hours Phoebe has gone 18.75 km.**

**c** Average speed $= \dfrac{18.75 - 8.75}{4}$

$= 2.5$ km/h

**Phoebe's average speed is 2.5 km/h.**

**3** $P = 180t + \dfrac{180}{t+1}$

Rate $= \dfrac{P(8) - P(0)}{8 - 0}$

$= \dfrac{180 \times 8 + \dfrac{180}{8+1} - \left(180 \times 0 + \dfrac{180}{0+1}\right)}{8}$

$= \mathbf{160}$ **tonnes per hour**

**4** $h = 320 - 5t^2$

When $t = 0$,

$h = 320 - 5 \times 0^2$

$= 320$

When $t = 7$,

$h = 320 - 5 \times 7^2$

$= 75$

Average rate of change $= \dfrac{75 - 320}{7}$

$= -35$ m/s

**The average rate of change is a fall of 35 m per second.**

## THE DERIVATIVE FUNCTION AND ITS GRAPH

### 1 The derivative from first principles ⇒ p. 103

**1** $f(x) = x^2$

$f'(x) = \lim\limits_{h \to 0} \dfrac{f(x+h) - f(x)}{h}$

$= \lim\limits_{h \to 0} \dfrac{(x+h)^2 - x^2}{h}$

$= \lim\limits_{h \to 0} \dfrac{x^2 + 2xh + h^2 - x^2}{h}$

$= \lim\limits_{h \to 0} \dfrac{h(2x + h)}{h}$

$= \lim\limits_{h \to 0} (2x + h)$

$= \mathbf{2x}$

**2** $f(x) = 3x^2 + 2x$

$f'(x) = \lim\limits_{h \to 0} \dfrac{f(x+h) - f(x)}{h}$

$= \lim\limits_{h \to 0} \dfrac{3(x+h)^2 + 2(x+h) - (3x^2 + 2x)}{h}$

$= \lim\limits_{h \to 0} \dfrac{3x^2 + 6xh + 3h^2 + 2x + 2h - 3x^2 - 2x}{h}$

$= \lim\limits_{h \to 0} \dfrac{6xh + 3h^2 + 2h}{h}$

$= \lim\limits_{h \to 0} (6x + 3h + 2)$

$= \mathbf{6x + 2}$

**3** $f(x) = 1 - x^2$

$f'(x) = \lim\limits_{h \to 0} \dfrac{f(x+h) - f(x)}{h}$

$= \lim\limits_{h \to 0} \dfrac{1 - (x+h)^2 - (1 - x^2)}{h}$

$= \lim\limits_{h \to 0} \dfrac{1 - (x^2 + 2xh + h^2) - 1 + x^2}{h}$

$= \lim\limits_{h \to 0} \dfrac{-2xh - h^2}{h}$

$= \lim\limits_{h \to 0} \dfrac{h(-2x - h)}{h}$

$= \lim\limits_{h \to 0} (-2x - h)$

$= -2x$

$f'(2) = -2 \times 2$

$= \mathbf{-4}$

4  $f(x) = 7x$

$$f'(x) = \lim_{h \to 0} \frac{f(x+h) - f(x)}{h}$$

$$= \lim_{h \to 0} \frac{7(x+h) - 7x}{h}$$

$$= \lim_{h \to 0} \frac{7x + 7h - 7x}{h}$$

$$= \lim_{h \to 0} \frac{7h}{h}$$

$$= \lim_{h \to 0}(7)$$

$$= 7$$

## 2 The gradient function ⊃ p. 105

1  a  $y = 6x^2 - 5x$

$$\frac{dy}{dx} = \lim_{h \to 0} \frac{f(x+h) - f(x)}{h}$$

$$= \lim_{h \to 0} \frac{6(x+h)^2 - 5(x+h) - (6x^2 - 5x)}{h}$$

$$= \lim_{h \to 0} \frac{6x^2 + 12xh + 6h^2 - 5x - 5h - 6x^2 + 5x}{h}$$

$$= \lim_{h \to 0} \frac{12xh + 6h^2 - 5h}{h}$$

$$= \lim_{h \to 0} \frac{h(12x + 6h - 5)}{h}$$

$$= \lim_{h \to 0}(12x + 6h - 5)$$

$$= 12x - 5$$

   b  i  $\dfrac{dy}{dx} = 12x - 5$

      When $x = 3$,

      $$\frac{dy}{dx} = 12 \times 3 - 5$$

      $$= 31$$

      ii  When $x = 0$,

      $$\frac{dy}{dx} = 12 \times 0 - 5$$

      $$= -5$$

      iii  When $x = -2$,

      $$\frac{dy}{dx} = 12 \times -2 - 5$$

      $$= -29$$

2  a  $f(x) = 3 - 2x^2$

$$f'(x) = \lim_{h \to 0} \frac{f(x+h) - f(x)}{h}$$

$$= \lim_{h \to 0} \frac{3 - 2(x+h)^2 - (3 - 2x^2)}{h}$$

$$= \lim_{h \to 0} \frac{3 - 2x^2 - 4xh - 2h^2 - 3 + 2x^2}{h}$$

$$= \lim_{h \to 0} \frac{h(-4x - 2h)}{h}$$

$$= \lim_{h \to 0}(-4x - 2h)$$

$$= -4x$$

b

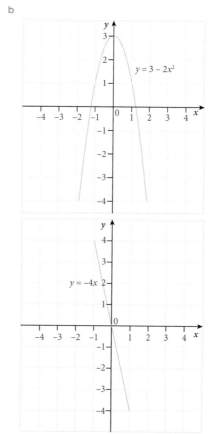

c  The graph of $y = f'(x)$ shows the gradient of the curve at every point. From the graph of $y = f'(x)$ we can see that the gradient function is positive when $x < 0$, where the curve is increasing. The gradient is negative when $x > 0$, when the curve is decreasing and the gradient is zero at $x = 0$, when the curve is at its maximum value.

3  a  $y = 5x - 8$

$$f'(x) = \lim_{h \to 0} \frac{f(x+h) - f(x)}{h}$$

$$= \lim_{h \to 0} \frac{5(x+h) - 8 - (5x - 8)}{h}$$

$$= \lim_{h \to 0} \frac{5x + 5h - 8 - 5x + 8}{h}$$

$$= \lim_{h \to 0} \frac{5h}{h}$$

$$= \lim_{h \to 0}(5)$$

$$= 5$$

   b  The gradient is constant. It is the same for all values of $x$.

## CALCULATING WITH DERIVATIVES

### 1 The derivative of $x^n$ ⊃ p. 105

1   $y = x^4$

$$\frac{dy}{dx} = 4x^3$$

2  $f(x) = x^8$

   $f'(x) = 8x^7$

3  $\dfrac{d}{dx}(x^{11}) = 11x^{10}$

4  $y = x^{-3}$

   $\dfrac{dy}{dx} = -3x^{-4}$

5  $y = x^{\frac{1}{2}}$

   $\dfrac{dy}{dx} = \dfrac{1}{2}x^{-\frac{1}{2}}$

6  $y = x^{2.4}$

   $\dfrac{dy}{dx} = 2.4x^{1.4}$

## 2 Further rules for differentiation ⊃ p. 106

1  $y = 17$

   $\dfrac{dy}{dx} = 0$

2  $f(x) = x^4 - x^3 + x$

   $f'(x) = 4x^3 - 3x^2 + 1$

3  $y = 12x^9$

   $y' = 12 \times 9x^8$

   $\quad = 108x^8$

4  $y = 3x^6 - 2x^5 + 5x^3 - 4x^2 - 3$

   $\dfrac{dy}{dx} = 18x^5 - 10x^4 + 15x^2 - 8x$

5  $y = 2 - 3x^{-4}$

   $\dfrac{dy}{dx} = 12x^{-5}$

6  $y = \dfrac{x^2}{2}$

   $y' = \dfrac{2x}{2}$

   $\quad = x$

## 3 Notations ⊃ p. 107

1  $s = 9t^3 + 6t^2 - t$

   $\dfrac{ds}{dt} = 27t^2 + 12t - 1$

2  $h = -m^4 + 5m^3 - 2m - 3$

   $\dfrac{dh}{dm} = -4m^3 + 15m^2 - 2$

3  $g(a) = -4a^5 - 7a^3 + 9a - 1$

   $g'(a) = -20a^4 - 21a^2 + 9$

4  $\dfrac{d}{du}(u^3 + 5u^2 - 7u) = 3u^2 + 10u - 7$

5  $f(p) = \dfrac{p^6}{3}$

   $f'(p) = \dfrac{6p^5}{3}$

   $\quad\ = 2p^5$

6  $f(y) = \dfrac{1}{2}y^2 - \dfrac{2}{3}y^3$

   $f'(y) = y - 2y^2$

## 4 Derivatives of rational expressions ⊃ p. 108

1  $y = \dfrac{1}{x^7}$

   $\quad = x^{-7}$

   $\dfrac{dy}{dx} = -7x^{-8}$

   $\quad = -\dfrac{7}{x^8}$

2  $f(x) = \dfrac{1}{x} - \dfrac{3}{x^2}$

   $\quad\ = x^{-1} - 3x^{-2}$

   $f'(x) = -x^{-2} + 6x^{-3}$

   $\quad\ = -\dfrac{1}{x^2} + \dfrac{6}{x^3}$

3  $y = 4\sqrt{x}$

   $\quad = 4x^{\frac{1}{2}}$

   $\dfrac{dy}{dx} = 2x^{-\frac{1}{2}}$

   $\quad = \dfrac{2}{\sqrt{x}}$

4  $y = \sqrt[4]{x^3}$

   $\quad = x^{\frac{3}{4}}$

   $y' = \dfrac{3}{4}x^{-\frac{1}{4}}$

   $\quad = \dfrac{3}{4\sqrt[4]{x}}$

5  $f(x) = x^2\sqrt{x}$

   $\quad\ = x^2 \times x^{\frac{1}{2}}$

   $\quad\ = x^{\frac{5}{2}}$

   $f'(x) = \dfrac{5}{2}x^{\frac{3}{2}}$

   $\quad\ = \dfrac{5x\sqrt{x}}{2}$

6  $y = \dfrac{1}{\sqrt[5]{x}}$

   $\quad = x^{-\frac{1}{5}}$

   $\dfrac{dy}{dx} = -\dfrac{1}{5}x^{-\frac{6}{5}}$

   $\quad = -\dfrac{1}{5\sqrt[5]{x^6}}$

## 5 The product rule ⊃ p. 108

1  $y = x(x^2 - 3x + 4)$

   $\quad = x^3 - 3x^2 + 4x$

   $\dfrac{dy}{dx} = 3x^2 - 6x + 4$

2  $y = (x - 2)(x + 7)$

   $\quad u = x - 2 \qquad v = x + 7$

   $\quad \dfrac{du}{dx} = 1 \qquad \dfrac{dv}{dx} = 1$

   $\dfrac{dy}{dx} = u\dfrac{dv}{dx} + v\dfrac{du}{dx}$

$$= (x - 2) \times 1 + (x + 7) \times 1$$
$$= x - 2 + x + 7$$
$$= \mathbf{2x + 5}$$

3  $y = (x - 3)(x^2 + x - 3)$

$$u = x - 3 \qquad v = x^2 + x - 3$$
$$\frac{du}{dx} = 1 \qquad \frac{dv}{dx} = 2x + 1$$

$$\frac{dy}{dx} = u\frac{dv}{dx} + v\frac{du}{dx}$$
$$= (x - 3) \times (2x + 1) + (x^2 + x - 3) \times 1$$
$$= 2x^2 + x - 6x - 3 + x^2 + x - 3$$
$$= \mathbf{3x^2 - 4x - 6}$$

4  $y = (x^2 - x + 1)(x^3 - 1)$

$$\frac{dy}{dx} = u\frac{dv}{dx} + v\frac{du}{dx}$$
$$= (x^2 - x + 1) \times \frac{d}{dx}(x^3 - 1) + (x^3 - 1) \times \frac{d}{dx}(x^2 - x + 1)$$
$$= (x^2 - x + 1) \times 3x^2 + (x^3 - 1) \times (2x - 1)$$
$$= 3x^4 - 3x^3 + 3x^2 + 2x^4 - x^3 - 2x + 1$$
$$= \mathbf{5x^4 - 4x^3 + 3x^2 - 2x + 1}$$

5  $y = (x^4 - 2)(5 - 3x - x^2)$

$$\frac{dy}{dx} = u\frac{dv}{dx} + v\frac{du}{dx}$$
$$= (x^4 - 2) \times (-3 - 2x) + (5 - 3x - x^2) \times 4x^3$$
$$= -3x^4 - 2x^5 + 6 + 4x + 20x^3 - 12x^4 - 4x^5$$
$$= \mathbf{-6x^5 - 15x^4 + 20x^3 + 4x + 6}$$

## 6 The quotient rule ⊃ pp. 109–110

1  $y = \dfrac{x-1}{x+3}$

$$u = x - 1 \qquad v = x + 3$$
$$\frac{du}{dx} = 1 \qquad \frac{dv}{dx} = 1$$

$$\frac{dy}{dx} = \frac{v\dfrac{du}{dx} - u\dfrac{dv}{dx}}{v^2}$$
$$= \frac{(x+3)\times 1 - (x-1)\times 1}{(x+3)^2}$$
$$= \frac{x+3-x+1}{(x+3)^2}$$
$$= \frac{\mathbf{4}}{(x+3)^2}$$

2  $y = \dfrac{2x}{x^3-5}$

$$u = 2x \qquad v = x^3 - 5$$
$$\frac{du}{dx} = 2 \qquad \frac{dv}{dx} = 3x^2$$

$$\frac{dy}{dx} = \frac{v\dfrac{du}{dx} - u\dfrac{dv}{dx}}{v^2}$$
$$= \frac{(x^3-5)\times 2 - 2x \times 3x^2}{(x^3-5)^2}$$
$$= \frac{2x^3 - 10 - 6x^3}{(x^3-5)^2}$$
$$= \frac{\mathbf{-4x^3 - 10}}{(x^3-5)^2}$$

3  $f(x) = \dfrac{x^2-3x-1}{x}$

$$u = x^2 - 3x - 1 \qquad v = x$$
$$\frac{du}{dx} = 2x - 3 \qquad \frac{dv}{dx} = 1$$

$$f'(x) = \frac{v\dfrac{du}{dx} - u\dfrac{dv}{dx}}{v^2}$$
$$= \frac{x \times (2x-3) - (x^2-3x-1)\times 1}{x^2}$$
$$= \frac{2x^2 - 3x - x^2 + 3x + 1}{x^2}$$
$$= \frac{\mathbf{x^2 + 1}}{x^2}$$

4  $y = \dfrac{5}{x^2-2}$

$$\frac{dy}{dx} = \frac{v\dfrac{du}{dx} - u\dfrac{dv}{dx}}{v^2}$$
$$= \frac{(x^2-2)\times \dfrac{d}{dx}(5) - 5 \times \dfrac{d}{dx}(x^2-2)}{(x^2-2)^2}$$
$$= \frac{(x^2-2)\times 0 - 5 \times 2x}{(x^2-2)^2}$$
$$= \frac{\mathbf{-10x}}{(x^2-2)^2}$$

5  $y = \dfrac{x^2+5x-7}{x^2-4x+3}$

$$\frac{dy}{dx} = \frac{v\dfrac{du}{dx} - u\dfrac{dv}{dx}}{v^2}$$
$$= \frac{(x^2-4x+3)\times(2x+5) - (x^2+5x-7)\times(2x-4)}{(x^2-4x+3)^2}$$
$$= \frac{2x^3+5x^2-8x^2-20x+6x+15-2x^3+4x^2-10x^2+20x+14x-28}{(x^2-4x+3)^2}$$
$$= \frac{\mathbf{-9x^2 + 20x - 13}}{(x^2-4x+3)^2}$$

## 7 The chain rule ⊃ p. 110

1  $y = (4x + 3)^3$

$$\frac{dy}{dx} = \frac{dy}{du} \times \frac{du}{dx}$$
$$= 3(4x+3)^2 \times \frac{d}{dx}(4x+3)$$
$$= 3(4x+3)^2 \times 4$$
$$= \mathbf{12(4x+3)^2}$$

2  $y = (x^3 - 5)^7$

$$\frac{dy}{dx} = \frac{dy}{du} \times \frac{du}{dx}$$
$$= 7(x^3-5)^6 \times \frac{d}{dx}(x^3-5)$$
$$= 7(x^3-5)^6 \times 3x^2$$
$$= \mathbf{21x^2(x^3-5)^6}$$

3   $f(x) = (x^2 + 7x - 6)^4$

$$f'(x) = 4(x^2 + 7x - 6)^3 \times \frac{d}{dx}(x^2 + 7x - 6)$$

$$= 4(x^2 + 7x - 6)^3 \times (2x + 7)$$

$$= \mathbf{4(2x + 7)(x^2 + 7x - 6)^3}$$

4   $y = \dfrac{1}{5x - 9}$

$$= (5x - 9)^{-1}$$

$$\frac{dy}{dx} = -(5x - 9)^{-2} \times \frac{d}{dx}(5x - 9)$$

$$= -(5x - 9)^{-2} \times 5$$

$$= -\frac{\mathbf{5}}{\mathbf{(5x - 9)^2}}$$

5   $y = \sqrt{16 - x^2}$

$$= \left(16 - x^2\right)^{\frac{1}{2}}$$

$$\frac{dy}{dx} = \frac{1}{2}\left(16 - x^2\right)^{-\frac{1}{2}} \times \frac{d}{dx}\left(16 - x^2\right)$$

$$= \frac{1}{2} \times \frac{1}{\sqrt{16 - x^2}} \times -2x$$

$$= -\frac{\mathbf{x}}{\sqrt{\mathbf{16 - x^2}}}$$

6   $y = \dfrac{1}{(2x + 3)^5}$

$$= (2x + 3)^{-5}$$

$$\frac{dy}{dx} = -5(2x + 3)^{-6} \times \frac{d}{dx}(2x + 3)$$

$$= -5(2x + 3)^{-6} \times 2$$

$$= -\frac{\mathbf{10}}{\mathbf{(2x + 3)^6}}$$

## 8 Combinations of the rules ⊃ pp. 111–112

1   $y = x(x^2 - 1)^5$

$$\frac{dy}{dx} = x \times \frac{d}{dx}(x^2 - 1)^5 + (x^2 - 1)^5 \times \frac{d}{dx}(x)$$

$$= x \times 5(x^2 - 1)^4 \times 2x + (x^2 - 1)^5 \times 1$$

$$= 10x^2(x^2 - 1)^4 + (x^2 - 1)^5$$

$$= (x^2 - 1)^4[10x^2 + (x^2 - 1)]$$

$$= \mathbf{(x^2 - 1)^4(11x^2 - 1)}$$

2   $y = x^3(5 - 4x)^4$

$$\frac{dy}{dx} = x^3 \times \frac{d}{dx}((5 - 4x)^4) + (5 - 4x)^4 \times \frac{d}{dx}(x^3)$$

$$= x^3 \times 4(5 - 4x)^3 \times -4 + (5 - 4x)^4 \times 3x^2$$

$$= -16x^3(5 - 4x)^3 + 3x^2(5 - 4x)^4$$

$$= x^2(5 - 4x)^3[-16x + 3(5 - 4x)]$$

$$= x^2(5 - 4x)^3[-16x + 15 - 12x]$$

$$= \mathbf{x^2(5 - 4x)^3(-28x + 15)}$$

3   $y = \dfrac{(5x + 3)^5}{x}$

$$\frac{dy}{dx} = \frac{x \times \frac{d}{dx}\left((5x + 3)^5\right) - (5x + 3)^5 \times \frac{d}{dx}(x)}{x^2}$$

$$= \frac{x \times 5(5x + 3)^4 \times 5 - (5x + 3)^5 \times 1}{x^2}$$

$$= \frac{25x(5x + 3)^4 - (5x + 3)^5}{x^2}$$

$$= \frac{(5x + 3)^4\left(25x - (5x + 3)\right)}{x^2}$$

$$= \frac{\mathbf{(20x - 3)(5x + 3)^4}}{\mathbf{x^2}}$$

4   $y = \dfrac{2x - 1}{(x + 1)^3}$

$$\frac{dy}{dx} = \frac{(x + 1)^3 \times 2 - (2x - 1) \times 3(x + 1)^2 \times 1}{\left((x + 1)^3\right)^2}$$

$$= \frac{2(x + 1)^3 - 3(2x - 1)(x + 1)^2}{(x + 1)^6}$$

$$= \frac{(x + 1)^2\left(2(x + 1) - 3(2x - 1)\right)}{(x + 1)^6}$$

$$= \frac{2x + 2 - 6x + 3}{(x + 1)^4}$$

$$= \frac{\mathbf{-4x + 5}}{\mathbf{(x + 1)^4}}$$

5   $f(x) = 4x\sqrt{1 - x}$

$$= 4x(1 - x)^{\frac{1}{2}}$$

$$f'(x) = 4x \times \frac{1}{2}(1 - x)^{-\frac{1}{2}} \times -1 + (1 - x)^{\frac{1}{2}} \times 4$$

$$= \frac{-2x}{\sqrt{1 - x}} + 4\sqrt{1 - x}$$

$$= \frac{-2x}{\sqrt{1 - x}} + \frac{4(1 - x)}{\sqrt{1 - x}}$$

$$= \frac{4 - 6x}{\sqrt{1 - x}}$$

$$= \frac{\mathbf{2(2 - 3x)}}{\sqrt{\mathbf{1 - x}}}$$

6   $y = (7x - 1)^2(5x + 2)^3$

$$\frac{dy}{dx} = (7x - 1)^2 \times 3(5x + 2)^2 \times 5 + (5x + 2)^3 \times 2(7x - 1) \times 7$$

$$= 15(7x - 1)^2(5x + 2)^2 + 14(7x - 1)(5x + 2)^3$$

$$= (7x - 1)(5x + 2)^2[15(7x - 1) + 14(5x + 2)]$$

$$= (7x - 1)(5x + 2)^2[105x - 15 + 70x + 28]$$

$$= \mathbf{(7x - 1)(5x + 2)^2(175x + 13)}$$

## 9 Equations of tangents ⊃ p. 113

1   $y = x^2 + 6x - 7$

$$\frac{dy}{dx} = 2x + 6$$

When $x = 2$,

$$\frac{dy}{dx} = 2 \times 2 + 6$$
$$= 10$$
$$\therefore \ m = 10, \quad (2, 9)$$
$$y - y_1 = m(x - x_1)$$
$$y - 9 = 10(x - 2)$$
$$y - 9 = 10x - 20$$
$$y = 10x - 11$$

$\therefore$ **the equation of the tangent is $y = 10x - 11$.**

2  $y = x^3 - 4x^2 + 9x - 11$
$$\frac{dy}{dx} = 3x^2 - 8x + 9$$
When $x = 3$,
$$\frac{dy}{dx} = 3 \times 3^2 - 8 \times 3 + 9$$
$$= 12$$
$$\therefore \ m = 12$$
When $x = 3$,
$$y = 3^3 - 4 \times 3^2 + 9 \times 3 - 11$$
$$= 7$$
$$m = 12, \quad (3, 7)$$
$$y - y_1 = m(x - x_1)$$
$$y - 7 = 12(x - 3)$$
$$y - 7 = 12x - 36$$
$$y = 12x - 29$$

**The equation of the tangent is $y = 12x - 29$.**

3  $y = 15 - x$ is the equation of the tangent at $P$.

$\therefore$ the gradient of the tangent at $P$ is $-1$.
$$y = x^3 + 2x^2 - 5x + 7$$
$$\frac{dy}{dx} = 3x^2 + 4x - 5$$
At $P$,  $\dfrac{dy}{dx} = -1$
$$\therefore \ 3x^2 + 4x - 5 = -1$$
$$3x^2 + 4x - 4 = 0$$
$$(3x - 2)(x + 2) = 0$$
$$3x - 2 = 0 \quad \text{or} \quad x + 2 = 0$$
$$x = \frac{2}{3} \quad \text{or} \quad x = -2$$
When $x = \dfrac{2}{3}$,
$$y = \left(\frac{2}{3}\right)^3 + 2 \times \left(\frac{2}{3}\right)^2 - 5 \times \frac{2}{3} + 7$$
$$= 4\frac{23}{27}$$
When $x = -2$,
$$y = (-2)^3 + 2 \times (-2)^2 - 5 \times -2 + 7$$
$$= 17$$
Now $P$ lies on the line $y = 15 - x$.
When $x = \dfrac{2}{3}$,
$$y = 15 - \frac{2}{3}$$
$$= 14\frac{1}{3} \quad \left(\neq 4\frac{23}{27}\right)$$

When $x = -2$,
$$y = 15 - (-2)$$
$$= 17$$
$\therefore$ **$P$ is the point $(-2, 17)$.**

4  $y = \dfrac{1}{x}$
$$= x^{-1}$$
$$\frac{dy}{dx} = -x^{-2}$$
$$= -\frac{1}{x^2}$$
When $x = -1$,
$$\frac{dy}{dx} = -\frac{1}{(-1)^2}$$
$$= -1$$
$$\therefore \ m = -1$$
When $x = -1$,
$$y = \frac{1}{-1}$$
$$= -1$$
$$m = -1, \quad (-1, -1)$$
$$y - y_1 = m(x - x_1)$$
$$y - (-1) = -1(x - (-1))$$
$$y + 1 = -x - 1$$
$$y = -x - 2$$

**The equation of the tangent is $y = -x - 2$.**

## 10 The equation of a normal to a curve ⊃ p. 114

1  $y = x - x^2$
$$\frac{dy}{dx} = 1 - 2x$$
When $x = 1$,
$$\frac{dy}{dx} = 1 - 2 \times 1$$
$$= -1$$
$\therefore$ the gradient of the tangent is $-1$.

$\therefore$ the gradient of the normal is $1$.
$$m = 1, \quad (1, 0)$$
$$y - y_1 = m(x - x_1)$$
$$y - 0 = 1(x - 1)$$
$$y = x - 1$$

$\therefore$ **the equation of the normal is $y = x - 1$.**

2  $y = \dfrac{3}{x}$
$$= 3x^{-1}$$
$$\frac{dy}{dx} = -3x^{-2}$$
$$= -\frac{3}{x^2}$$
When $x = 6$,
$$\frac{dy}{dx} = -\frac{3}{6^2}$$
$$= -\frac{1}{12}$$
$\therefore$ the gradient of the tangent is $-\dfrac{1}{12}$.

$\therefore$ the gradient of the normal is $12$.

When $x = 6$,

$$y = \frac{3}{6}$$

$$= \frac{1}{2}$$

$$m = 12, \quad \left(6, \frac{1}{2}\right)$$

$$y - y_1 = m(x - x_1)$$

$$y - \frac{1}{2} = 12(x - 6)$$

$$y - \frac{1}{2} = 12x - 72$$

$$y = 12x - 71\frac{1}{2}$$

∴ the equation of the normal is $y = 12x - 71\frac{1}{2}$.

3  a   $y = \dfrac{x^2}{8}$

$$\frac{dy}{dx} = \frac{2x}{8}$$

$$= \frac{x}{4}$$

When $x = 4$,

$$\frac{dy}{dx} = \frac{4}{4}$$

$$= 1$$

∴ the gradient of the tangent is 1.

The gradient of the normal is –1.

$$m = -1, \quad (4, 2)$$

$$y - y_1 = m(x - x_1)$$

$$y - 2 = -1(x - 4)$$

$$y - 2 = -x + 4$$

$$y = -x + 6$$

**The equation of the normal is $y = -x + 6$.**

b  The points of intersection of the parabola and the normal occur when:

$$\frac{x^2}{8} = -x + 6$$

$$x^2 = -8x + 48$$

$$x^2 + 8x - 48 = 0$$

$$(x + 12)(x - 4) = 0$$

$$x + 12 = 0 \quad \text{or} \quad x - 4 = 0$$

$$x = -12 \quad \text{or} \quad x = 4$$

Now $P$ is the point where $x = 4$.

∴ $Q$ is the point where $x = -12$.

When $x = -12$, $y = -(-12) + 6$

$$= 18$$

**So $Q$ is the point (–12, 18).**

4   $y = (2x - 1)^4$

$$\frac{dy}{dx} = 4(2x - 1)^3 \times 2$$

$$= 8(2x - 1)^3$$

When $x = 1$,

$$\frac{dy}{dx} = 8(2 \times 1 - 1)^3$$

$$= 8$$

∴ the gradient of the tangent is 8.

The gradient of the normal is $-\dfrac{1}{8}$.

When $x = 1$,

$$y = (2 \times 1 - 1)^4$$

$$= 1$$

$$m = -\frac{1}{8}, \quad (1, 1)$$

$$y - y_1 = m(x - x_1)$$

$$y - 1 = -\frac{1}{8}(x - 1)$$

$$y - 1 = -\frac{1}{8}x + \frac{1}{8}$$

$$y = -\frac{1}{8}x + 1\frac{1}{8}$$

∴ the equation of the normal is $y = -\dfrac{1}{8}x + 1\dfrac{1}{8}$.

## 11 Rates of change ⊃ p. 116

1   $V = 7t^2 + 4t + 6$

$$\frac{dV}{dt} = 14t + 4$$

When $t = 3$,

$$\frac{dV}{dt} = 14 \times 3 + 4$$

$$= 46$$

**The volume is increasing at the rate of 46 L per second.**

2  a   $V = t^2 - 420t + 8000$

When $t = 0$,

$$V = 0^2 - 420 \times 0 + 8000$$

$$= 8000$$

**The capacity of the vat is 8000 L.**

b  When $t = 20$,

$$V = 20^2 - 420 \times 20 + 8000$$

$$= 0$$

∴ the vat is empty after 20 minutes.

c  When $V = 1925$,

$$t^2 - 420t + 8000 = 1925$$

$$t^2 - 420t + 6075 = 0$$

$$t = \frac{-b \pm \sqrt{b^2 - 4ac}}{2a}$$

$$= \frac{420 \pm \sqrt{(-420)^2 - 4 \times 1 \times 6075}}{2 \times 1}$$

$$t = 15 \quad \text{or} \quad t = 405$$

But the vat is empty when $t = 20$.

∴ $t = 15$

$$V = t^2 - 420t + 8000$$

$$\frac{dV}{dt} = 2t - 420$$

When $t = 15$,

$$\frac{dV}{dt} = 2 \times 15 - 420$$

$$= -390$$

∴ the water is flowing out of the vat at the rate of 390 L per minute.

3  a   $N = 833 + 32t^2 - t^4$

When $t = 0$,

$$N = 833 + 32 \times 0^2 - 0^4$$

$$= 833$$

**There are approximately 833 people at the concert at 6 pm.**

**b** When $t = 7$,

$N = 833 + 32 \times 7^2 - 7^4$

$\quad = 0$

**There are no people left at the concert after 7 hours.**

**c** $N = 833 + 32t^2 - t^4$

$\dfrac{dN}{dt} = 64t - 4t^3$

When $t = 1$,

$\dfrac{dN}{dt} = 64 \times 1 - 4 \times 1^3$

$\quad = 60$

When $t = 6$,

$\dfrac{dN}{dt} = 64 \times 6 - 4 \times 6^3$

$\quad = -480$

**After 1 hour the number of people is increasing by 60 people per hour but after 6 hours the number of people is decreasing by 480 people per hour.**

**4 a** While filling the bottom 6 cm, the depth of the water will be increasing constantly. $\dfrac{dh}{dt}$ will be a positive constant.

**b** The depth of water in the bottle will be increasing at its fastest rate at the narrowest part of the bottle. $\dfrac{dh}{dt}$ will be a maximum.

**c** The graph will be an increasing curve. The curve will be a straight line for $0 \leq h \leq 6$. The height is then increasing at an increasing rate so the curve will be concave up until $h = 8$, where it will change concavity. The height will be increasing at a decreasing rate for $8 \leq h \leq 10$ and then will be a straight line for $10 \leq h \leq 15$. The pattern will repeat so the curve will be concave up until $h = 17$, concave down until $h = 19$ and straight until $h = 25$.

**5 a** $V = 6t - \dfrac{t^2}{90}$

$\dfrac{dV}{dt} = 6 - \dfrac{2t}{90}$

$\quad\quad = 6 - \dfrac{t}{45}$

When $t = 0$,

$\dfrac{dV}{dt} = 6 - \dfrac{0}{45}$

$\quad\quad = 6$

**Initially the fuel is flowing at 6 L/s.**

**b** Fuel stops flowing when $\dfrac{dV}{dt} = 0$,

i.e. $0 = 6 - \dfrac{t}{45}$

$\dfrac{t}{45} = 6$

$\quad t = 270$

**The fuel stops flowing after 270 seconds or $4\dfrac{1}{2}$ minutes.**

**c** When $t = 270$,

$V = 6 \times 270 - \dfrac{270^2}{90}$

$\quad = 810$

**So 810 L flows during that time.**

12 Displacement, velocity and acceleration ⊃ p. 117

**1 a** $x = 18t - t^2$

$\dfrac{dx}{dt} = 18 - 2t$

**So an expression for the velocity is $v = 18 - 2t$.**

**b** When $t = 6$,

$v = 18 - 2 \times 6$

$\quad = 6$

**When $t = 6$, the velocity is 6 ms$^{-1}$.**

**c** When $x = 81$,

$\quad\quad\quad 81 = 18t - t^2$

$t^2 - 18t + 81 = 0$

$\quad (t - 9)^2 = 0$

$\quad\quad\quad\quad t = 9$

When $t = 9$,

$v = 18 - 2 \times 9$

$\quad = 0$

**The velocity is 0 when $x = 81$.**

**2** $x = 2t^2 - 7t + 8$

$v = \dfrac{dx}{dt}$

$\quad = 4t - 7$

$a = \dfrac{dv}{dt}$

$\quad = 4$

$\therefore$ **the acceleration is constant.**

**3 a** $x = 11 + 20t - 2t^2$

$v = 20 - 4t$

The particle is at rest when $v = 0$,

i.e. $20 - 4t = 0$

$\quad\quad 4t = 20$

$\quad\quad\quad t = 5$

When $t = 5$,

$x = 11 + 20 \times 5 - 2 \times 5^2$

$\quad = 61$

$\therefore$ **the particle is at rest after 5 seconds at a position 61 m to the right of $O$.**

**b** $v = 20 - 4t$

$a = -4$

$\therefore$ **the particle will move to the left because the acceleration is negative.**

**4** $x = 1 + 4t + 15t^2 - t^3$

$v = \dfrac{dx}{dt}$

$\quad = 4 + 30t - 3t^2$

$a = \dfrac{dv}{dt}$

$\quad = 30 - 6t$

If $a = 0$,

$\quad 0 = 30 - 6t$

$\quad 6t = 30$

$\quad\quad t = 5$

So, the acceleration is zero after 5 seconds.

When $t = 5$,

$v = 4 + 30 \times 5 - 3 \times 5^2$

$\quad = 79$

**The velocity is 79 ms$^{-1}$ when the acceleration is zero.**

## Part A

**1  D**  Only D is continuous.

**2  A**  $y = 3x - 5$

$m = 3$

So $\tan \theta = 3$

$\theta = \tan^{-1} 3$

$= 71.5650511...°$

$= 72°$   (nearest degree)

**3  C**  $y = x^2 + 3$,   $x_1 = 1$,   $x_2 = 2$

$m = \dfrac{f(x_2) - f(x_1)}{x_2 - x_1}$

$= \dfrac{(2^2 + 3) - (1^2 + 3)}{2 - 1}$

$= 3$

∴ the gradient of the secant is 3.

**4  C**  $f(x')$ is not a correct notation for the derivative of $y = f(x)$.

**5  D**  $y = \dfrac{1}{2}x - 7$

The gradient of the tangent is $\dfrac{1}{2}$.

So the gradient of the normal is $-2$.

**6  C**  $y = \dfrac{1}{x^2}$

$= x^{-2}$

$\dfrac{dy}{dx} = -2x^{-3}$

$= -\dfrac{2}{x^3}$

**7  B**  $(x^3 + 1)(x^2 + x + 1)$ is a product.

So, of the options, the product rule would be best.

**8  B**  $v = 5 - 3t$

$a = \dfrac{dv}{dt}$

$= -3$

**9  A**  $V = 8t^2 - 6t + 7$

$\dfrac{dV}{dt} = 16t - 6$

**10  B**  $f(x) = 9 - 3x^2$

$f'(x) = -6x$

$f'(2) = -6 \times 2$

$= -12$

**11  A**  If the curve is increasing the gradient of the tangent will be positive.

**12  D**  $y = (5x^2 - 2)^7$

$\dfrac{dy}{dx} = 7(5x^2 - 2)^6 \times 10x$

$= 70x(5x^2 - 2)^6$

## Part B

**13**  $f(x) = x^6 - 2x^3 + 7x$

$f'(x) = 6x^5 - 6x^2 + 7$   ✓

**14**  $\dfrac{d}{du}\left(\dfrac{u}{2}\right) = \dfrac{1}{2}$   ✓

**15  a**  $f(x) = x^2 - 6x + 5$

$f'(x) = 2x - 6$   ✓

**b**  The gradient is zero when $f'(x) = 0$,

i.e. $2x - 6 = 0$

$2x = 6$

$x = 3$   ✓

Now $f(3) = 3^2 - 6 \times 3 + 5$

$= -4$

**So the gradient of the tangent is zero at (3, –4).**   ✓

**c**  The curve will be stationary at that point.   ✓

**16**  $y = \dfrac{1}{1-x}$

$= (1 - x)^{-1}$

$\dfrac{dy}{dx} = -(1 - x)^{-2} \times -1$   ✓

$= (1 - x)^{-2}$

$= \dfrac{1}{(1-x)^2}$   ✓

**17  a**  $y = \dfrac{3}{x^5}$

$= 3x^{-5}$

$\dfrac{dy}{dx} = -15x^{-6}$   ✓

$= -\dfrac{15}{x^6}$   ✓

**b**  $y = \sqrt[3]{x}$

$= x^{\frac{1}{3}}$

$\dfrac{dy}{dx} = \dfrac{1}{3}x^{-\frac{2}{3}}$   ✓

$= \dfrac{1}{3\sqrt[3]{x^2}}$   ✓

**c**  $y = x(7 - 4x)^9$

$\dfrac{dy}{dx} = x \times 9(7 - 4x)^8 \times -4 + (7 - 4x)^9 \times 1$   ✓

$= -36x(7 - 4x)^8 + (7 - 4x)^9$

$= (7 - 4x)^8(-36x + (7 - 4x))$

$= (7 - 40x)(7 - 4x)^8$   ✓

**d**  $y = \dfrac{2x+1}{2x-1}$

$\dfrac{dy}{dx} = \dfrac{(2x-1) \times 2 - (2x+1) \times 2}{(2x-1)^2}$   ✓

$= \dfrac{4x - 2 - 4x - 2}{(2x-1)^2}$

$= \dfrac{-4}{(2x-1)^2}$   ✓

**18**  $f(x) = x^2 + 12x - 5$

$f'(x) = 2x + 12$   ✓

The function is increasing when $f'(x) > 0$,

i.e.  $2x + 12 > 0$

$2x > -12$

$x > -6$   ✓

**19** $y = \sqrt{x}$

$\quad = x^{\frac{1}{2}}$

$\dfrac{dy}{dx} = \dfrac{1}{2}x^{-\frac{1}{2}}$

$\quad = \dfrac{1}{2\sqrt{x}}$ ✓

When $x = 4$,

$\dfrac{dy}{dx} = \dfrac{1}{2\sqrt{4}}$

$\quad = \dfrac{1}{4}$ ✓

$\therefore$ the gradient of the tangent is $\dfrac{1}{4}$.

**The gradient of the normal is –4.** ✓

**20** $f(x) = (x - 2)^2$

$\quad f'(x) = 2(x - 2) \times 1$

$\qquad = 2x - 4$

$\quad f'(3) = 2 \times 3 - 4$

$\qquad = 2$

$\therefore$ the gradient of the tangent is 2. ✓

$f(3) = (3 - 2)^2$

$\quad = 1$

$m = 2, \quad (3, 1)$

$y - y_1 = m(x - x_1)$

$y - 1 = 2(x - 3)$

$y - 1 = 2x - 6$

$\quad y = 2x - 5$

**The equation of the tangent is $y = 2x - 5$.** ✓

**21 a** $f(x) = x^3$

$\quad f'(x) = 3x^2$ ✓

**b**

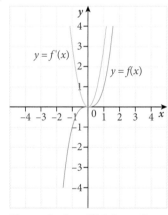

✓✓

**c** The graph of $y = f'(x)$ shows the gradient of the curve $y = f(x)$ at each point. When the curve is negative $f'(x)$ is decreasing and when the curve is positive $f'(x)$ is increasing. The curve is always increasing except when $x = 0$, when it is stationary. The gradient function is always positive except when $x = 0$, when it is zero. ✓

**22** $f(x) = x^2 + 6x$

$\quad f'(x) = \lim\limits_{h \to 0} \dfrac{f(x+h) - f(x)}{h}$

$\qquad = \lim\limits_{h \to 0} \dfrac{(x+h)^2 + 6(x+h) - (x^2 + 6x)}{h}$ ✓

$\qquad = \lim\limits_{h \to 0} \dfrac{x^2 + 2xh + h^2 + 6x + 6h - x^2 - 6x}{h}$

$\qquad = \lim\limits_{h \to 0} \dfrac{2xh + h^2 + 6h}{h}$

$\qquad = \lim\limits_{h \to 0} \dfrac{h(2x + h + 6)}{h}$

$\qquad = \lim\limits_{h \to 0} (2x + h + 6)$

$\qquad = 2x + 6$ ✓

**23 a** $x = t^2 - 8t - 7$

When $t = 0$,

$x = 0^2 - 8 \times 0 - 7$

$\quad = -7$

**The particle is initially 7 m left of the origin.** ✓

**b** $x = t^2 - 8t - 7$

$v = \dfrac{dx}{dt}$

$\quad = 2t - 8$ ✓

**c** The particle is at rest when $v = 0$,

i.e. $2t - 8 = 0$

$\qquad 2t = 8$

$\qquad t = 4$

**The particle is at rest after 4 seconds.** ✓

**d** $v = 2t - 8$

$a = \dfrac{dv}{dt}$

$\quad = 2$ ✓

**24 a** $V = t^2 - 200t + 10\,000$

When $t = 0$,

$V = 0^2 - 200 \times 0 + 10\,000$

$\quad = 10\,000$

$\therefore$ **An amount of 10 000 L was in the tank before it began to be emptied.** ✓

**b** When $t = 10$,

$V = 10^2 - 200 \times 10 + 10\,000$

$\quad = 8100$ ✓

Average rate of change $= \dfrac{10\,000 - 8100}{0 - 10}$

$\qquad\qquad\qquad\qquad = -190 \text{ L per minute}$ ✓

**c** $V = t^2 - 200t + 10\,000$

$\dfrac{dV}{dt} = 2t - 200$ ✓

When $t = 60$,

$\dfrac{dV}{dt} = 2 \times 60 - 200$

$\qquad = -80 \text{ L/min}$

**The water is flowing out of the tank at the rate of 80 L/min.** ✓

# CHAPTER 4
## LOGARITHMS AND EXPONENTIALS

TOPIC 4:
EXPONENTIAL
AND LOGARITHMIC
FUNCTIONS

## Introducing logarithms

### 1 Review of index laws

→ In the expression $a^m$, $a$ is the **base** and $m$ the **index** (or power or exponent).

→ The index tells us how many **factors** of the base are multiplied together; for example, $x^4 = x \times x \times x \times x$.

→ Familiarity with the **index laws** is essential.

$$a^x \times a^y = a^{x+y} \quad a^x \div a^y = a^{x-y} \quad (a^x)^y = a^{xy}$$
$$a^1 = a \quad a^0 = 1$$

→ The definitions extend to all **powers** that are **real numbers**.

$$a^{-1} = \frac{1}{a} \qquad a^{-x} = \frac{1}{a^x}$$

$$\text{If } a \geq 0, \qquad a^{\frac{1}{2}} = \sqrt{a} \qquad a^{\frac{1}{x}} = \sqrt[x]{a} \qquad a^{\frac{x}{y}} = \sqrt[y]{a^x} = \left(\sqrt[y]{a}\right)^x$$

### EXAMPLE 1

Evaluate $7^{-1.5}$, giving the answer correct to two significant figures.

$$7^{-1.5} = 0.053\,994\,9247\ldots$$
$$= 0.054 \quad \text{(2 sig. fig.)}$$

*We can use a calculator to evaluate any powers, even irrational ones like $3^\pi$ or $5^{\sqrt{2}}$.*

### EXAMPLE 2

Express $27^{-\frac{2}{3}}$ as a fraction in simplest form.

$$27^{-\frac{2}{3}} = \frac{1}{\left(\sqrt[3]{27}\right)^2}$$
$$= \frac{1}{3^2}$$
$$= \frac{1}{9}$$

*A calculator could be used to get this result but it is important to understand the process.*

### EXAMPLE 3

Solve $4^x = 8$.

$$4^x = 8$$
$$(2^2)^x = 2^3$$
$$2^{2x} = 2^3$$
$$\therefore 2x = 3$$
$$x = 1.5$$

*If expressions involving powers of the same base are equal then the actual indices must be equal.*

### → PRACTICE

1  Evaluate $5^{-2.4}$, giving the answer correct to two significant figures.

2  Express $16^{-\frac{3}{4}}$ as a fraction in simplest form.

3  Solve $100^x = 100\,000$.

4*  Solve $(1 - r)^6 = 0.621$, giving the value of $r$ correct to three decimal places.

Answers ⊃ p. 148

## 2 Introduction to logarithms

→ A logarithm is an **index**. The word logarithm is often abbreviated to **log**.

→ The notation $\log_a b$ is used for logarithms. The **base** is $a$ [$a > 0$, $a \neq 1$].

→ The logarithm of a number to any (positive) base is the **index** when the number is expressed as a power of the base. For example, because $3^2 = 9$, the logarithm to the base 3 of 9 is 2, i.e. $\log_3 9 = 2$.

→ $\log_a y = x$ is an **equivalent** statement to $a^x = y$.

For example:   $7^2 = 49$  so  $\log_7 49 = 2$   and
$\log_3 243 = 5$  because  $3^5 = 243$.

→ Logarithms to base 10 are often referred to as **common logarithms**. The logarithm to base 10 of any number can be found using a calculator, normally by using the 'log' button. The 'ln' button is for natural logarithms or logarithms to base $e$ which are dealt with later in this chapter.

## EXAMPLE 1

**What is the value of $\log_2 32$?**

$\log_2 32 = 5$

The question asks 'What power of 2 is 32?'. The answer is 5 because $2^5 = 32$.

## EXAMPLE 2

**Evaluate $\log_{10} 2.3$, giving the answer correct to four decimal places.**

$\log_{10} 2.3 = 0.361\,727\,83\ldots$
$\qquad = 0.3617 \quad (4\text{ d.p.})$

Make sure you know how to use your calculator to find a log to base 10.

## EXAMPLE 3

**Find $x$ if $\log_3 x = 4$.**

$\log_3 x = 4$
$\therefore x = 3^4$
$\quad x = 81$

Write the statement in indices rather than logs and the answer becomes apparent.

## EXAMPLE 4

**Find $a$ if $\log_a 16 = 2$.**

$\log_a 16 = 2$
$\therefore a^2 = 16$
$\quad a = 4 \quad (a > 0)$

By definition, the base must be positive.

## EXAMPLE 5

**Evaluate $\log_4 2$.**

Let $\log_4 2 = x$
$\therefore 4^x = 2$
$\quad (2^2)^x = 2$
$\quad 2^{2x} = 2^1$
$\quad 2x = 1$
$\quad x = \dfrac{1}{2}$
$\therefore \log_4 2 = \dfrac{1}{2}$

You might simply recognise that $2 = \sqrt{4} = 4^{\frac{1}{2}}$.

→ **PRACTICE**

1  Find the value of $\log_2 16$.

2  Evaluate $\log_{10} 27$, giving the answer correct to four decimal places.

3  Find $x$ if $\log_2 x = 5$.

4  Find $a$ if $\log_a 81 = 4$.

5  Evaluate $\log_9 3$.

6*  What is $\log_a 7$ if $a^{1.77} = 7$?

Answers ⊃ p. 148

## 3 The graphs of $y = a^x$, $y = a^{-x}$ and $y = \log_a x$

→ The **graph of $y = a^x$** is an exponential curve. It passes through the points $(0, 1)$ and $(1, a)$.

→ The **graph of $y = a^{-x}$** passes through $(0, 1)$ and $(-1, a)$. It is the reflection of $y = a^x$ in the $y$-axis.

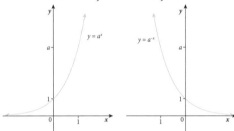

→ The **graph of $y = \log_a x$** is a reflection of the graph of $y = a^x$ in the line $y = x$. It passes through the points $(1, 0)$ and $(a, 1)$.

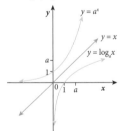

## EXAMPLE 1

**Sketch the graph of $y = 4^x$.**

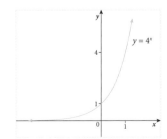

The $x$-axis is an asymptote of the curve. The curve gets closer and closer to the $x$-axis but never touches it.

## EXAMPLE 2

Sketch the graph of $y = 3^{-x}$.

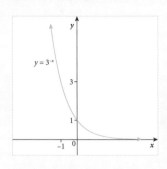

As $x$ gets larger, $y$ gets closer and closer to 0.

## EXAMPLE 3

On the same set of axes sketch $y = 2^x$ and $y = \log_2 x$.

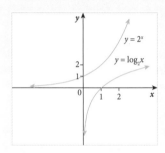

Imagine the graph folded along the line $y = x$ and the two curves should match exactly.

## EXAMPLE 4

Sketch the graph of $y = \log_{10} x$.

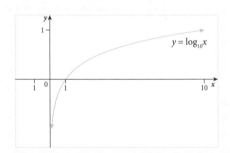

The $y$-axis is an asymptote.

### → PRACTICE

1   Sketch the graph of $y = 5^x$.

2   Sketch the graph of $y = 4^{-x}$.

3   On the same set of axes sketch $y = 3^x$ and $y = \log_3 x$.

4   Sketch the graph of $y = \log_6 x$.

5*  On the same diagram sketch the graphs of $y = 7^{-x}$ and $y = \log_7 x$. Hence give an approximate value of $x$ for which $7^{-x} = \log_7 x$.

Answers ➲ pp. 148–149

## Logarithmic laws and applications

### 1 The logarithmic laws

→ There is an **equivalent law involving logarithms** for each of the **index laws**.

→ The **log laws** are:

- $\log_a(mn) = \log_a m + \log_a n$
  (When multiplying, add the indices.)

- $\log_a \dfrac{m}{n} = \log_a m - \log_a n$
  (When dividing, subtract the indices.)

- $\log_a m^n = n\log_a m$
  (When raising a power to a power, multiply the indices.)

- $\log_a 1 = 0$      (because $a^0 = 1$)

- $\log_a a = 1$      (because $a^1 = a$)

- $\log_a \dfrac{1}{x} = -\log_a x$   (because $\dfrac{1}{x} = x^{-1}$)

## EXAMPLE 1

Express $\log_a 3 + \log_a 7$ as a single logarithm.

$\log_a 3 + \log_a 7 = \log_a 21$

The indices have been added so we need to multiply $3 \times 7$.

## EXAMPLE 2

Find the value of $\log_5 15 - \log_5 3$.

$\begin{aligned} \log_5 15 - \log_5 3 &= \log_5\left(\dfrac{15}{3}\right) \\ &= \log_5 5 \\ &= 1 \end{aligned}$

The indices have been subtracted so 15 is divided by 3.

## EXAMPLE 3

Evaluate $\log_4 8 + \log_4 2$.

$\begin{aligned} \log_4 8 + \log_4 2 &= \log_4(8 \times 2) \\ &= \log_4 16 \\ &= 2 \end{aligned}$

We know that $4^2 = 16$ so it follows that $\log_4 16 = 2$. Alternatively $\log_4 16 = \log_4 4^2 = 2\log_4 4 = 2 \times 1 = 2$.

## EXAMPLE 4

Find the value of $\log_3 72 - 3\log_3 2$.

$$\begin{aligned}
\log_3 72 - 3\log_3 2 &= \log_3 72 - \log_3 2^3 \\
&= \log_3 72 - \log_3 8 \\
&= \log_3 9 \\
&= 2
\end{aligned}$$

*In this case we use a log law in reverse: $3\log_3 2 = \log_3 2^3$.*

## EXAMPLE 5

Evaluate $\log_2 \dfrac{1}{4} + \log_4 \dfrac{1}{2}$.

$$\begin{aligned}
\log_2 \frac{1}{4} + \log_4 \frac{1}{2} &= \log_2 2^{-2} + \log_4 4^{-\frac{1}{2}} \\
&= -2 + -\frac{1}{2} \\
&= -2\frac{1}{2}
\end{aligned}$$

*Remember that the log laws only work when the base is the same.*

---

### → PRACTICE

1  Express $\log_m 5 + \log_m 6$ as a single logarithm.

2  Find the value of $\log_2 10 - \log_2 5$.

3  Evaluate $\log_6 12 + \log_6 3$.

4  Find the value of $\log_2 36 - 2\log_2 3$.

5  Evaluate $\log_9 \dfrac{1}{3} - \log_3 \dfrac{1}{9}$.

6*  Simplify $2\log_a a^5 - \log_a a^3$.

Answers ⊃ p. 149

---

### 2 Simplifying and evaluating logarithmic expressions

→  It is important to be able to quickly change an expression from **exponential** form (index form) to **logarithmic** form and vice versa. If $y = a^x$ then $\log_a y = x$ and, conversely, if $x = \log_a y$ then $y = a^x$.

→  $a^{\log_a b} = b$

→  Don't forget that a logarithm is an **index**.

→  When using the log laws with more than one logarithm the **base** must be the same.

## EXAMPLE 1

If $\log_a 5 = 0.827$ and $\log_a 2 = 0.356$ find the value of $\log_a 1.25$.

$$\begin{aligned}
\log_a 1.25 &= \log_a \frac{5}{4} \\
&= \log_a 5 - \log_a 4 \\
&= \log_a 5 - \log_a 2^2 \\
&= \log_a 5 - 2\log_a 2 \\
&= 0.827 - 2 \times 0.356 \\
&= 0.115
\end{aligned}$$

*We could determine the value of $a$ but it is not necessary.*

## EXAMPLE 2

Simplify $\dfrac{\log_a 32}{\log_a 8}$.

$$\begin{aligned}
\frac{\log_a 32}{\log_a 8} &= \frac{\log_a 2^5}{\log_a 2^3} \\
&= \frac{5\log_a 2}{3\log_a 2} \\
&= \frac{5}{3}
\end{aligned}$$

*There is no law to divide one logarithm by another.*

## EXAMPLE 3

Find the value of $x$ if $5\log_3 2 - \log_3 x = \dfrac{1}{2}\log_3 16$.

$$\begin{aligned}
5\log_3 2 - \log_3 x &= \frac{1}{2}\log_3 16 \\
\log_3 2^5 - \log_3 x &= \log_3 16^{\frac{1}{2}} \\
\log_3 32 - \log_3 x &= \log_3 4 \\
\log_3 x &= \log_3 32 - \log_3 4 \\
&= \log_3 8 \\
\therefore x &= 8
\end{aligned}$$

*We know that $32 \div 8$ is 4 so we might see the solution in the third line and solve by inspection there.*

## EXAMPLE 4

Find the value of $x$ if $\log_x 3 = \log_8 2$.

$$\begin{aligned}
\log_x 3 &= \log_8 2 \\
&= \log_8 8^{\frac{1}{3}} \\
&= \frac{1}{3}
\end{aligned}$$

So $x^{\frac{1}{3}} = 3$

$$\begin{aligned}
x &= 3^3 \\
&= 27
\end{aligned}$$

*We might recognise that 8 is the cube of 2 so $x$ must be the cube of 3.*

## EXAMPLE 5

Solve $\log_{10}x^2 + \log_{10}8x = 3$.

$$\log_{10}x^2 + \log_{10}8x = 3$$
$$\log_{10}8x^3 = 3$$
$$\therefore 8x^3 = 10^3$$
$$x^3 = 125$$
$$x = 5$$

> In this case we can use a calculator to find $\log_{10}25 + \log_{10}40$ and check that our answer is correct.

**→ PRACTICE**

1   If $\log_a 3 = 0.458$ and $\log_a 2 = 0.289$ find the value of $\log_a 4.5$.

2   Simplify $\dfrac{\log_a 100}{\log_a 1000}$.

3   Find the value of $x$ if $3\log_2 6 - \log_2 x = \dfrac{1}{2}\log_2 144$.

4   Find the value of $x$ if $\log_x 8 = \log_9 3$.

5   Solve $\log_6 3x^2 + \log_6 16x = 4$.

6*  Express $2\log_a x + \dfrac{1}{2}\log_a y - \log_a z$ as a single log.

Answers ⊃ p. 149

## 3 Inverse functions

→ $f(x) = a^x$ and $f(x) = \log_a x$ are **inverse functions**. One function undoes what the other function does.

→ $\log_a a^x = x$ and $a^{\log_a x} = x$

→ The **graphs** of $y = a^x$ and $y = \log_a x$ are reflections in the line $y = x$.

→ We can use the properties of inverse functions to **solve equations**. This might involve taking the log of both sides of an equation. We can use a calculator to find the log to base 10.

## EXAMPLE 1

Evaluate $\log_n n^6$.

$$\log_n n^6 = 6$$

> Write the answer using the definition $\log_a a^x = x$.

## EXAMPLE 2

Find the value of $3^{2\log_3 5}$.

$$3^{2\log_3 5} = 3^{\log_3 5^2}$$
$$= 5^2$$
$$= 25$$

> Inverse functions are not reciprocals. Don't confuse them.

## EXAMPLE 3

Find the value of $x$ if $\log_7(6x + 1) = 3$.

$$\log_7(6x + 1) = 3$$
$$\therefore 6x + 1 = 7^3$$
$$6x + 1 = 343$$
$$6x = 342$$
$$x = 57$$

> By changing a log into index form we make the equation much simpler.

## EXAMPLE 4

Find the smallest integer $n$ for which $0.7^n < 0.003$.

$$0.7^n < 0.003$$
$$\log_{10}0.7^n < \log_{10}0.003$$
$$n\log_{10}0.7 < \log_{10}0.003$$
$$n > \log_{10}0.003 \div \log_{10}0.7$$
$$n > 16.286\,9388\ldots$$

$\therefore$ the smallest integer for which $0.7^n < 0.003$ is $n = 17$.

> The log of any number between 0 and 1 is negative. The inequality has to be reversed when we divide by a negative number.

**→ PRACTICE**

1   Evaluate $\log_m m^8$.

2   Find the value of $2^{3\log_2 5}$

3   Find the value of $x$ if $\log_3(7x + 3) = 7$.

4   Find the smallest integer $n$ for which $0.4^n < 0.0002$.

5*  A water filter removes 12% of the impurities each time water flows through it.

    a   Show that 77.44% of impurities remain after the water has passed through the filter twice.

    b   How many times must the water flow through the filter so that at least 95% of the impurities are removed?

Answers ⊃ pp. 149–150

## 4 Change of base

→ **The change of base formula** allows us to change a logarithm in any base to a logarithm in a different base.

→ The formula is $\log_a x = \dfrac{\log_b x}{\log_b a}$.

→ By changing the log to base 10 (or base $e$) a **calculator** can be used to evaluate any logarithm.

### EXAMPLE 1

**Find the value, to three decimal places, of $\log_7 11$.**

$$\log_7 11 = \frac{\log_{10} 11}{\log_{10} 7}$$
$$= 1.232\,274\,40\ldots$$
$$= 1.232 \quad (3\text{ d.p.})$$

*We change the log from base 7 to base 10 so that we can use a calculator to find the value.*

### EXAMPLE 2

**Without using a calculator, evaluate $\log_8 16$.**

$$\log_8 16 = \frac{\log_2 16}{\log_2 8}$$
$$= \frac{\log_2 2^4}{\log_2 2^3}$$
$$= \frac{4\log_2 2}{3\log_2 2}$$
$$= \frac{4}{3}$$
$$= 1\frac{1}{3}$$

*We change the log to base 2 because both 8 and 16 are powers of 2.*

### EXAMPLE 3

**Write $\log_2 6 + \log_4 9$ as a single log.**

$$\log_2 6 + \log_4 9 = \log_2 6 + \frac{\log_2 9}{\log_2 4}$$
$$= \log_2 6 + \frac{1}{2}\log_2 9$$
$$= \log_2 6 + \log_2 9^{\frac{1}{2}}$$
$$= \log_2 6 + \log_2 3$$
$$= \log_2 (6 \times 3)$$
$$= \log_2 18$$

*We could have instead changed $\log_2 6$ to a base 4 number, but it is better to use the lowest base.*

### EXAMPLE 4

**Simplify $\log_9 25 - \log_3 5$.**

$$\log_9 25 - \log_3 5 = \frac{\log_3 25}{\log_3 9} - \log_3 5$$
$$= \frac{\log_3 5^2}{\log_3 3^2} - \log_3 5$$
$$= \frac{2\log_3 5}{2\log_3 3} - \log_3 5$$
$$= \log_3 5 - \log_3 5 \qquad \text{\small Remember: } \log_a a = 1.$$
$$= 0$$

### EXAMPLE 5

**Solve $\log_4 x - \log_8 x = 2$.**

$$\log_4 x - \log_8 x = 2$$
$$\frac{\log_2 x}{\log_2 4} - \frac{\log_2 x}{\log_2 8} = 2$$
$$\frac{\log_2 x}{2} - \frac{\log_2 x}{3} = 2$$
$$3\log_2 x - 2\log_2 x = 12$$
$$\log_2 x = 12$$
$$x = 2^{12}$$
$$x = 4096$$

*You will not be expected to remember the change of base formula. It is given on the reference sheet.*

### → PRACTICE

1　Find the value to three decimal places of $\log_5 8$.

2　Without using a calculator, evaluate $\log_9 27$. (Give the answer as a decimal.)

3　Write $\log_8 27 + \log_2 7$ as a single log.

4　Simplify $\log_3 12 - \log_9 16$.

5　Solve $\log_8 x + \log_4 x = 5$.

6*　Simplify $\log_8 81 - \log_2\left(\sqrt[3]{3}\right)$.

*Answers ⊃ p. 150*

## 5 Further applications of logs

→ Logs are used in many fields, including science, finance and industry. We apply our understanding of logs to **solve problems** in these areas.

→ A **logarithmic scale** allows a large range of quantities to be compared. The difference between values on the scale are multiples rather than units. Examples of logarithmic scales are the Richter scale for earthquakes, octaves in music and pH levels of acidity.

## EXAMPLE 1

The change in the level of sound, in decibels, between two signals is given by $L = 10 \log_{10}\left(\dfrac{P_2}{P_1}\right)$ where $P_1$ is the power of the first signal and $P_2$ the power of the second. If the second signal is twice the power of the first what is the increase in sound?

$$L = 10 \log_{10}\left(\frac{P_2}{P_1}\right)$$

Now $P_2 = 2P_1$

$\therefore \quad L = 10 \log_{10}2$

$\quad\quad = 3.010\,299\,95\ldots$

$\quad\quad = 3 \text{ dB} \quad \text{(nearest unit)}$

There is a 3 dB, to the nearest decibel, increase in the level of sound.

Use the given information to answer the question. You do not need to understand why the equation works.

## EXAMPLE 2

The magnitude of an earthquake is given by $M = \log_{10}\left(\dfrac{I}{S}\right)$ where $M$ is the magnitude, $I$ is the intensity (or strength) of the earthquake and $S$ is a constant. The earthquake that occurred in Newcastle in 1989 had a magnitude of 5.6. The strongest earthquake recorded in Australia had an intensity 40 times stronger than the Newcastle one. What was the magnitude of the strongest earthquake?

$$M = \log_{10}\left(\frac{I}{S}\right)$$

Let $x$ be the intensity of the Newcastle earthquake.

$\therefore 5.6 = \log_{10}\left(\dfrac{x}{S}\right)$

The strongest earthquake had intensity $40x$.

$M = \log_{10}\left(\dfrac{40x}{S}\right)$

$\quad = \log_{10}40 + \log_{10}\left(\dfrac{x}{S}\right)$

$\quad = 1.602\,059\,99\ldots + 5.6$

$\quad = 7.2 \quad \text{(1 d.p.)}$

The magnitude of the strongest earthquake was 7.2.

An earthquake of magnitude 7 is 10 times stronger than one of magnitude 6, 100 times stronger than one of magnitude 5, and 1000 times stronger than one of magnitude 4.

## → PRACTICE

1  The change in the level of sound, in decibels, between two signals is given by $L = 10 \log_{10}\left(\dfrac{P_2}{P_1}\right)$ where $P_1$ is the power of the first signal and $P_2$ the power of the second. If the power of the second signal is three times that of the first, what is the increase in sound?

2  The magnitude of an earthquake is given by $M = \log_{10}\left(\dfrac{I}{S}\right)$ where $M$ is the magnitude, $I$ is the intensity (or strength) of the earthquake and $S$ is a constant. An earthquake in New Zealand had a magnitude of 6.3. Another earthquake recorded a few years later had an intensity 31.6 times stronger than the earlier one. What was the magnitude of the stronger earthquake?

3*  The pH of a solution is defined as the log to base 10 of the reciprocal of its hydrogen ion activity ($a_{H^+}$). Find the pH of a solution that has hydrogen ion activity of $7.8 \times 10^{-7}$.

Answers ⊃ p. 150

## The exponential function and natural logarithms

### 1 The number $e$

→ By **first principles** we can show that if $y = a^x$ then $\dfrac{dy}{dx} = \left(\lim_{h \to 0}\dfrac{a^h - 1}{h}\right)a^x$.

→ Using a calculator we can find an **approximate value of this limit** for different values of $a$. For example, if $a$ is 10 the limit is about 2.3. If $a = 2$ the limit is about 0.69 and if $a = 3$ the limit is about 1.1. Obviously there must be a value of $a$ for which this limit is equal to 1 (and that value of $a$ must be between 2 and 3 and closer to 3). That value can be found, using a calculator, to be about 2.7.

→ The **number $e$** is called **Euler's number** and its value of $2.718\,281\,828\,45\ldots$ is the value for which $\lim_{h \to 0}\dfrac{a^h - 1}{h} = 1$.

→ The value of $e$ can be found on a **calculator** and used in calculations.

### EXAMPLE 1

Find the value, to four significant figures, of $\dfrac{e^2}{3}$.

$\dfrac{e^2}{3} = 2.463\,018\ldots$

$\quad\quad = 2.463 \quad \text{(4 sig. fig.)}$

On many calculators $e$ is found as the second function on the 'ln' button.

## EXAMPLE 2

Find the value of $\dfrac{3-e}{2e+1}$. Give the answer correct to three decimal places.

$\dfrac{3-e}{2e+1} = 0.043\,768\,4122\ldots$

On the calculator you might have to put $e^1$ to get $e$.

$\quad\quad = 0.044 \quad$ (3 d.p.)

### → PRACTICE

1  Find the value, to four significant figures, of $\dfrac{e^3}{2}$.

2  Find the value of $\dfrac{5-3e}{4e+2}$. Give the answer correct to three decimal places.

3*  Find the value, to four decimal places, of $\sqrt{e}$.

Answers ⊃ p. 150

## 2 The derivative of $e^x$

→ If $f(x) = e^x$ then $f'(x) = e^x$ or, using a different notation, $\dfrac{d}{dx}(e^x) = e^x$.

→ $e^x$ is the only **function** that is **equal** to its **derivative**.

→ If $e^x$ is **multiplied by a constant** its derivative is also multiplied by the same constant:

$\dfrac{d}{dx}(ke^x) = ke^x$

→ $\dfrac{d}{dx}(e^{ax}) = ae^{ax}$ by the **chain rule**.

### EXAMPLE 1

Find the derivative, with respect to $x$, of $y = 5e^x$.

$y = 5e^x$

$\dfrac{dy}{dx} = 5e^x$

Remember: $e$ is a number. It is not a variable that we might differentiate.

### EXAMPLE 2

Differentiate $y = 7 - e^x$.

$y = 7 - e^x$

$\dfrac{dy}{dx} = -e^x$

The derivative of a sum of functions is the sum of the derivatives of the functions.

## EXAMPLE 3

If $f(x) = 3e^x$ find $f'(2)$.

$f(x) = 3e^x$
$f'(x) = 3e^x$
$f'(2) = 3e^2$

Leave the answer in exact form rather than a decimal approximation, unless told otherwise.

## EXAMPLE 4

Find the gradient of the tangent to the curve $y = e^x$ at the point where $x = 1$.

$y = e^x$

$\dfrac{dy}{dx} = e^x$

When $x = 1$, $\dfrac{dy}{dx} = e^1$

The gradient function is equal to the function.

$\quad\quad\quad\quad\quad = e$

$\therefore$ the gradient of the tangent is $e$.

## EXAMPLE 5

Find the derivative of $y = 4e^{3x}$.

$y = 4e^{3x}$

$\dfrac{dy}{dx} = 4e^{3x} \times 3$

$3x$ is a function of $x$ so we need to use the chain rule.

$\quad\quad = 12e^{3x}$

### → PRACTICE

1  Find the derivative, with respect to $x$, of $y = 4e^x$.

2  Differentiate $y = 2 + e^x$.

3  If $f(x) = 2e^x$ find $f'(3)$.

4  Find the gradient of the tangent to the curve $y = e^x$ at the point where $x = 0$.

5  Find the derivative of $y = 5e^{4x}$.

6*  Differentiate $\dfrac{e^x}{2} + e^{\frac{x}{2}}$.

Answers ⊃ p. 151

## 3 Natural logarithms

→ Logarithms to **base $e$** are called **natural logarithms**.

→ $y = \log_e x$ is the **inverse** or opposite function to $y = e^x$.

→ If $y = \log_e x$ then $x = e^y$.

→ $y = \ln x$ is another **notation** for $y = \log_e x$.

→ Your **calculator** allows you to find the value of natural logs (often with a button marked 'ln').

## EXAMPLE 1

**Find ln 3 correct to three decimal places.**

$\ln 3 = 1.098\,612\,28\ldots$
$\quad = 1.099 \quad \text{(3 d.p.)}$

> Sometimes the notation $y = \log x$ is used for base 10 logarithms and sometimes it is used for natural logs. To avoid confusion always write the 10 for base 10 logs and use either $\log_e$ or ln for natural logs.

## EXAMPLE 2

**Find the value, to five significant figures, of $4 \log_e 5$.**

$4 \log_e 5 = 6.437\,7516\ldots$
$\quad = 6.4378 \quad \text{(5 sig. figs.)}$

> On most calculators $\log_e$ is found using the ln button so just press 4 ln 5 =.

→ PRACTICE

1  Find ln 4, correct to three decimal places.

2  Find the value, to five significant figures, of $2 \log_e 8$.

3*  Find the value, to four decimal places, of $\dfrac{2\ln 9}{3\ln 6}$.

Answers ⊃ p. 151

## 4 The log laws with natural logs

→ Like all logarithms, $\ln x$ is only **defined** for $x > 0$.

→ The **log laws** all apply to natural logarithms:

- $\ln x + \ln y = \ln (xy)$
- $\ln x - \ln y = \ln \dfrac{x}{y}$
- $\ln x^n = n \ln x$

→ It is helpful to remember these **special results**:
$\ln e = 1 \quad \text{and} \quad \ln 1 = 0.$

## EXAMPLE 1

**Find the value of $\ln \dfrac{1}{e}$.**

$\ln \dfrac{1}{e} = \ln e^{-1}$
$\quad = -\ln e$
$\quad = -1$

> $\ln e^x = x$

## EXAMPLE 2

**Simplify $\log_e 24 - 3 \log_e 2$.**

$\log_e 24 - 3 \log_e 2 = \log_e 24 - \log_e 2^3$
$\quad = \log_e 24 - \log_e 8$
$\quad = \log_e 3$

> Using $\ln x - \ln \dfrac{x}{y}$

## EXAMPLE 3

**Find the value of $x$ if $\ln x + 2 \ln 6 = 3 \ln 3$.**

$\ln x + 2 \ln 6 = 3 \ln 3$
$\ln x + \ln 6^2 = \ln 3^3$
$\ln x + \ln 36 = \ln 27$
$\quad \ln x = \ln 27 - \ln 36$
$\quad\quad = \ln \dfrac{27}{36}$
$\quad\quad = \ln \dfrac{3}{4}$
$\therefore x = \dfrac{3}{4}$

> Equating logs

## EXAMPLE 4

**Find the value of $x$ if $2 \ln x = \ln (x + 6)$.**

$2 \ln x = \ln (x + 6)$
$\ln x^2 = \ln (x + 6)$
$\therefore x^2 = x + 6$
$x^2 - x - 6 = 0$
$(x - 3)(x + 2) = 0$
$\quad x = 3 \quad \text{or} \quad x = -2$
But $x > 0$,
$\therefore x = 3$

> Never forget that we can't have logs of negative numbers.

→ PRACTICE

1  Find the value of $\ln \dfrac{1}{e^2}$.

2  Simplify $\log_e 36 - 2 \log_e 3$.

3  Find the value of $x$ if $\ln x + 5 \ln 2 = 2 \ln 4$.

4  Find the value of $x$ if $2 \ln x = \ln (x + 12)$.

5*  Find the value of $\dfrac{1}{2}\ln \dfrac{1}{\sqrt{e}}$.

Answers ⊃ p. 151

# Graphs and applications of exponential and logarithmic functions

## 1 Solving equations with exponentials

→ $e^{\ln x} = x$   and   $\ln e^x = x$

→ By taking the **log of both sides** of an equation we can often eliminate exponentials and hence solve equations.

→ **Take care** to do the same to both sides of the equation and carefully follow the log laws.

### EXAMPLE 1

Find the value of $x$, correct to three decimal places, for which $e^x = 8$.

$e^x = 8$
$\therefore x = \ln 8$
$\quad = 2.079\,441\,54\ldots$
$\quad = 2.079$   (3 d.p.)

*Taking logs of both sides:*
*$\ln e^x = \ln 8$.*

### EXAMPLE 2

Find the value of $x$ for which $e^{2x} + 1 = 17$. Give the answer correct to four decimal places.

$e^{2x} + 1 = 17$
$\quad e^{2x} = 16$
$\quad 2x = \ln 16$
$\quad x = \dfrac{1}{2}\ln 16$
$\quad\quad = 1.386\,294\,36\ldots$
$\quad\quad = 1.3863$   (4 d.p.)

*$\frac{1}{2}\ln 16$ could be simplified to $\ln 4$ before evaluating.*

### EXAMPLE 3

Solve $5^x = 37$, giving the answer correct to three decimal places.

$5^x = 37$
$\ln 5^x = \ln 37$
$x \ln 5 = \ln 37$
$\quad x = \dfrac{\ln 37}{\ln 5}$
$\quad\quad = 2.243\,589\,44\ldots$
$\quad\quad = 2.244$   (3 d.p.)

*Stop to think whether your answer makes sense. For example, $5^2$ is 25 so the answer here must be slightly larger than 2.*

### EXAMPLE 4

Find the value of $n$, to one decimal place, if $25\,000(1.08)^n = 37\,485$.

$25\,000\,(1.08)^n = 37\,485$
$\quad 1.08^n = \dfrac{37\,485}{25\,000}$
$\quad \ln 1.08^n = \ln\left(\dfrac{37\,485}{25\,000}\right)$
$\quad n \ln 1.08 = \ln\left(\dfrac{37\,485}{25\,000}\right)$
$\quad n = \ln\left(\dfrac{37\,485}{25\,000}\right) \div \ln 1.08$
$\quad\quad = 5.263\,247\,76\ldots$
$\quad\quad = 5.3$   (1 d.p.)

*We could have used log to base 10 instead.*

### → PRACTICE

1   Find the value of $x$, correct to three decimal places, for which $e^x = 11$.

2   Find the value of $x$ for which $e^{3x} + 2 = 15$. Give the answer correct to four decimal places.

3   Solve $7^x = 29$, giving the answer correct to three decimal places.

4   Find the value of $n$, to one decimal place, if $50\,000\,(1.07)^n = 75\,482$.

5*   Find the value of $x$ for which $6e^{2x-1} = 13$. Give the answer correct to three decimal places.

Answers ⊃ pp. 151–152

## 2 Further graphs of exponential curves

→ All **exponential curves** have a similar shape. Any curve of the form $y = a^x \,(a > 0)$, has the $x$-axis as an asymptote and cuts the $y$-axis at $(0, 1)$.

→ **Adding a constant to the equation** $y = a^x$ has the effect of moving the graph up (or down) the $y$-axis. $y = a^x + c$ will cut the $y$-axis at $(0, 1 + c)$.

→ **Adding a constant to the exponential** value will move the graph right (or left). $y = a^{x+c}$ will pass through the point $(-c, 1)$ and cut the $y$-axis at $(0, a^c)$.

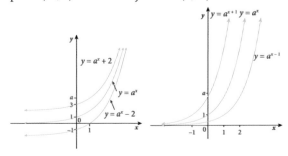

→ **Multiplying an exponential** by a constant will change the steepness of the curve. Any curve of the form $y = ka^x$ will cut the $y$-axis at $(0, k)$ and pass through $(1, ka)$.

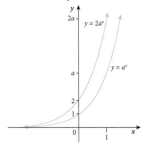

## EXAMPLE 1

a On the same diagram sketch the graphs of $y = e^x$ and $y = e^{-x}$

b Hence find the solution(s) of the equation $e^x - e^{-x} = 0$.

a

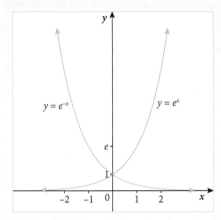

b $e^x - e^{-x} = 0$

$\therefore e^x = e^{-x}$

$x = 0$

From the graph the only solution is $x = 0$.

## EXAMPLE 2

Consider the curve $y = 4^x - 2$.

a What is the equation of any asymptote?

b Where will the curve cut the $y$-axis?

c Does the curve cut the $x$-axis? If so, at what point?

d Sketch the curve.

a The equation of the asymptote is $y = -2$.

The curve $y = 4^x$ has asymptote $y = 0$ and this curve has moved down 2 units.

b $y = 4^x - 2$

When $x = 0$, $y = 4^0 - 2$

$\qquad = -1$

The curve cuts the $y$-axis at $y = -1$.

c When $y = 0$,

$4^x - 2 = 0$

$4^x = 2$

$2^{2x} = 2^1$

$2x = 1$

$x = \dfrac{1}{2}$

You could use logs to solve the equation, or simply realise that 2 is the square root of 4 so $4^{\frac{1}{2}} = 2$.

The curve cuts the $x$-axis at $\left(\dfrac{1}{2}, 0\right)$.

d

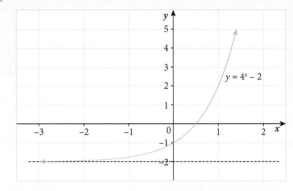

## EXAMPLE 3

A graphics calculator was used to graph the two functions $y = 2^{x+1}$ and $y = 2 \times 2^x$. Explain why only one graph is drawn.

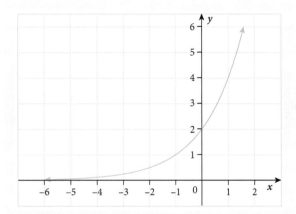

$2 \times 2^x = 2^1 \times 2^x$

$\qquad = 2^{x+1}$

Don't overlook the simple index laws.

So the two functions are identical. The second graph is exactly the same as the first.

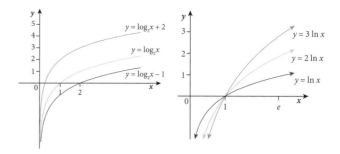

## → PRACTICE

1   **a**  On the same diagram sketch the graphs of $y = 6^x$ and $y = 6^{-x}$.

    **b**  Hence find the solution(s) of the equation $6^x - 6^{-x} = 0$.

2   Consider the curve $y = 3^x - 3$.

    **a**  What is the equation of any asymptote?

    **b**  Where will the curve cut the $y$-axis?

    **c**  Does the curve cut the $x$-axis? If so, at what point?

    **d**  Sketch the curve.

3   A graphics calculator was used to graph the two functions $y = 2^{-x}$ and $y = \left(\dfrac{1}{2}\right)^x$. Explain why only one graph is drawn.

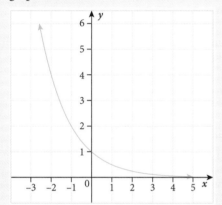

4*  Sketch the graph of $y = 2(5^x) + 3$ showing essential features.

Answers ⊃ p. 152

## 3 Further graphs of logarithmic curves

→ All **logarithmic curves** have a similar shape. Any curve of the form $y = \log_a x \ (a > 0)$ has the $y$-axis as an asymptote and cuts the $x$-axis at $(1, 0)$.

→ **Adding a constant to the equation** $y = \log_a x$ has the effect of moving the graph up (or down).

→ **Multiplying the logarithm by a constant** will change the steepness of the curve.

→ Any logarithmic function is the **inverse of an exponential function** and the graphs will be reflections of each other in the line $y = x$.

## EXAMPLE 1

  **a**  Find the solution(s) to the equation $5 \log_3 x = 3 \log_3 x$ and hence write down the point(s) of intersection of the curves $y = 5 \log_3 x$ and $y = 3 \log_3 x$.

  **b**  Sketch the curves.

  **a**  $5 \log_3 x = 3 \log_3 x$

      $2 \log_3 x = 0$

        $\log_3 x = 0$      *$\log_a 1 = 0$ for all values of $a$ for which logs are defined.*

           $x = 1$

The only point of intersection is $(1, 0)$.

  **b**

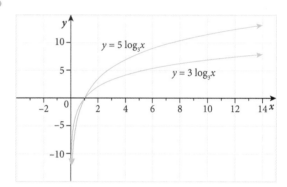

## EXAMPLE 2

A graphing program produced this graph which passes through $(1, -2)$ and $(4, -1)$.

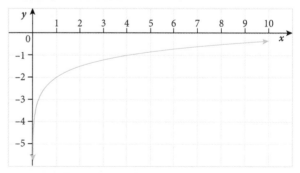

  **a**  If the graph is of the form $y = \log_a x + c$, find the values of $a$ and $c$.

  **b**  Where does the graph cut the $x$-axis?

a $y = \log_a x + c$
When $x = 1$, $y = -2$
$-2 = \log_a 1 + c$
But $\log_a 1 = 0$
$\therefore c = -2$
$\therefore y = \log_a x - 2$
When $x = 4$, $y = -1$
$-1 = \log_a 4 - 2$
$1 = \log_a 4$
But $\log_4 4 = 1$
$\therefore a = 4$

b $y = \log_4 x - 2$
When $y = 0$,
$0 = \log_4 x - 2$
$\log_4 x = 2$
$x = 4^2$
$= 16$
The curve cuts the $x$-axis at $(16, 0)$.

> The coordinates of all points on the graph must satisfy its equation.

Answers ➲ pp. 152–153

### → PRACTICE

1 a Find the solution(s) to the equation
$7 \log_5 x = 4 \log_5 x$ and hence write down the
point(s) of intersection of the curves $y = 7 \log_5 x$
and $y = 4 \log_5 x$.

b Sketch the curves.

2 A graphing program produced this graph which
passes through $(1, -4)$ and $(4, -2)$.

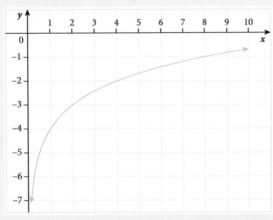

a If the graph was of the form $y = \log_a x + c$, find
the values of $a$ and $c$.

b Where does the graph cut the $x$-axis?

3* Consider the curve $y = \log_8 x + \dfrac{1}{3}$.

a Where does the curve cut the $x$-axis?

b Find the value of $y$ when $x = 4$.

c Sketch the curve.

## 4 Applications of exponential functions

→ Exponential and logarithmic functions have many
**practical applications** in subjects such as science,
industry, medicine and finance.

→ To solve problems, **interpret the given information**, and
translate it into mathematical expressions or equations.

→ Remember that logarithms and exponentials are **inverses**
and use that to help solve problems.

→ Consider a **graphical** solution to some problems.

### EXAMPLE 1

$20\,000$ is invested at 6% p.a. interest, compounded
monthly. How long does it take to double in value?
(The compound interest formula is $A = P(1 + r)^n$ where
$A$ is the final balance, $P$ is the initial quantity, $r$ is the
percentage interest rate per period expressed as a
decimal and $n$ is the number of periods.)

6% p.a. = $(6 \div 12)$% per month
$= 0.5$% per month
Now $A = P(1 + r)^n$
$40\,000 = 20\,000(1 + 0.005)^n$
$2 = 1.005^n$
$\ln 2 = \ln 1.005^n$
$= n \ln 1.005$
So $n = \dfrac{\ln 2}{\ln 1.005}$
$= 138.975\,721....$
$\approx 139$ months

> The actual amount invested doesn't matter. Any amount invested at 6% p.a. interest, compounded monthly, will take about 11 years and 7 months to double.

The amount takes about 11 years and 7 months to
double.

### EXAMPLE 2

A radioactive substance decomposes over time. The
mass $M$ in grams of a particular radioactive substance
can be expressed as $M = M_0 e^{-0.03t}$, where $t$ is the time in
years and $M_0$ is the original mass.

a If the original mass was 80 g, find the mass of the
substance after 5 years.

b After about how many years will half of the
substance remain?

a $M = M_0 e^{-0.03t}$, $M_0 = 80$
$\therefore M = 80 e^{-0.03t}$

When $t = 5$,
$M = 80e^{-0.03 \times 5}$
$\quad = 68.8566381...$
$\quad = 68.9 \quad (1 \text{ d.p.})$

After 5 years the mass of the substance is about 68.9 g.

b $\quad 40 = 80e^{-0.03t}$

$\quad 0.5 = e^{-0.03t}$

$\quad \ln 0.5 = \ln e^{-0.03t}$

$\quad\quad\quad = -0.03t$

$\quad\quad t = \ln 0.5 \div -0.03$

$\quad\quad\quad = 23.1049060...$

$\quad\quad\quad \approx 23 \text{ years}$

This is an example of exponential decay.

After about 23 years half of the mass will remain.

## EXAMPLE 3

The population of a country is known to be growing exponentially. At a given time $t$, in years, the population $P(t)$ is given by $P(t) = P(0)e^{kt}$, where $k$ is a constant.

a If the population was 1.2 million at the beginning of 2010 and was 1.5 million at the beginning of 2015, show that $k = \dfrac{1}{5} \ln 1.25$.

b Determine the expected population at the beginning of 2025.

c In what year will the population reach 3 million?

a Let $t = 0$ at the beginning of 2010.

$\therefore P(0) = 1\,200\,000$

So $P(t) = 1\,200\,000e^{kt}$

Now $P(5) = 1\,500\,000$

So $1\,200\,000e^{k \times 5} = 1\,500\,000$

$\quad\quad\quad e^{5k} = 1.25$

$\quad\quad \ln e^{5k} = \ln 1.25$

$\quad\quad\quad 5k = \ln 1.25$

$\quad\quad\quad k = \dfrac{1}{5} \ln 1.25$

b At the beginning of 2025, $t = 15$

$P(15) = 1\,200\,000e^{k \times 15}$

$\quad\quad = 2\,343\,750$

So the expected population at the beginning of 2025 is about 2.3 million.

c $1\,200\,000e^{kt} = 3\,000\,000$

$\quad\quad e^{kt} = 2.5$

$\quad\quad kt = \ln 2.5$

$t = \dfrac{\ln 2.5}{k}$

$\quad = 20.531418...$

$\quad = 20.5 \text{ years} \quad (1 \text{ d.p.})$

$\therefore$ the population should reach 3 million in the year 2030.

We use the exact value of $k$ throughout the question, not a decimal approximation.

→ **PRACTICE**

1 $\$30\,000$ is invested at 3% p.a. interest, compounded monthly. How long does it take to double in value? (The compound interest formula is $A = P(1 + r)^n$ where $A$ is the final balance, $P$ is the initial quantity, $r$ is the percentage interest rate per period expressed as a decimal and $n$ is the number of periods.)

2 The mass $M$ in grams of a particular radioactive substance can be expressed as $M = M_0 e^{-0.04t}$, where $t$ is the time in years and $M_0$ is the original mass.

   a If the original mass was 100 g, find the mass of the substance after 6 years.

   b After about how many years will half of the substance remain?

3 The population of a country is known to be growing exponentially. At a given time $t$, in years, the population $P(t)$ is given by $P(t) = P(0)e^{kt}$, where $k$ is a constant.

   a If the population was 1.5 million at the beginning of 2010 and was 1.8 million at the beginning of 2017, show that $k = \dfrac{1}{7} \ln 1.2$.

   b Determine the expected population at the beginning of 2030.

   c In what year will the population reach 4 million?

4* The mass $M$ g of a radioactive substance present after $t$ years is given by the formula $M = M_0 e^{-kt}$ where $k$ is a positive constant. The half-life of a radioactive substance is the time for it to reduce to half of its original mass. A substance has a half-life of 256 years. If the original mass was 12 g:

   a show that $k = \dfrac{\ln 2}{256}$

   b find the amount by which the mass has reduced in 50 years

Answers ⊃ p. 153

**Total marks: 50**

## PART A

(Suggested time: 15 minutes)

(1 mark each)

1   Between which two values does $\log_2 7$ lie?

   **A**  0 and 1

   **B**  1 and 2

   **C**  2 and 3

   **D**  3 and 4

2   Which is equivalent to $\log_a x - \log_a y$?

   **A**  $\log_a \dfrac{x}{y}$

   **B**  $\log_a \dfrac{y}{x}$

   **C**  $\dfrac{\log_a x}{\log_a y}$

   **D**  $\dfrac{\log_a y}{\log_a x}$

3   What is the value of $\log_9 27$?

   **A**  3

   **B**  $\dfrac{1}{3}$

   **C**  $\dfrac{2}{3}$

   **D**  $\dfrac{3}{2}$

4   Which is equivalent to $\ln e^{x^2}$?

   **A**  $e^{2x}$             **B**  $2e^x$

   **C**  $2x$              **D**  $x^2$

5   What could be the equation of this graph?

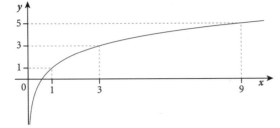

   **A**  $y = \log_3 x + 1$

   **B**  $y = \log_2 x + 1$

   **C**  $y = 2\log_3 x + 1$

   **D**  $y = 3\log_2 x + 1$

6   Which is equivalent to $\dfrac{\log_x 8}{\log_x 2}$?

   **A**  3

   **B**  4

   **C**  $\log_x 4$

   **D**  $\log_x 6$

7   Which statement is correct?

   **A**  $\log_a 3 + \log_a 5 = \log_a 8$

   **B**  $\log_a 3 + \log_a 5 = \log_a 15$

   **C**  $\log_a 3 \times \log_a 5 = \log_a 8$

   **D**  $\log_a 3 \times \log_a 5 = \log_a 15$

8   $\dfrac{d}{dx}(3e^x) =$

   **A**  $e^x$

   **B**  $3e^x$

   **C**  $e^{3x}$

   **D**  3

9   If $\log_a x = 1.11$ what is the value of $\log_a a^2 x$?

   **A**  1.23

   **B**  2.11

   **C**  2.22

   **D**  3.11

10   Which is **not** correct?

   **A**  $\log_e \dfrac{1}{2} = -\log_e 2$

   **B**  $3 + \log_e e = 3e$

   **C**  $\log_e 1 = 0$

   **D**  $\log_e 8 = 3\log_e 2$

11   What is the value of $7\log_5 9$ to three decimal places?

   **A**  1.787

   **B**  5.981

   **C**  9.556

   **D**  10.882

12   Consider these statements:

   I $\log_a\left(\dfrac{1}{4}\right) = -\log_a 4$       II $\log_a\left(\dfrac{1}{4}\right) = 2\log_a\left(\dfrac{1}{2}\right)$

   Which is correct?

   **A**  both I and II

   **B**  neither I nor II

   **C**  I but not II

   **D**  II but not I

**PART B**  (Suggested time: 45 minutes)

Show all working.

**13** Find the value, to three significant figures, of $\log_e 7$.  (1 mark)

**14** Differentiate:

    **a**   $e^x + 8$  (1 mark)

    **b**   $8e^{2x}$  (1 mark)

**15** Express as an integer:

    **a**   $\log_3 27$  (1 mark)

    **b**   $\log_6 18 + \log_6 12$  (2 marks)

    **c**   $\log_a 2 + \log_a \dfrac{1}{2}$  (2 marks)

**16** Find the value of $x$ if

    $\dfrac{1}{4}\log_a 16 = 6 \log_a 2 - \log_a x$.  (2 marks)

**17** If $a^{3.17} = 9$, find:

    **a**   $\log_a 9$  (1 mark)

    **b**   $\log_a\left(\dfrac{1}{81}\right)$  (2 marks)

**18** On the same set of axes sketch $y = 7^x$ and $y = \log_7 x$.  (2 marks)

**19** Find the value of $x$ correct to four decimal places if $e^x = 5$.  (1 mark)

**20** If $\log_m 2 = 0.63$ and $\log_m 5 = 1.46$, evaluate $\log_m 40$.  (2 marks)

**21** Solve $2 \ln x = \ln (2x + 8)$.  (3 marks)

**22** The mass, $M$ grams, of an element at time $t$ days is given by $M = M_0 e^{-kt}$ where $k$ is a positive constant.

    **a**   A mass of 500 g reduces to 400 g in 87 days. Show that $k = \dfrac{\ln 1.25}{87}$.  (3 marks)

    **b**   How much of the mass would remain after a further 23 days?  (1 mark)

**23** Find the smallest integer $n$ for which $0.8^n < 0.007$.  (3 marks)

**24** The change in the level of sound arising from an increase in power is given by $10 \log_{10}\left(\dfrac{P}{P_0}\right)$ where $P$ is the power and $P_0$ the initial power.

    **a**   If $P = \dfrac{V^2}{R}$, where $V$ is the voltage for that power and $R$ is a constant, show that the gain $G$ (in decibels) in the level of sound is given by $G = 20 \log_{10}\left(\dfrac{V}{V_0}\right)$.  (2 marks)

    **b**   Find the gain when $V = 5$ and $V_0 = 0.02$.  (1 mark)

**25**  **a**   On the same set of axes sketch the graphs of $y = e^x + 1$ and $y = e^{-x} - 1$.  (2 marks)

    **b**   Show that the point of intersection of the two curves occurs when $e^{2x} + 2e^x - 1 = 0$.  (2 marks)

    **c**   Hence show that the lines intersect when $x \approx -0.88$.  (3 marks)

# ANSWERS

PRACTICE

## INTRODUCING LOGARITHMS

### 1 Review of index laws ➲ p. 132

1.   $5^{-2.4} = 0.021\,012\,2224\ldots$
      $= \mathbf{0.021}$   (2 sig.fig.)

2.   $16^{-\frac{3}{4}} = \dfrac{1}{\left(\sqrt[4]{16}\right)^3}$
           $= \dfrac{1}{2^3}$
           $= \dfrac{\mathbf{1}}{\mathbf{8}}$

3.   $100^x = 100\,000$
    $(10^2)^x = 10^5$
     $10^{2x} = 10^5$
    $\therefore 2x = 5$
       $x = \mathbf{2.5}$

4.   $(1 - r)^6 = 0.621$
    $1 - r = \pm\sqrt[6]{0.621}$
  $\therefore$   $r = 1 - \sqrt[6]{0.621}$   or   $r = 1 + \sqrt[6]{0.621}$
      $r = 0.076\,333\,3426\ldots$  or  $r = 0.923\,666\,65\ldots$
      $r = \mathbf{0.076}$     or    $r = \mathbf{1.924}$   (3 d.p.)

### 2 Introduction to logarithms ➲ p. 133

1.   $\mathbf{\log_2 16 = 4}$

2.   $\log_{10} 27 = 1.431\,363\,76\ldots$
           $= \mathbf{1.4314}$   (4 d.p.)

3.   $\log_2 x = 5$
    $\therefore x = 2^5$
       $x = \mathbf{32}$

4.   $\log_a 81 = 4$
    $\therefore a^4 = 81$
      $a = \sqrt[4]{81}$   $(a > 0)$
      $a = \mathbf{3}$

5.   Let $\log_9 3 = x$
    $\therefore 9^x = 3$
    $(3^2)^x = 3$
     $3^{2x} = 3^1$
      $2x = 1$
       $x = \dfrac{1}{2}$
  $\therefore \mathbf{\log_9 3 = \dfrac{1}{2}}$

6.   $a^{1.77} = 7$
    $\therefore \mathbf{\log_a 7 = 1.77}$

### 3 The graphs of $y = a^x$, $y = a^{-x}$ and $y = \log_a x$ ➲ p. 134

1.
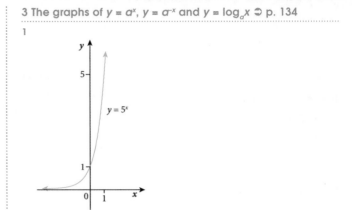

2.
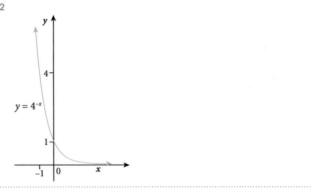

3.
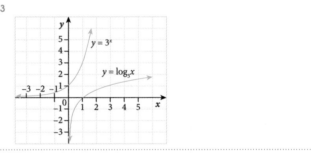

4.
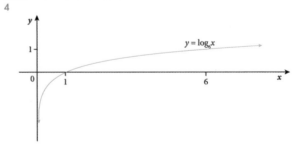

**5** An approximate value of $x$ for which $7^{-x} = \log_7 x$ is
$x = 1.2$.

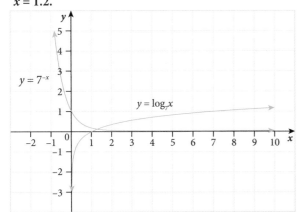

## LOGARITHMIC LAWS AND APPLICATIONS

### 1 The logarithmic laws ⊃ p. 135

**1** $\log_m 5 + \log_m 6 = \log_m 30$

**2** $\log_2 10 - \log_2 5 = \log_2 \left(\dfrac{10}{5}\right)$
$= \log_2 2$
$= 1$

**3** $\log_6 12 + \log_6 3 = \log_6 (12 \times 3)$
$= \log_6 36$
$= 2$

**4** $\log_2 36 - 2\log_2 3 = \log_2 36 - \log_2 3^2$
$= \log_2 36 - \log_2 9$
$= \log_2 4$
$= 2$

**5** $\log_9 \dfrac{1}{3} - \log_3 \dfrac{1}{9} = \log_9 9^{-\frac{1}{2}} - \log_3 3^{-2}$
$= -\dfrac{1}{2} - (-2)$
$= 1\dfrac{1}{2}$

**6** $2\log_a a^5 - \log_a a^3 = 2 \times 5 - 3$
$= 7$

### 2 Simplifying and evaluating logarithmic expressions ⊃ p. 136

**1** $\log_a 4.5 = \log_a \dfrac{9}{2}$
$= \log_a 9 - \log_a 2$
$= \log_a 3^2 - \log_a 2$
$= 2\log_a 3 - \log_a 2$
$= 2 \times 0.458 - 0.289$
$= 0.627$

**2** $\dfrac{\log_a 100}{\log_a 1000} = \dfrac{\log_a 10^2}{\log_a 10^3}$
$= \dfrac{2\log_a 10}{3\log_a 10}$
$= \dfrac{2}{3}$

**3** $3\log_2 6 - \log_2 x = \dfrac{1}{2}\log_2 144$
$\log_2 6^3 - \log_2 x = \log_2 144^{\frac{1}{2}}$
$\log_2 216 - \log_2 x = \log_2 12$
$\log_2 x = \log_2 216 - \log_2 12$
$= \log_2 18$
$\therefore x = 18$

**4** $\log_x 8 = \log_9 3$
$= \log_9 9^{\frac{1}{2}}$
$= \dfrac{1}{2}$
So $x^{\frac{1}{2}} = 8$
$x = 8^2$
$= 64$

**5** $\log_6 3x^2 + \log_6 16x^2 = 4$
$\log_6 48x^3 = 4$
$48x^3 = 6^4$
$x^3 = \dfrac{6^4}{48}$
$= 27$
$\therefore x = 3$

**6** $2\log_a x + \dfrac{1}{2}\log_a y - \log_a z$
$= \log_a x^2 + \log_a y^{\frac{1}{2}} - \log_a z$
$= \log_a \left(\dfrac{x^2 \sqrt{y}}{z}\right)$

### 3 Inverse functions ⊃ p. 136

**1** $\log_m m^8 = 8$

**2** $2^{3\log_2 5} = 2^{\log_2 5^3}$
$= 5^3$
$= 125$

**3** $\log_3 (7x + 3) = 7$
$\therefore 7x + 3 = 3^7$
$7x + 3 = 2187$
$7x = 2184$
$x = 312$

**4** $0.4^n < 0.0002$
$\log_{10} 0.4^n < \log_{10} 0.0002$
$n\log_{10} 0.4 < \log_{10} 0.0002$
$n > \log_{10} 0.0002 \div \log_{10} 0.4$
$n > 9.295\,295\,58\ldots$
$\therefore$ the smallest integer for which $0.4^n < 0.0002$ is $n = 10$.

**5 a** In the first pass 12% of the impurities are removed.
Remaining impurities = 88%
In the second pass 12% of 88% are removed.
Remaining impurities = 88% of 88%
$= 77.44\%$

b After $n$ passes the remaining impurities $= 0.88^n$

If at least 95% are removed then less than 5% remain.

$$0.88^n < 0.05$$
$$\log_{10} 0.88^n < \log_{10} 0.05$$
$$n \log_{10} 0.88 < \log_{10} 0.05$$
$$n > \frac{\log_{10} 0.05}{\log_{10} 0.88}$$
$$n > 23.434\,6652\ldots$$

**The water would need to flow through the filter 24 times to be sure that at least 95% of the impurities are removed.**

## 4 Change of base ➲ p. 137

1  $\log_5 8 = \dfrac{\log_{10} 8}{\log_{10} 5}$
   $= 1.292\,029\,67\ldots$
   $= \mathbf{1.292}$  (3 d.p.)

2  $\log_9 27 = \dfrac{\log_3 27}{\log_3 9}$
   $= \dfrac{\log_3 3^3}{\log_3 3^2}$
   $= \dfrac{3\log_3 3}{2\log_3 3}$
   $= \dfrac{3}{2}$
   $= \mathbf{1.5}$

3  $\log_8 27 + \log_2 7 = \dfrac{\log_2 27}{\log_2 8} + \log_2 7$
   $= \dfrac{\log_2 27}{3} + \log_2 7$
   $= \dfrac{1}{3}\log_2 27 + \log_2 7$
   $= \log_2 27^{\frac{1}{3}} + \log_2 7$
   $= \log_2 3 + \log_2 7$
   $= \mathbf{\log_2 21}$

4  $\log_3 12 - \log_9 16 = \log_3 12 - \dfrac{\log_3 16}{\log_3 9}$
   $= \log_3 12 - \dfrac{\log_3 16}{2}$
   $= \log_3 12 - \dfrac{1}{2}\log_3 16$
   $= \log_3 12 - \log_3 4$
   $= \log_3 3$
   $= \mathbf{1}$

5  $\log_8 x + \log_4 x = 5$
   $\dfrac{\log_2 x}{\log_2 8} + \dfrac{\log_2 x}{\log_2 4} = 5$
   $\dfrac{\log_2 x}{3} + \dfrac{\log_2 x}{2} = 5$
   $2\log_2 x + 3\log_2 x = 30$
   $5\log_2 x = 30$
   $\log_2 x = 6$
   $x = 2^6$
   $= \mathbf{64}$

6  $\log_8 81 - \log_2\left(\sqrt[3]{3}\right) = \dfrac{\log_2 81}{\log_2 8} - \log_2 3^{\frac{1}{3}}$
   $= \dfrac{\log_2 81}{3} - \dfrac{1}{3}\log_2 3$
   $= \dfrac{1}{3}(\log_2 81 - \log_2 3)$
   $= \dfrac{1}{3}\log_2 27$
   $= \log_2 27^{\frac{1}{3}}$
   $= \mathbf{\log_2 3}$

## 5 Further applications of logs ➲ p. 138

1  $L = 10\log_{10}\left(\dfrac{P_2}{P_1}\right)$

Now $P_2 = 3P_1$

$\therefore\ L = 10\log_{10} 3$
   $= 4.771\,212\,54\ldots$
   $= 4.8\text{ dB}$  (1 d.p.)

**There is a 4.8 dB, to one decimal place, increase in the level of sound.**

2  $M = \log_{10}\left(\dfrac{I}{S}\right)$

Let $x$ be the intensity of the earlier earthquake.

$\therefore\ 6.3 = \log_{10}\left(\dfrac{x}{S}\right)$

The stronger earthquake had intensity $31.6x$.

$M = \log_{10}\left(\dfrac{31.6x}{S}\right)$
   $= \log_{10} 31.6 + \log_{10}\left(\dfrac{x}{S}\right)$
   $= 1.499\,687\,08\ldots + 6.3$
   $= 7.8$  (1 d.p.)

**The magnitude of the stronger earthquake was 7.8.**

3  $\text{pH} = \log_{10}\left(\dfrac{1}{a_{H^+}}\right)$
   $= \log_{10}\left(\dfrac{1}{7.8\times10^{-7}}\right)$
   $= 6.107\,905\,39\ldots$
   $= 6.1$  (1 d.p.)

**The pH of the solution is 6.1 to one decimal place.**

## THE EXPONENTIAL FUNCTION AND NATURAL LOGARITHMS

### 1 The number $e$ ➲ p. 139

1  $\dfrac{e^3}{2} = 10.042\,7684\ldots$
   $= \mathbf{10.04}$  (4 sig. fig.)

2  $\dfrac{5-3e}{4e+2} = -0.245\,072\,188\ldots$
   $= \mathbf{-0.245}$  (3 d.p.)

3  $\sqrt{e} = 1.648\,721\,27\ldots$
   $= \mathbf{1.6487}$  (4 d.p.)

## 2 The derivative of $e^x$ ⊃ p. 139

**1** $y = 4e^x$

$$\frac{dy}{dx} = 4e^x$$

**2** $y = 2 + e^x$

$$\frac{dy}{dx} = e^x$$

**3** $f(x) = 2e^x$

$f'(x) = 2e^x$

$f'(3) = \mathbf{2e^3}$

**4** $y = e^x$

$$\frac{dy}{dx} = e^x$$

When $x = 0$, $\dfrac{dy}{dx} = e^0$

$$= 1$$

∴ **the gradient of the tangent is 1.**

**5** $y = 5e^{4x}$

$$\frac{dy}{dx} = 5e^{4x} \times 4$$

$$= \mathbf{20e^{4x}}$$

**6** $y = \dfrac{e^x}{2} + e^{\frac{x}{2}}$

$$\frac{dy}{dx} = \frac{e^x}{2} + \frac{1}{2}e^{\frac{x}{2}}$$

$$= \mathbf{\frac{1}{2}\left(e^x + e^{\frac{x}{2}}\right)}$$

## 3 Natural logarithms ⊃ p. 140

**1** $\ln 4 = 1.386\,294\,36\ldots$

$\quad = \mathbf{1.386}$ (3 d.p.)

**2** $2\log_e 8 = 4.158\,883\,08\ldots$

$\quad = \mathbf{4.1589}$ (5 sig. fig.)

**3** $\dfrac{2\ln 9}{3\ln 6} = 0.817\,529\,590\ldots$

$\quad = \mathbf{0.8175}$ (4 d.p.)

## 4 The log laws with natural logs ⊃ p. 140

**1** $\ln \dfrac{1}{e^2} = \ln e^{-2}$

$\quad = \mathbf{-2}$

**2** $\log_e 36 - 2\log_e 3 = \log_e 36 - \log_e 3^2$

$\qquad\qquad = \log_e 36 - \log_e 9$

$\qquad\qquad = \mathbf{\log_e 4}$

**3** $\ln x + 5\ln 2 = 2\ln 4$

$\ln x + \ln 2^5 = \ln 4^2$

$\ln x + \ln 32 = \ln 16$

$\qquad \ln x = \ln 16 - \ln 32$

$\qquad\qquad = \ln \dfrac{16}{32}$

$\qquad\qquad = \ln \dfrac{1}{2}$

$\qquad\quad \therefore x = \mathbf{\dfrac{1}{2}}$

**4** $2\ln x = \ln(x + 12)$

$\ln x^2 = \ln(x + 12)$

$\therefore x^2 = x + 12$

$x^2 - x - 12 = 0$

$(x - 4)(x + 3) = 0$

$x = 4$ or $x = -3$

But $x > 0$,

$\qquad \therefore \mathbf{x = 4}$

**5** $\dfrac{1}{2}\ln\dfrac{1}{\sqrt{e}} = \dfrac{1}{2}\ln e^{-\frac{1}{2}}$

$\qquad\qquad = -\dfrac{1}{4}\ln e$

$\qquad\qquad = \mathbf{-\dfrac{1}{4}}$

# GRAPHS AND APPLICATIONS OF EXPONENTIAL AND LOGARITHMIC FUNCTIONS

## 1 Solving equations with exponentials ⊃ p. 141

**1** $e^x = 11$

$\therefore x = \ln 11$

$\quad = 2.397\,895\,27\ldots$

$\quad = \mathbf{2.398}$ (3 d.p.)

**2** $e^{3x} + 2 = 15$

$e^{3x} = 13$

$3x = \ln 13$

$x = \dfrac{1}{3}\ln 13$

$\quad = 0.854\,983\,119\ldots$

$\quad = \mathbf{0.8550}$ (4 d.p.)

**3** $7^x = 29$

$\ln 7^x = \ln 29$

$x\ln 7 = \ln 29$

$x = \dfrac{\ln 29}{\ln 7}$

$\quad = 1.730\,447\,74\ldots$

$\quad = \mathbf{1.730}$ (3 d.p.)

**4** $50\,000\,(1.07)^n = 75\,482$

$1.07^n = \dfrac{75\,482}{50\,000}$

$\ln 1.07^n = \ln\left(\dfrac{75\,482}{50\,000}\right)$

$n\ln 1.07 = \ln\left(\dfrac{75\,482}{50\,000}\right)$

$n = \ln\left(\dfrac{75\,482}{50\,000}\right) \div \ln 1.07$

$\quad = 6.087\,488\,01\ldots$

$\quad = \mathbf{6.1}$ (1 d.p.)

5  $6e^{2x-1} = 13$

$e^{2x-1} = \dfrac{13}{6}$

$2x - 1 = \ln\left(\dfrac{13}{6}\right)$

$2x = \ln\left(\dfrac{13}{6}\right) + 1$

$x = \dfrac{\ln\left(\dfrac{13}{6}\right) + 1}{2}$

$= 0.886\,594\,944...$

$= \mathbf{0.887}$   (3 d.p.)

## 2 Further graphs of exponential curves ⊃ p. 143

1  a

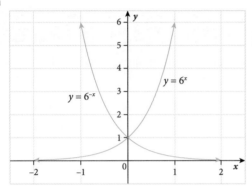

b  $6^x - 6^{-x} = 0$

∴ $6^x = 6^{-x}$

$\mathbf{x = 0}$

2  a  $y = 3^x - 3$

The equation of the asymptote is $y = -3$.

b        $y = 3^x - 3$

When $x = 0$,

$y = 3^0 - 3$

$= -2$

The curve cuts the $y$-axis at $y = -2$.

c  When $y = 0$,

$3^x - 3 = 0$

$3^x = 3$

$x = 1$

The curve cuts the $x$-axis at $(1, 0)$.

d

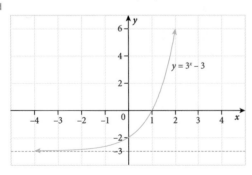

3  $\left(\dfrac{1}{2}\right)^x = (2^{-1})^x$

$= 2^{-x}$

**So the two functions are identical. The second graph is exactly the same as the first.**

4

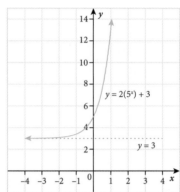

## 3 Further graphs of logarithmic curves ⊃ p. 144

1  a  $7\log_5 x = 4\log_5 x$

$3\log_5 x = 0$

$\log_5 x = 0$

$x = 1$

**The only point of intersection is $(1, 0)$.**

b

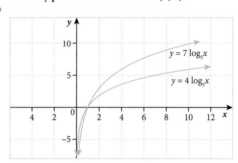

2  a      $y = \log_a x + c$

When $x = 1$, $y = -4$

$-4 = \log_a 1 + c$

But $\log_a 1 = 0$

∴ $\mathbf{c = -4}$

∴ $y = \log_a x - 4$

When $x = 4$, $y = -2$

$-2 = \log_a 4 - 4$

$2 = \log_a 4$

∴ $a^2 = 4$

$\mathbf{a = 2}$   $(a > 0)$

b  $y = \log_2 x - 4$

When $y = 0$,

$0 = \log_2 x - 4$

$\log_2 x = 4$

$x = 2^4$

$= 16$

**The curve cuts the $x$-axis at $(16, 0)$.**

**3 a** $y = \log_8 x + \dfrac{1}{3}$

When $y = 0$,

$$\log_8 x + \dfrac{1}{3} = 0$$

$$\log_8 x = -\dfrac{1}{3}$$

$$x = 8^{-\frac{1}{3}}$$

$$= \dfrac{1}{2}$$

**The curve cuts the $x$-axis at $\left(\dfrac{1}{2}, 0\right)$.**

**b** When $x = 4$,

$$y = \log_8 4 + \dfrac{1}{3}$$

$$= \dfrac{\log_2 4}{\log_2 8} + \dfrac{1}{3}$$

$$= \dfrac{2\log_2 2}{3\log_2 2} + \dfrac{1}{3}$$

$$= \dfrac{2}{3} + \dfrac{1}{3}$$

$$= 1$$

**c**

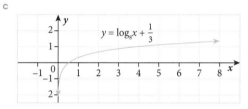

## 4 Applications of exponential functions ⊃ p. 145

**1** 3% p.a. = 0.25% per month

Now $A = P(1 + r)^n$

$$60\,000 = 30\,000(1 + 0.0025)^n$$

$$2 = 1.0025^n$$

$$\ln 2 = \ln 1.0025^n$$

$$= n \ln 1.0025$$

So $n = \dfrac{\ln 2}{\ln 1.0025}$

$$= 277.605\,301\ldots$$

$$\approx 278 \text{ months}$$

**The amount takes about 23 years and 2 months to double.**

**2 a** $M = M_0 e^{-0.04t}$, $M_0 = 100$

$$\therefore M = 100e^{-0.04t}$$

When $t = 6$,

$$M = 100e^{-0.04 \times 6}$$

$$= 78.662\,7861\ldots$$

$$= 78.7 \quad (1 \text{ d.p.})$$

**After 6 years the mass of the substance is about 78.7 g.**

**b** $50 = 100e^{-0.04t}$

$$0.5 = e^{-0.04t}$$

$$\ln 0.5 = \ln e^{-0.04t}$$

$$= -0.04t$$

$$t = \ln 0.5 \div -0.04$$

$$= 17.328\,6795\ldots$$

$$\approx 17 \text{ years}$$

**After about 17 years half of the mass will remain.**

**3 a** Let $t = 0$ at the beginning of 2010.

$$\therefore P(0) = 1\,500\,000$$

So $P(t) = 1\,500\,000e^{kt}$

Now $P(7) = 1\,800\,000$

So $1\,500\,000e^{k \times 7} = 1\,800\,000$

$$e^{7k} = 1.2$$

$$\ln e^{7k} = \ln 1.2$$

$$7k = \ln 1.2$$

$$k = \dfrac{1}{7}\ln 1.2$$

**b** At the beginning of 2030, $t = 20$

$$P(20) = 1\,500\,000e^{k \times 20}$$

$$= 2\,525\,360.54\ldots$$

**So the expected population at the beginning of 2030 is about 2.5 million.**

**c** $1\,500\,000e^{kt} = 4\,000\,000$

$$e^{kt} = \dfrac{8}{3}$$

$$kt = \ln \dfrac{8}{3}$$

$$t = \dfrac{1}{k}\ln \dfrac{8}{3}$$

$$= 37.657\,6686\ldots$$

$$= 37.7 \text{ years} \quad (1 \text{ d.p.})$$

**∴ the population should reach 4 million in the year 2047.**

**4 a** $M = M_0 e^{-kt}$

But $M_0 = 12$

$$\therefore M = 12e^{-kt}$$

When $t = 256$, $M = 6$.

$$6 = 12e^{-k \times 256}$$

$$0.5 = e^{-256k}$$

$$\ln 0.5 = -256k$$

$$\dfrac{\ln 0.5}{-256} = k$$

But $\ln 0.5 = \ln 2^{-1}$

$$= -\ln 2$$

So $\dfrac{-\ln 2}{-256} = k$

$$\therefore k = \dfrac{\ln 2}{256}$$

**b** $M = 12e^{-kt}$

When $t = 50$,

$$M = 12e^{-50k}$$

$$= 10.480\,6043\ldots$$

$$= 10.5 \quad (1 \text{ d.p.})$$

**So the mass present after 50 years is about 10.5 g.**

**So the mass has reduced by about 1.5 g in 50 years.**

## YEAR 11 EXAM-TYPE QUESTIONS

### Part A

**1 C** $\log_2 4 = 2$ and $\log_2 8 = 3$

So $\log_2 7$ will lie between 2 and 3.

**2 A** $\log_a x - \log_a y = \log_a \dfrac{x}{y}$

**3  D**  $\log_9 27 = \dfrac{\log_3 27}{\log_3 9}$

$\qquad\qquad = \dfrac{3}{2}$

---

**4  D**  $\ln e^{x^2} = x^2$

---

**5  C**  Of the options only $y = 2\log_3 x + 1$ passes through $(1, 1)$, $(3, 3)$ and $(9, 5)$.

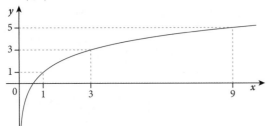

---

**6  A**  $\dfrac{\log_x 8}{\log_x 2} = \dfrac{\log_x 2^3}{\log_x 2}$

$\qquad\qquad = \dfrac{3\log_x 2}{\log_x 2}$

$\qquad\qquad = 3$

---

**7  B**  $\log_a 3 + \log_a 5 = \log_a(3 \times 5)$

$\qquad\qquad\qquad = \log_a 15$

---

**8  B**  $\dfrac{d}{dx}(3e^x) = 3e^x$

---

**9  D**  $\log_a x = 1.11$

$\log_a a^2 x = \log_a a^2 + \log_a x$

$\qquad\qquad = 2 + \log_a x$

$\qquad\qquad = 2 + 1.11$

$\qquad\qquad = 3.11$

---

**10  B**  Consider each option:

$\log_e \dfrac{1}{2} = \log_e 2^{-1} = -\log_e 2$

$3 + \log_e e = 3 + 1 = 4$

$\log_e 1 = 0$

$\log_e 8 = \log_e 2^3$

$\qquad\quad = 3\log_e 2$

So $3 + \log_e e = 3e$ is not correct.

---

**11  C**  $7\log_5 9 = \dfrac{7\ln 9}{\ln 5}$

$\qquad\qquad = 9.55648672\ldots$

$\qquad\qquad = 9.556 \quad (3 \text{ d.p.})$

---

**12  A**  $\log_a\left(\dfrac{1}{4}\right) = \log_a 4^{-1}$

$\qquad\qquad\quad = -\log_a 4$

So statement I is correct.

$\log_a\left(\dfrac{1}{4}\right) = \log_a\left(\dfrac{1}{2}\right)^2$

$\qquad\qquad\quad = 2\log_a\left(\dfrac{1}{2}\right)$

So both statements are correct.

---

**Part B**

**13**  $\log_e 7 = 1.94591014\ldots$

$\qquad\quad = \mathbf{1.95} \quad (3 \text{ sig. fig.})$ ✓

---

**14  a**  $y = e^x + 8$

$\qquad \dfrac{dy}{dx} = e^x$ ✓

$\;\;$**b**  $y = 8e^{2x}$

$\qquad \dfrac{dy}{dx} = 8e^{2x} \times 2$

$\qquad\qquad = \mathbf{16e^{2x}}$ ✓

---

**15  a**  $\log_3 27 = \log_3 3^3$

$\qquad\qquad = \mathbf{3}$ ✓

$\;\;$**b**  $\log_6 18 + \log_6 12 = \log_6(18 \times 12)$

$\qquad\qquad\qquad\quad = \log_6 216$ ✓

$\qquad\qquad\qquad\quad = \log_6 6^3$

$\qquad\qquad\qquad\quad = \mathbf{3}$ ✓

$\;\;$**c**  $\log_a 2 + \log_a \dfrac{1}{2} = \log_a\left(2 \times \dfrac{1}{2}\right)$

$\qquad\qquad\qquad\quad = \log_a 1$ ✓

$\qquad\qquad\qquad\quad = \mathbf{0}$ ✓

---

**16**  $\dfrac{1}{4}\log_a 16 = 6\log_a 2 - \log_a x$

$\quad \log_a 16^{\frac{1}{4}} = \log_a 2^6 - \log_a x$

$\qquad \log_a 2 = \log_a 64 - \log_a x$ ✓

$\qquad \log_a x = \log_a 64 - \log_a 2$

$\qquad\qquad = \log_a 32$

$\qquad \therefore \boldsymbol{x = 32}$ ✓

---

**17**  $a^{3.17} = 9$

$\;\;$**a**  $\boldsymbol{\log_a 9 = 3.17}$ ✓

$\;\;$**b**  $\log_a\left(\dfrac{1}{81}\right) = \log_a 9^{-2}$

$\qquad\qquad\qquad = -2\log_a 9$ ✓

$\qquad\qquad\qquad = -2 \times 3.17$

$\qquad\qquad\qquad = \mathbf{-6.34}$ ✓

---

**18**

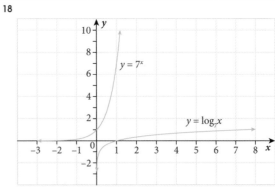

✓✓

---

**19**  $e^x = 5$

$\quad x = \ln 5$

$\qquad = 1.60943791\ldots$

$\qquad = \mathbf{1.6094} \quad (4 \text{ d.p.})$ ✓

---

**20**  $\log_m 2 = 0.63 \quad \log_m 5 = 1.46$

$\quad \log_m 40 = \log_m(8 \times 5)$

$\qquad\qquad = \log_m 8 + \log_m 5$

$\qquad\qquad = \log_m 2^3 + \log_m 5$ ✓

---

$$= 3 \log_m 2 + \log_m 5$$
$$= 3 \times 0.63 + 1.46$$
$$= \mathbf{3.35} \quad \checkmark$$

**21** 
$$2 \ln x = \ln (2x + 8)$$
$$\ln x^2 = \ln (2x + 8)$$
$$\therefore x^2 = 2x + 8 \quad \checkmark$$
$$x^2 - 2x - 8 = 0$$
$$(x - 4)(x + 2) = 0$$
$$x - 4 = 0 \quad \text{or} \quad x + 2 = 0$$
$$x = 4 \quad \text{or} \quad x = -2 \quad \checkmark$$
But $x > 0$,
$$\therefore \boldsymbol{x = 4} \quad \checkmark$$

**22 a** $\quad M = M_0 e^{-kt}$
$$M_0 = 500, \quad M = 400 \text{ when } t = 87$$
$$400 = 500 e^{-k \times 87}$$
$$\frac{4}{5} = e^{-87k} \quad \checkmark$$
$$\ln \frac{4}{5} = \ln e^{-87k}$$
$$-87k = \ln \frac{4}{5}$$
$$k = \frac{-\ln \frac{4}{5}}{87} \quad \checkmark$$
But $-\ln \dfrac{4}{5} = \ln \left(\dfrac{4}{5}\right)^{-1}$
$$= \ln \frac{5}{4}$$
$$= \ln 1.25$$
$$\therefore k = \frac{\mathbf{\ln 1.25}}{\mathbf{87}} \quad \checkmark$$

**b** After a further 23 days, $t = 87 + 23$
$$= 110$$
$$M = 500 e^{-k \times 110}$$
$$= 377.085\,734...$$
**So approximately 377 g will remain after a further 23 days.** $\quad \checkmark$

**23** 
$$0.8^n < 0.007$$
$$\ln 0.8^n < \ln 0.007$$
$$n \ln 0.8 < \ln 0.007 \quad \checkmark$$
$$n > \frac{\ln 0.007}{\ln 0.8} \quad \checkmark$$
$$n > 22.236\,1125...$$
**So the smallest integer $n$ such that $0.8^n < 0.007$ is 23.** $\quad \checkmark$

**24 a** $\quad G = 10 \log_{10} \left(\dfrac{P}{P_0}\right)$

Now $P = \dfrac{V^2}{R}$ where $R$ is a constant. So $P_0 = \dfrac{V_0^2}{R}$.

$$G = 10 \log_{10} \left(\frac{\frac{V^2}{R}}{\frac{V_0^2}{R}}\right)$$
$$= 10 \log_{10} \left(\frac{V^2}{V_0^2}\right) \quad \checkmark$$
$$= 10 \log_{10} \left(\frac{V}{V_0}\right)^2$$
$$= \mathbf{20 \log_{10}} \left(\frac{\boldsymbol{V}}{\boldsymbol{V_0}}\right) \quad \checkmark$$

**b** When $V = 5$ and $V_0 = 0.02$,
$$G = 20 \log_{10} \left(\frac{5}{0.02}\right)$$
$$= 47.958\,8001...$$
$$= 48 \quad \text{(nearest unit)}$$
**The gain is about 48 decibels.** $\quad \checkmark$

**25 a**

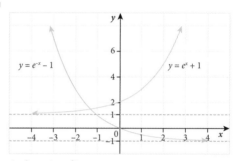

$\checkmark\checkmark$

**b** At the point of intersection
$$e^x + 1 = e^{-x} - 1$$
$$e^x - e^{-x} + 2 = 0 \quad \checkmark$$
$$e^x(e^x - e^{-x} + 2) = e^x \times 0$$
$$e^{2x} - e^0 + 2e^x = 0$$
$$\boldsymbol{e^{2x} + 2e^x - 1 = 0} \quad \checkmark$$

**c** Let $u = e^x$
$$u^2 + 2u - 1 = 0$$
$$u = \frac{-b \pm \sqrt{b^2 - 4ac}}{2a}$$
$$= \frac{-2 \pm \sqrt{2^2 - 4 \times 1 \times -1}}{2 \times 1}$$
$$= \frac{-2 \pm \sqrt{8}}{2}$$
$$= \frac{-2 \pm 2\sqrt{2}}{2}$$
$$= -1 \pm \sqrt{2} \quad \checkmark$$
So $e^x = -1 + \sqrt{2}$ or $e^x = -1 - \sqrt{2}$
$$= 0.414\,213\,562... \text{ or } -2.414\,213\,56...$$
But $e^x > 0$ for all values of $x$.
So $e^x = 0.414\,213\,562...$ $\quad \checkmark$
$$x = \ln(0.414\,213\,562...)$$
$$= -0.881\,373\,58...$$
$$= \boldsymbol{-0.88} \quad \text{(2 d.p.)} \quad \checkmark$$

# PROBABILITY AND DISCRETE PROBABILITY DISTRIBUTIONS

## Probability and Venn diagrams

### 1 The probability of an event

→ **Outcomes** of experiments are the results that could possibly occur. For example, if a coin is tossed the possible outcomes are a head or a tail.

→ Outcomes are **equally likely** if every outcome has an equal chance of occurring.

→ The **sample space** is the set of all possible outcomes of an event.

→ If each of the outcomes that produce event $A$ are equally likely then the **probability of event** $A$, $P(A)$, is given by:

$$P(A) = \frac{\text{number of outcomes that produce } A}{\text{total number of outcomes}}.$$

→ If an event is **impossible** the probability is **zero**. If an event is **certain** the probability is **one**. In all other cases the probability will be **between 0 and 1**.

### EXAMPLE 1

A dice is tossed once. What is the probability that the number shown on the uppermost face is:

a  5?

b  an even number?

c  less than 5?

a  $P(5) = \dfrac{1}{6}$

There are six equally likely outcomes.

b  $P(\text{even}) = \dfrac{3}{6} = \dfrac{1}{2}$

There are three favourable outcomes.

c  $P(<5) = \dfrac{4}{6} = \dfrac{2}{3}$

### EXAMPLE 2

500 tickets are sold in a raffle. What is the probability that you will win first prize if you buy 20 tickets? Give the answer as a percentage.

$P(\text{winning}) = \dfrac{20}{500} \times 100\%$

$= 4\%$

Probability is often given as a fraction, but can also be expressed as a decimal or percentage.

### EXAMPLE 3

'When I arrive at any set of traffic lights, there are three possible outcomes; the lights could be red, amber or green. Therefore the probability that a particular set of lights will be amber when I reach them is $\dfrac{1}{3}$.' Briefly explain why this statement is false.

The statement is false because the set of lights are not equally likely to display each of the three colours. The lights are amber for a much shorter time than they are either red or green and so the probability that they will be amber is much less than $\dfrac{1}{3}$.

It is important in probability to consider whether the outcomes are equally likely. Many false statements result from failing to observe this rule.

### → PRACTICE

1  A dice is tossed once. What is the probability that the number shown on the uppermost face is:
   a  2?
   b  an odd number?
   c  more than 4?

2  750 tickets are sold in a raffle. What is the probability that you will win first prize if you buy 15 tickets? Give the answer as a percentage.

3  'Tomorrow it might rain or it might not. Therefore the probability that it will rain tomorrow is $\dfrac{1}{2}$.' Briefly explain why this statement is false.

4*  A bag holds five red, four green and three blue marbles. If one marble is chosen at random, what is the probability that it is:
   a  red?
   b  yellow?
   c  red, green or blue?
   d  red or blue?

Answers ⊃ p. 176

## 2 Relative frequency

→ In an **experiment or trial** the **frequency** of an event is the number of times that event occurs.

→ The **relative frequency** is found by dividing the frequency of the event by the total frequency.

→ The relative frequency can be used to predict **future outcomes**.

→ Using a large number of trials gives a **more accurate** relative frequency which in turn is **more effective** at future predictions.

### EXAMPLE 1

A spinner has sectors in five different colours. It was spun a number of times and the results are shown in this table.

| Red | Green | Pink | Yellow | Blue |
|-----|-------|------|--------|------|
| 6   | 7     | 6    | 5      | 8    |

a   What is the relative frequency of pink?

b   Based on these results how many times would you expect to land on blue in 50 spins?

a   Total frequency = 6 + 7 + 6 + 5 + 8

$$= 32$$

Relative frequency of pink $= \dfrac{6}{32}$

$$= \dfrac{3}{16}$$

b   Relative frequency of blue $= \dfrac{8}{32}$

$$= \dfrac{1}{4}$$

Expected number of blue in 50 spins $= \dfrac{1}{4} \times 50$

$$= 12.5$$

*It is only possible to get blue a whole number of times, but the expected result gives us an idea of about how many times it should occur.*

### EXAMPLE 2

A coin was tossed 60 times. The relative frequency of the coin showing a head was $\dfrac{2}{5}$.

a   How many times did the coin show a tail?

b   The coin was tossed a further 40 times. If the relative frequency of a head on this second trial was $\dfrac{3}{5}$, what is the relative frequency of tails for the whole experiment? (Give the answer as a decimal.)

a   Number of heads $= \dfrac{2}{5} \times 60$

$$= 24$$

Number of tails = 60 – 24

$$= 36$$

b   Second trial:
Number of heads $= \dfrac{3}{5} \times 40$

$$= 24$$

Number of tails = 40 – 24

$$= 16$$

Whole experiment:
Total tails = 36 + 16

$$= 52$$

Total tosses = 60 + 40

$$= 100$$

Relative frequency of tails $= \dfrac{52}{100}$

$$= 0.52$$

*Because there were a different number of tosses in each trial it isn't correct to just average the two results.*

### → PRACTICE

1   A dice was rolled a number of times and the results are shown in the table.

| 1 | 2 | 3 | 4 | 5 | 6 |
|---|---|---|---|---|---|
| 3 | 5 | 4 | 6 | 4 | 2 |

a   What is the relative frequency of 5?

b   Based on these results, how many times would you expect to roll 4 in 30 rolls of the dice?

2   A coin was tossed 30 times. The relative frequency of the coin showing a tail was $\dfrac{7}{15}$.

a   How many times did the coin show a head?

b   The coin was tossed a further 50 times. If the relative frequency of a tail on this second trial was $\dfrac{14}{25}$, what is the relative frequency of heads for the whole experiment? (Give the answer as a decimal.)

3*  A survey had three possible responses: 'yes', 'no' or 'don't know'. The relative frequency of 'yes' was $\dfrac{2}{9}$ and the relative frequency of 'no' was $\dfrac{1}{3}$.

a   What was the relative frequency of 'don't know'?

b   If 72 people responded to the survey, how many answered 'no'?

Answers ⊃ p. 176

## 3 Multi-stage events

→ **Multi-stage events** are events which have more than one simple stage.

→ The **outcome of a subsequent stage** might or might not depend upon the result of the previous stage.

→ The **number of possible outcomes** for a multi-stage event is found by multiplying the number of outcomes at each stage.

→ An **array, table or list** might help us keep track of possible outcomes.

→ The probability that $A$ and $B$ will both occur, called the **product of $A$ and $B$**, is given by $P(AB) = P(A) \times P(B)$.

### EXAMPLE 1

**Seven people are standing for an election. In how many different ways can their names appear on the ballot paper?**

Number of arrangements $= 7 \times 6 \times 5 \times 4 \times 3 \times 2 \times 1$
$$= 5040$$
The names could appear in 5040 different arrangements.

There are seven choices for first position. Once the first place has been chosen there are six choices for second, and so on.

Factorial notation is a way of writing a product such as this one. The symbol ! means factorial. $3! = 3 \times 2 \times 1$ and $5! = 5 \times 4 \times 3 \times 2 \times 1$. You may use this notation if you wish but it is not required for this course.

### EXAMPLE 2

**Five cards are placed in a hat. The cards are identical except that one card is marked with an A, one with a H, one with a Y and two with P. If a card is drawn at random and placed on a table, followed by another, and so on until all five cards are laid out in the order in which they were drawn, what is the probability that they spell HAPPY?**

$P(\text{HAPPY}) = P(\text{H}) \times P(\text{A}) \times P(\text{P}) \times P(\text{P}) \times P(\text{Y})$
$$= \frac{1}{5} \times \frac{1}{4} \times \frac{2}{3} \times \frac{1}{2} \times 1$$
$$= \frac{1}{60}$$

The probability that the cards spell HAPPY is $\frac{1}{60}$.

Originally there are five cards and one shows H. Once H has been selected there are four cards left and one shows A. Then there are three cards left and two show P. Then one of two cards show P and the final card is Y.

### EXAMPLE 3

**Sam buys four tickets in a raffle in which 100 tickets are sold. Two different tickets are drawn for the first and second prize. What is the probability that Sam wins both prizes?**

$P(\text{both prizes}) = P(\text{first}) \times P(\text{second})$
$$= \frac{4}{100} \times \frac{3}{99}$$
$$= \frac{1}{825}$$

∴ the probability that Sam wins both prizes is $\frac{1}{825}$.

Sam has four tickets out of 100 at first, but if he wins first prize he only has three tickets left and there are 99 tickets left.

### EXAMPLE 4

**A biased coin is twice as likely to show heads as tails.**

a   **What is the probability that it shows heads when it is tossed?**

b   **Troy plays a game in which he tosses the coin and then rolls a dice (which is equally likely to land on any of its six sides, numbered one to six). List all the possible results.**

c   **What is the probability that Troy throws a head and a six?**

a   There are two chances of tossing heads and one of tails.
$$P(\text{heads}) = \frac{2}{3}$$

b

| H1 | H2 | H3 | H4 | H5 | H6 |
|----|----|----|----|----|----|
| T1 | T2 | T3 | T4 | T5 | T6 |

c   $P(\text{H6}) = \frac{2}{3} \times \frac{1}{6} = \frac{1}{9}$

Although there are 12 arrangements, they are not equally likely.

→ **PRACTICE**

1  A concert program is made up of eight different acts. In how many different ways could the acts be arranged?

..............................................................

2  A box holds four cards. The cards are identical except for the letters written on them. One card has D, one card has F and two cards show O. If the cards are drawn at random, one after the other, and laid out on a table in the order that they are drawn, what is the probability that they spell FOOD?

..............................................................

3  Sara buys five tickets in a raffle in which 200 tickets are sold. Two different tickets are drawn for the first and second prize. What is the probability that Sara wins both prizes?

..............................................................

4  A biased coin is three times as likely to show tails as heads.

   a  What is the probability that it shows tails when it is tossed?

   b  Erin plays a game in which she tosses two coins, the biased one and a fair one. List all the possible results.

   c  What is the probability that Erin throws two tails?

..............................................................

5*  50 tickets are sold in a raffle. Kelly buys six tickets. Three different tickets are drawn for the first, second and third prizes. What is the probability that Kelly:

   a  wins first prize?

   b  wins all three prizes?

   c  does **not** win a prize?

Answers ⊃ pp. 176–177

## 4 Tree diagrams

→ A **tree diagram** is a tool that helps to keep track of certain probabilities.

→ When the outcomes of different events are not equally likely the **probabilities** can be written on the **branches** of the tree.

→ The **sum of all the probabilities** on branches beginning at a single point must always be **one**.

### EXAMPLE 1

a  A family consists of four children. Assuming that each child has an equal chance of being a girl or a boy, draw a tree diagram showing the possible makeup of the family.

b  What is the probability that the family is made up of:

   i  four boys?

   ii  two girls and two boys?

   iii  at least two girls?

   iv  the oldest and youngest being the same sex?

a
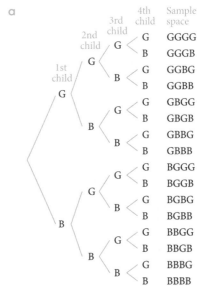

b  i  $P(BBBB) = \dfrac{1}{16}$

   ii  $P(2\text{girls}, 2\text{ boys}) = \dfrac{6}{16}$

      $= \dfrac{3}{8}$

   iii  $P(\text{at least 2 girls}) = \dfrac{11}{16}$

   iv  $P(\text{first and last same}) = \dfrac{8}{16}$

      $= \dfrac{1}{2}$

Logically, it doesn't matter what the first child is, there is a fifty-fifty chance that the last child will be the same sex.

### EXAMPLE 2

A box holds four blue and three red discs. One disc is selected at random, the colour noted and the disc replaced. A second disc is then selected.

a  Draw a tree diagram to show the possible outcomes.

b  What is the probability that:

   i  both discs are blue?

   ii  both discs are red?

   iii  one disc is blue and one is red?

**a**

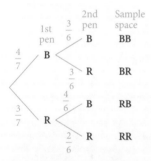

1st disc $\frac{4}{7}$

2nd disc / Sample space

$\frac{4}{7}$ B — B — BB

B — $\frac{3}{7}$ R — BR

$\frac{3}{7}$ R — $\frac{4}{7}$ B — RB

$\frac{3}{7}$ R — RR

> Writing the probabilities on the branches simplifies the tree diagram.

**b  i**  $P(\text{BB}) = \dfrac{4}{7} \times \dfrac{4}{7}$

$= \dfrac{16}{49}$

> The outcomes are not equally likely.

**ii**  $P(\text{RR}) = \dfrac{3}{7} \times \dfrac{3}{7}$

$= \dfrac{9}{49}$

**iii**  $P(\text{1 red, 1 blue}) = P(\text{BR}) + P(\text{RB})$

$= \dfrac{4}{7} \times \dfrac{3}{7} + \dfrac{3}{7} \times \dfrac{4}{7}$

$= \dfrac{24}{49}$

## EXAMPLE 3

There are four black and three red pens in a box. Two pens are removed, one after the other without replacement. What is the probability that the pens are the same colour?

1st pen / 2nd pen $\frac{3}{6}$ / Sample space

$\frac{4}{7}$ B — $\frac{3}{6}$ B — BB

B — $\frac{3}{6}$ R — BR

$\frac{3}{7}$ R — $\frac{4}{6}$ B — RB

R — $\frac{2}{6}$ R — RR

$P(\text{same colour}) = P(\text{BB}) + P(\text{RR})$

$= \dfrac{4}{7} \times \dfrac{3}{6} + \dfrac{3}{7} \times \dfrac{2}{6}$

$= \dfrac{3}{7}$

> For the first pen drawn, four out of seven are black and three out of seven are red. After the first pen has been selected only six pens remain. If the first pen was black, three of the remaining pens are black and three are red. If the first pen was red, four of the remaining pens are black and two are red.

## EXAMPLE 4

The chance of the person going first winning a game of chance is 0.5. The chance of that person losing is 0.4 and there is a 0.1 chance of a draw. If Gareth goes first in two games, what is the probability that he wins at least one game?

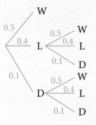

0.5 W

    0.5 W
0.4 L   0.4 L
    0.1 D

0.1 D
    0.5 W
    0.4 L
    0.1 D

> A tree diagram can be simplified by only showing the outcomes that are required. If Gareth wins the first game it doesn't matter what happens in the second game because he has scored at least one win.

$P(\text{wins at least 1 game})$
$= 0.5 + 0.4 \times 0.5 + 0.1 \times 0.5$
$= 0.75$

### → PRACTICE

**1**  A coin is tossed three times. Draw a tree diagram showing the possible results. What is the probability that:

  **a**  all show heads?

  **b**  there are two heads and one tail?

  **c**  there are at least two tails?

  **d**  the first and last toss are the same?

**2**  A box holds five green and two yellow tickets. One ticket is selected at random, the colour noted and the ticket replaced. A second ticket is then selected.

  **a**  Draw a tree diagram to show the possible outcomes.

  **b**  What is the probability that:

    **i**  both tickets are green?

    **ii**  both tickets are yellow?

    **iii**  one ticket is green and one is yellow?

**3**  There are five green and two blue marbles in a bag. Two marbles are removed, one after the other without replacement. What is the probability that the marbles are the same colour?

**4**  The chance of the person who has the first turn in a game winning the game is 0.6. The chance of that person losing is 0.3 and there is a 0.1 chance of a draw. If Bernadette goes first in two games, what is the probability that she loses at least one game?

5* There are six white and four red balls in a box. Two are selected at random, one after the other, without replacement.

a Draw a tree diagram to show the possible outcomes.

b Ted comments that there is a slightly better than 50 per cent chance that the balls will be different colours. Do you agree? Justify your answer.

Answers ➲ p. 177

## 5 Venn diagrams

➜ A Venn diagram is a **tool** used in probability.

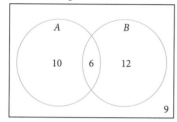

➜ A Venn diagram is made up of **intersecting circles.** Each circle represents a particular event and the numbers involved with that event are shown. Numbers found in the overlapping parts of the circles are those involved in both of the intersecting circles. For example, in this Venn diagram there are 10 + 6 = 16 for event $A$, six of those are also involved in event $B$. Nine are not involved in either event.

### EXAMPLE 1

A Venn diagram has been drawn to show the number of children who have won one or more ribbons of different colours in a sports competition. The ribbons are either blue, red or yellow.

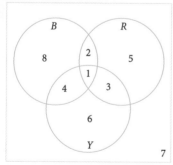

a Altogether, how many children won blue ribbons?

b How many children won both blue and red ribbons but not yellow?

c What is the probability that a child, chosen at random from the group, has won a yellow ribbon?

d What is the probability that a child has won ribbons in at least two different colours?

a Number winning blue ribbons
$= 8 + 2 + 1 + 4$
$= 15$

> Add all the numbers found in the circle marked B for blue.

b Number winning both blue and red but not yellow $= 2$

> This is the number that lies in both the blue and red circles, but not in the yellow one.

c Total in the group $= 15 + 5 + 3 + 6 + 7$
$= 36$

> There is a 7 lying outside the circles. So seven children would not have won any ribbons.

Number winning yellow $= 6 + 4 + 1 + 3$
$= 14$

$P(\text{yellow}) = \dfrac{14}{36}$

$= \dfrac{7}{18}$

d Number winning at least 2 different ribbons
$= 2 + 4 + 1 + 3$
$= 10$

$P(\text{at least 2 ribbons}) = \dfrac{10}{36}$

$= \dfrac{5}{18}$

### EXAMPLE 2

In a group of 150 students, 87 study physics, 72 study chemistry and 39 study both.

a Show the information in a Venn diagram.

b What is the probability that one of the students, selected at random, studies neither physics nor chemistry?

a

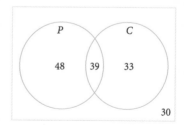

> First fill in the 39 who study both. Then 87 − 39 = 48 study physics only and 72 − 39 = 33 study chemistry only. The total must be 150 so 30 lies outside the intersecting circles meaning these students study neither.

b $P(\text{study neither}) = \dfrac{30}{150}$

$= \dfrac{1}{5}$

## EXAMPLE 3

Of the 72 people working at a particular business, all but four regularly travel to work by either car, bus or train or some combination of these. Altogether 36 travel by car, 22 by bus and 31 by train. If five travel by both bus and car, eight by both bus and train and 10 by both car and train, what is the probability that a worker chosen at random travels by car, bus and train to get to work?

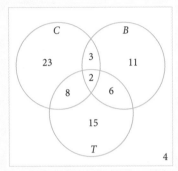

Number travelling = 72 − 4

$\qquad = 68$

Now 36 + 22 + 31 = 89

$\qquad$ Difference = 89 − 68

$\qquad = 21$

Number travelling by at least 2 different means

= 5 + 8 + 10

= 23

Number travelling by all 3 = 23 − 21

$\qquad = 2$

$P(\text{travels by all 3}) = \dfrac{2}{72}$

$\qquad = \dfrac{1}{36}$

Using a Venn diagram makes it easy to check that all the numbers are correct.

### → PRACTICE

1  A Venn diagram has been drawn to show the number of athletes who have won one or more medals (either gold, silver or bronze) in a sports competition.

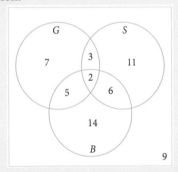

a  Altogether, how many athletes won gold medals?

b  How many athletes won both silver and bronze medals but not gold?

c  What is the probability that an athlete, chosen at random from the group, has won a silver medal?

d  What is the probability that an athlete has won medals of at least two different types?

2  In a group of 120 students, 68 study history, 45 study economics and 26 study both.

a  Show the information in a Venn diagram.

b  What is the probability that one of the students, selected at random, studies neither history nor economics?

3  Of the 84 people taking part in a triathlon, all but nine responded to a survey about the best leg of the race. Altogether 46 mentioned the swim leg, 39 the cycle leg and 28 the run. Of those, 19 mentioned both the swim and cycle legs, 11 the cycle and run, and 14 the swim and run. What is the probability that one of the competitors, chosen at random, mentioned all three legs of the race?

4*  A Venn diagram was drawn to show the results when a group of people were asked which of three fruits they had eaten the previous day, but some of the results are missing. Altogether 41 ate an apple, 38 ate a banana and 42 ate an orange.

a  Find the values of $x$, $y$ and $z$.

b  What is the probability that one of the people, chosen at random, ate an apple and banana but not an orange?

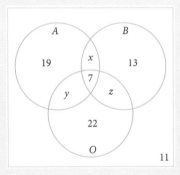

Answers ⊃ p. 178

## 6 Set notation

→ A **set** is a **group of objects** and each object belonging to the set is a member or **element** of the set. The elements in a set are shown in braces; for example, the set of odd numbers between 2 and 10 is {3, 5, 7, 9}.

→ The **sample space** is the set that contains **all possible outcomes** and is usually denoted by $S$.

→ If $A$ is an event then the **complement** of $A$ is the event that $A$ does not occur and is usually denoted by $\bar{A}$.

→ $A \cap B$ is the **intersection** of $A$ and $B$ and consists of all elements that are in $A$ and also in $B$.

→ $A \cup B$ is the **union** of $A$ and $B$ and consists of all elements in $A$ and all elements in $B$ (and both).

→ If there are no elements in a set it is called the **null set**.

## EXAMPLE 1

Suppose $S$ is the set of positive integers less than 10 and that $A$ is the set of even numbers and that $B$ is the set of prime numbers. Write down the sets:

a $\bar{A}$

b $A \cup B$

c $A \cap B$

d $\bar{A} \cup B$

e $A \cap \bar{B}$

$A = \{2, 4, 6, 8\}, \quad B = \{2, 3, 5, 7\}$

a $\bar{A} = \{1, 3, 5, 7, 9\}$

b $A \cup B = \{2, 3, 4, 5, 6, 7, 8\}$

c $A \cap B = \{2\}$       *$A \cap B$ is a subset of both set $A$ and set $B$.*

d $\bar{A} \cup B = \{1, 2, 3, 5, 7, 9\}$

e $\bar{B} = \{1, 4, 6, 8, 9\}$

    $A \cap \bar{B} = \{4, 6, 8\}$

## EXAMPLE 2

Find:

a $P(X \cap Y)$

b $P(X \cup Y)$

c $P(\bar{X} \cap Y)$

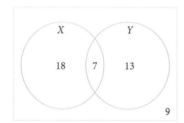

a   Total $= 18 + 7 + 13 + 9$

        $= 47$

   $P(X \cap Y) = \dfrac{7}{47}$

b   $18 + 7 + 13 = 38$

   $P(X \cup Y) = \dfrac{38}{47}$

c   $P(\bar{X} \cap Y) = \dfrac{13}{47}$      *This is the probability that an element lies in $Y$ but not in $X$.*

## EXAMPLE 3

Using set notation, what does the shaded region in the diagram represent?

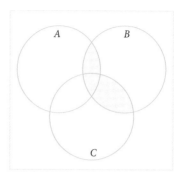

*Everything in $B$ that is also in $A$ or $C$ or both*

$B \cap (A \cup C)$

→ **PRACTICE**

1   Suppose $S$ is the set of positive integers less than 20 and that $A$ is the set of odd numbers and that $B$ is the set of multiples of 3. Write down the sets:

   a $\bar{A}$

   b $A \cup B$

   c $A \cap B$

   d $\bar{A} \cup B$

   e $A \cap \bar{B}$

2   Find:

   a $P(C \cap D)$

   b $P(C \cup D)$

   c $P(C \cap \bar{D})$

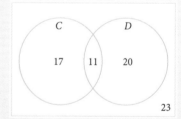

3   Using set notation, what does the shaded region in the diagram represent?

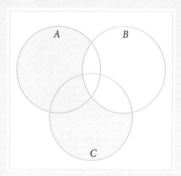

**4\*** If $A$ is the set of multiples of 5 greater than 1 and less than 25, $B$ is the set of multiples of 4 between 1 and 25 and $C$ is the set of multiples of 3 between 1 and 25, find:

a $A \cup (B \cap C)$

b $A \cap (B \cup C)$

c $(A \cup B) \cap C$

d $(A \cap B) \cup C$

Answers ⊃ p. 178

## 7 Further rules with probability

➔ $\bar{A}$ is the **complementary result** to $A$. It is the outcome that $A$ does not occur.

➔ $P(A) + P(\bar{A}) = 1$ because $A$ must either occur or not occur. $P(\bar{A}) = 1 - P(A)$.

➔ **Mutually exclusive outcomes** are outcomes that cannot both occur at the same time. For example, if a dice is tossed the outcomes odd and even are mutually exclusive because the result can be either even or odd but it cannot be both.

➔ If events $A$ and $B$ are **mutually exclusive** then $P(A \cup B) = P(A) + P(B)$.

➔ If events $A$ and $B$ are **not mutually exclusive** then $P(A \cup B) = P(A) + P(B) - P(A \cap B)$.

### EXAMPLE 1

Three men and two women play three games of chance, where each person has an equal chance of winning. What is the probability that at least one game is won by a woman?

$P(\text{man wins a game}) = \dfrac{3}{5}$

$P(\text{men win all 3 games}) = \dfrac{3}{5} \times \dfrac{3}{5} \times \dfrac{3}{5}$

$= \dfrac{27}{125}$

$P(\text{at least one is won by a woman}) = 1 - \dfrac{27}{125}$

$= \dfrac{98}{125}$

Whenever a question asks for the probability of 'at least …' often the easiest way to find the answer is to use the complementary result.

### EXAMPLE 2

The probability that a person has seen movie $A$ is 0.6 and movie $B$ is 0.7. What is the probability that a person has seen neither movie?

$P(\text{not seen } A) = 1 - 0.6$

$= 0.4$

$P(\text{not seen } B) = 1 - 0.7$

$= 0.3$

$P(\text{seen neither}) = 0.4 \times 0.3$

$= 0.12$

We are looking for $P(\bar{A} \cap \bar{B})$.

### EXAMPLE 3

A bag holds marbles in three different colours: red, green and blue. One marble is taken from the bag, without looking. The probability that the ball is red is $\dfrac{3}{8}$ and the probability that it is green is $\dfrac{1}{3}$. What is the probability that the ball is blue?

$P(R \cup G) = \dfrac{3}{8} + \dfrac{1}{3}$

$= \dfrac{17}{24}$

$P(B) = 1 - P(R \cup G)$

$= 1 - \dfrac{17}{24}$

$= \dfrac{7}{24}$

Getting a red marble and getting a green marble are mutually exclusive events.

The probability of getting a blue marble is $\dfrac{7}{24}$.

### EXAMPLE 4

A survey was taken of 60 people leaving a plant store. 27 had bought flowering plants, 20 had bought vegetable plants and 8 had bought both. What is the probability that a randomly selected person had bought flowering or vegetable plants?

$P(F \cup V) = P(F) + P(V) - P(F \cap V)$

$= \dfrac{27}{60} + \dfrac{20}{60} - \dfrac{8}{60}$

$= \dfrac{13}{20}$

We let $F$ be the event that a person bought a flowering plant and $V$ be the event that a person bought a vegetable plant.

## EXAMPLE 5

56% of residents of a certain town have (at least) one dog and 41% have a cat. If 27% of residents have both a dog and a cat, what is the probability that a resident, chosen at random, has a dog or cat?

$$P(D \cup C) = P(D) + P(C) - P(D \cap C)$$
$$= 56\% + 41\% - 27\%$$
$$= 70\%$$

If events $A$ and $B$ are mutually exclusive, then $P(A \cap B) = 0$ and the result $P(A \cup B) = P(A) + P(B) - P(A \cap B)$ still holds.

### → PRACTICE

1   Four girls and two boys play three games of chance. Each person is equally likely to win. What is the probability that at least one game is won by a boy?

2   The probability that a person has read book $A$ is 0.3 and book $B$ is 0.25. What is the probability that a person has read neither book?

3   A bag holds marbles in three different colours: black, white and yellow. One marble is taken from the bag, without looking. The probability that the ball is black is $\frac{2}{9}$ and the probability that it is white is $\frac{1}{4}$. What is the probability that the ball is yellow?

4   A survey was taken of 50 blocks of units. 35 were found to have swimming pools and 17 had gymnasiums. Of these, nine had both pools and gyms. Find the probability that a block, chosen at random from the surveyed group, had a pool or a gym.

5   68% of residents of a certain town are members of the local library and 42% of residents are members of the local club. If 26% of residents are members of both the library and the club, what is the probability that a resident, selected at random, is a member of the library or club?

6*  Students at a certain college must study either art or music or both. If the probability that a student at the college studies art is 0.65 and the probability that a student of the college studies music is 0.55, find the probability that a student of the college, chosen at random, studies both art and music.

Answers ⊃ p. 179

## 8 Conditional probability

→ If **certain restrictions or conditions** are applied to the sample space, then the resulting probability of an event is said to be **conditional**. For example, if a card is randomly selected from a pack of playing cards then $P(\text{queen of clubs}) = \frac{1}{52}$, but if the sample space is restricted to the clubs, $P(\text{queen of clubs}) = \frac{1}{13}$.

→ The notation $P(A|B)$ means the probability of $A$ given $B$; for example, the probability of a queen given that the card is a club.

→ If $P(B) \neq 0$, then $P(A|B) = \dfrac{P(A \cap B)}{P(B)}$. So, if $A$ is the event that the card is a queen and $B$ the event that the card is a club, then the probability that the card is both, is $P(A \cap B) = \frac{1}{52}$. The probability of a club is $P(B) = \frac{1}{4}$.

So $P(A|B) = \dfrac{\frac{1}{52}}{\frac{1}{4}} = \dfrac{1}{13}$.

### EXAMPLE 1

This two-way table was drawn to show how people travelled to an event.

|  | Car | Public transport |
|---|---|---|
| Male | 42 | 18 |
| Female | 36 | 24 |

What is the probability that:

a   a male person travelled by car?

b   a person who travelled by car is male?

a

|  | Car | Public transport | Total |
|---|---|---|---|
| Male | 42 | 18 | 60 |
| Female | 36 | 24 | 60 |
| Total | 78 | 42 | 120 |

Filling in the totals often makes the probabilities easier to identify.

$$P(\text{male travelled by car}) = \frac{42}{60}$$
$$= \frac{7}{10}$$

b   $P(\text{car traveller is male}) = \dfrac{42}{78}$
$$= \frac{7}{13}$$

Read the question carefully. The different conditions make a difference to the answer.

## EXAMPLE 2

If $P(A) = \dfrac{2}{3}$, $P(B) = \dfrac{3}{5}$ and $P(A \cap B) = \dfrac{4}{15}$ find:

a $P(A|B)$

b $P(B|A)$

a $P(A|B) = \dfrac{P(A \cap B)}{P(B)}$

$= \dfrac{\frac{4}{15}}{\frac{3}{5}}$

$= \dfrac{4}{9}$

*$P(A|B)$ is the probability of $A$, given $B$.*

b $P(B|A) = \dfrac{P(A \cap B)}{P(A)}$

$= \dfrac{\frac{4}{15}}{\frac{2}{3}}$

$= \dfrac{2}{5}$

*$P(A|B)$ is the probability of $B$, given $A$. The different conditions mean the answers are not the same.*

## EXAMPLE 3

Suppose the probability that, in a particular area, a house has a pool and at least four bedrooms is 0.36 and the probability that a house has at least four bedrooms is 0.48. What is the probability that a house in that area has a pool given that it has at least four bedrooms?

Let $B$ be the event that a house has four or more bedrooms and let $P$ be the event that a house has a pool.

$P(P|B) = \dfrac{P(P \cap B)}{P(B)}$

$= \dfrac{0.36}{0.48}$

$= 0.75$

So there is a 75% chance that a house has a pool given that it has at least four bedrooms.

*We would need more information to find the probability that a house has at least four bedrooms given that it has a pool.*

### → PRACTICE

1 This two-way table was drawn to show the results of a survey as to which team people supported in a sporting competition.

|  | Crows | Eagles |
|---|---|---|
| Male | 28 | 32 |
| Female | 33 | 17 |

What is the probability that:

a a female supports the Crows?

b a Crows supporter is female?

2 If $P(A) = \dfrac{4}{7}$, $P(B) = \dfrac{9}{14}$ and $P(A \cap B) = \dfrac{3}{14}$ find:

a $P(A|B)$

b $P(B|A)$

3 Suppose the probability that a construction will be on time and that there are no rain delays is 0.56 and the probability that there will be no rain delays is 0.72. What is the probability that a construction will be on time given that there are no rain delays?

4* From past experience in the local area it is known that the probability of a large fire over summer is 0.2. The probability that there will be a large fire and it will cause major damage is 0.08. What is the probability that, given that there is a large fire, it will **not** cause major damage?

Answers ⊃ p. 179

## 9 Independent events

→ Two events are **independent** if the outcome of one has no effect on the outcome of the other.

→ An event $A$ is independent of event $B$ if and only if $P(A|B) = P(A)$.

→ For independent events $A$ and $B$, $P(A \cap B) = P(A)\,P(B)$. This is called the **multiplication law**.

### EXAMPLE 1

In a litter of seven pups it is known that the first three born are all male. What is the probability that the next pup born will also be male?

$P(\text{male}) = \dfrac{1}{2}$

*It doesn't matter that the first three were male. The events are independent.*

### EXAMPLE 2

A small high school has 14 boys and 10 girls in year 11 and 9 boys and 11 girls in year 12. Two students, a boy and a girl, are chosen at random. What is the probability that:

a both students are from year 11?

b both students are from year 12?

c one student is from year 11 and one from year 12?

a $P(\text{both from year 11}) = \dfrac{14}{23} \times \dfrac{10}{21}$

$= \dfrac{20}{69}$

> There are 14 + 9 = 23 boys altogether and 10 + 11 = 21 girls. Choosing a boy and choosing a girl are independent events.

b $P(\text{both from year 12}) = \dfrac{9}{23} \times \dfrac{11}{21}$

$= \dfrac{33}{161}$

c $P(\text{different years}) = 1 - \left( \dfrac{20}{69} + \dfrac{33}{161} \right)$

$= \dfrac{244}{483}$

## EXAMPLE 3

70% of the residents of a town were vaccinated against a certain disease and the remainder were not. 5% of those who had been vaccinated and 75% of those who had not been vaccinated caught the disease. If a resident is chosen at random, what is the probability that he or she caught the disease?

$P(\text{disease}) = 0.05 \times 70\% + 0.75 \times 30\%$

$= 26\%$

> When we think in terms of 'and' the probabilities are multiplied. When we think in terms of 'or' the probabilities are added.

### → PRACTICE

1 A fair coin is tossed and shows heads five times in a row. On the sixth toss what is the probability that the coin will show heads?

2 A bag holds 12 red and nine green apples. Another bag holds 15 red and 12 green apples. One apple is randomly taken from each bag. What is the probability that:

a both apples are red?

b both apples are green?

c one apple is red and one is green?

3 80% of the people at a market are local and the rest are visitors. 90% of the locals and 30% of the visitors had attended the market previously. If a person at the market is chosen randomly, what is the probability that he or she had attended the market before?

4* In a litter of eight piglets, it is known that the first three born are female. What is the probability that:

a the fourth born is also female?

b if I choose one of the eight at random it will be a female?

Answers ⊃ pp. 179–180

## Discrete probability distributions

### 1 Definitions

→ Data is information that can be collected, arranged and analysed. Data can be classified as **categorical** (can be put into categories or groups) or **numerical** (involving numbers). Numerical data can be **discrete** (data that can be counted) or **continuous** (data that is measured).

→ A **random sample** is one where every element of the population has an equal chance of being included in the sample.

→ A **random variable** is the value associated with the outcome of an experiment.

→ A **discrete random variable** is one where the possible values are **finite or countably infinite** (meaning we could in theory count them but we might have to go on forever).

→ A **continuous random variable** can take any value in a particular **range**.

### EXAMPLE 1

Gavin wants to conduct a survey of rail commuters. He travels to a city station and decides to question the first 50 people who leave the station after a certain time. Is this a random sample? Explain why or why not.

No, it is not a random sample because every commuter does not have an equal chance of being selected. It is quite possible that all of those selected actually travelled on the same train, for example.

> This type of sample is systematic.

### EXAMPLE 2

Determine whether these random variables are discrete or continuous:

a the number of red jellybeans in a packet

b  the time to complete a lap of a racetrack

c  the height of trees in an orchard

d  the number of girls in families of five children

a  discrete

b  continuous          *Time is measured.*

c  continuous

d  discrete

---

### → PRACTICE

1  Gloria wants to conduct a survey of shoppers. She travels to a shopping centre and decides to question the first 60 people who come into the food court. Is this a random sample? Explain why or why not.

2  Determine whether these random variables are discrete or continuous:
   a  the weight of pups in a litter
   b  the number of correct responses in a multiple-choice test
   c  the length of time for meetings
   d  the number of sheep counted before you fall asleep

3*  Consider the random variable: the number of days in a month where the temperature exceeds 25°.

   Izzy said that it is a continuous random variable because it involves measurement of temperature. Is she correct? Justify your answer.

Answers ⊃ p. 180

---

## 2 Probability distributions

→ A probability distribution lists all the possible **values of a random variable**, $X$, and the **probability** of each.

→ Each probability, $x$, must be between 0 and 1 inclusive. $0 \leq P(x) \leq 1$

→ The **sum of all the probabilities** must be 1.

→ A **uniform distribution** is one where all the outcomes are equally likely.

### EXAMPLE 1

Let $X$ be the number of heads when four coins are tossed together. A probability distribution has been drawn up but the probability for two heads is missing. What should it be?

| X | 0 | 1 | 2 | 3 | 4 |
|---|---|---|---|---|---|
| P(X) | $\frac{1}{16}$ | $\frac{1}{4}$ | | $\frac{1}{4}$ | $\frac{1}{16}$ |

If four coins are tossed together there might be 0, 1, 2, 3 or 4 heads. $P(4 \text{ heads}) = \frac{1}{2} \times \frac{1}{2} \times \frac{1}{2} \times \frac{1}{2} = \frac{1}{16}$ for example.

Sum of given probabilities $= \frac{1}{16} + \frac{1}{4} + \frac{1}{4} + \frac{1}{16}$

$$= \frac{5}{8}$$

Missing probability $= 1 - \frac{5}{8}$     *The total of all the probabilities must be 1.*

$$= \frac{3}{8}$$

### EXAMPLE 2

This probability distribution was drawn to show the possible number of heads when a coin is tossed six times.

| X | 0 | 1 | 2 | 3 | 4 | 5 | 6 |
|---|---|---|---|---|---|---|---|
| P(X) | $\frac{1}{64}$ | $\frac{3}{32}$ | $\frac{15}{64}$ | $\frac{5}{16}$ | $\frac{15}{64}$ | $\frac{3}{32}$ | $\frac{1}{64}$ |

a  What is the probability of tossing:
   i  exactly five heads?
   ii  at least five heads?

b  In a test there are six questions that all need to be answered as true or false. If you guess the answers, what is the probability of getting at least four right?

a  i  $P(5 \text{ heads}) = \frac{3}{32}$

   ii  $P(\text{at least 5 heads}) = P(5 \text{ heads}) + P(6 \text{ heads})$

   $$= \frac{3}{32} + \frac{1}{64}$$

   $$= \frac{7}{64}$$

b  $P(\text{at least 4 heads}) = \frac{15}{64} + \frac{3}{32} + \frac{1}{64}$

   $$= \frac{11}{32}$$

So the probability of getting at least four questions right would also be $\frac{11}{32}$.

*This is a uniform distribution where the outcomes are equally likely. It can be used to model any phenomena with equally likely outcomes with the same probability.*

## EXAMPLE 3

There are two red, three blue and five white marbles in a box. A marble is taken from the box, its colour noted, and the marble returned before a second marble is drawn.

a Draw a tree diagram and determine the probability, as a decimal, for each possible outcome.

b Let $X$ be the number of blue marbles. Find the probability distribution.

a

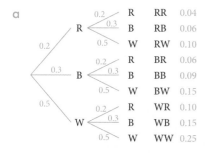

| | | |
|---|---|---|
| R | RR | 0.04 |
| B | RB | 0.06 |
| W | RW | 0.10 |
| R | BR | 0.06 |
| B | BB | 0.09 |
| W | BW | 0.15 |
| R | WR | 0.10 |
| B | WB | 0.15 |
| W | WW | 0.25 |

b
$$P(\text{no blue}) = P(RR) + P(RW) + P(WR) + P(WW)$$
$$= 0.04 + 0.10 + 0.10 + 0.25$$
$$= 0.49$$
$$P(1 \text{ blue}) = P(RB) + P(BR) + P(BW) + P(WB)$$
$$= 0.06 + 0.06 + 0.15 + 0.15$$
$$= 0.42$$

Let $X$ be the number of blue marbles.

| $X$ | 0 | 1 | 2 |
|---|---|---|---|
| $P(X)$ | 0.49 | 0.42 | 0.09 |

This is a non-uniform distribution. The outcomes are not equally likely.

→ **PRACTICE**

1 Let $X$ be the number of times 6 occurs when four dice are rolled together. The probability distribution was drawn but the probability for two 6s is missing. What should it be?

| $X$ | 0 | 1 | 2 | 3 | 4 |
|---|---|---|---|---|---|
| $P(X)$ | $\dfrac{625}{1296}$ | $\dfrac{125}{324}$ | | $\dfrac{5}{324}$ | $\dfrac{1}{1296}$ |

2 This probability distribution was drawn to show the possible number of tails when a coin is tossed five times.

| $X$ | 0 | 1 | 2 | 3 | 4 | 5 |
|---|---|---|---|---|---|---|
| $P(X)$ | $\dfrac{1}{32}$ | $\dfrac{5}{32}$ | $\dfrac{5}{16}$ | $\dfrac{5}{16}$ | $\dfrac{5}{32}$ | $\dfrac{1}{32}$ |

a What is the probability of tossing:
  i   exactly four tails?
  ii  at least four tails?

b A cat has five kittens. Assuming that each is equally likely to be male or female, what is the probability that at least two are female?

3 There are 10 green, eight orange and two black balls in a box. A ball is taken from the box, its colour noted, and the ball returned before a second ball is drawn.

a Draw a tree diagram and determine the probability, as a decimal, for each possible outcome.

b Let $X$ be the number of orange marbles. Find the probability distribution.

4* Sam needs to cross three level crossings, each controlled by lights and boom gates, on his way to work. He knows from experience that the probability that he has to stop at each is $\dfrac{1}{20}$. Find the probability distribution of the random variable describing the number of times he has to stop.

Answers ⊃ pp. 180–181

## 3 Mean or expected value

→ The **mean of a random variable**, $X$, is a measure of centre and is called the **expected value**. It is denoted by $E(X)$ or $\mu$. ($\mu$ is the Greek letter mu.)

→ The mean, or expected value, is the **weighted average**. Each value of $X$ is weighted by its probability.

→ To **find the mean**, multiply each value of $X$ by its probability and add all the products together.

## EXAMPLE 1

A card is randomly selected from a standard pack of playing cards, its suit noted and the card replaced. The probability distribution shows the number of hearts when three cards are drawn.

| $X$ | 0 | 1 | 2 | 3 |
|---|---|---|---|---|
| $P(X)$ | $\dfrac{27}{64}$ | $\dfrac{27}{64}$ | $\dfrac{9}{64}$ | $\dfrac{1}{64}$ |

What is the expected number of hearts?

$$E(X) = 0 \times \frac{27}{64} + 1 \times \frac{27}{64} + 2 \times \frac{9}{64} + 3 \times \frac{1}{64}$$
$$= \frac{3}{4}$$

In this case the expected number of hearts can't actually be achieved.

## EXAMPLE 2

A discrete random variable has this probability distribution. What is the mean?

| X | 0 | 1 | 2 | 3 | 4 |
|---|---|---|---|---|---|
| P(X) | 0.12 | 0.23 | 0.31 | 0.25 | 0.09 |

$\mu = 0 \times 0.12 + 1 \times 0.23 + 2 \times 0.31 + 3 \times 0.25 + 4 \times 0.09$
$= 1.96$

The mean is 1.96.

> Finding the mean for a probability distribution is an equivalent process to finding the usual average or mean.

## EXAMPLE 3

A biased coin is twice as likely to show a tail as a head. If it is tossed three times draw a probability distribution, letting $X$ be the number of heads, and find the mean.

$P(\text{heads}) = \dfrac{1}{3}$ and $P(\text{tails}) = \dfrac{2}{3}$

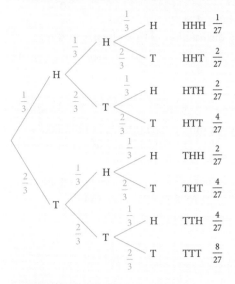

Let $X$ be the number of heads obtained.

| X | 0 | 1 | 2 | 3 |
|---|---|---|---|---|
| P(X) | $\dfrac{8}{27}$ | $\dfrac{4}{9}$ | $\dfrac{2}{9}$ | $\dfrac{1}{27}$ |

$\mu = 0 \times \dfrac{8}{27} + 1 \times \dfrac{4}{9} + 2 \times \dfrac{2}{9} + 3 \times \dfrac{1}{27}$
$= 1$

The expected number of heads is 1.

> The mean is called the expected number because it is exactly what you would expect. If a coin is twice as likely to show a tail as a head then, in three tosses, you would expect to get two tails and one head.

### → PRACTICE

1   A card is randomly selected from a standard pack of playing cards, its value noted and the card replaced. The probability distribution shows the number of picture cards when three cards are drawn.

| X | 0 | 1 | 2 | 3 |
|---|---|---|---|---|
| P(X) | $\dfrac{1000}{2197}$ | $\dfrac{900}{2197}$ | $\dfrac{270}{2197}$ | $\dfrac{27}{2197}$ |

What is the expected number of picture cards?

2   A discrete random variable has this probability distribution. What is the mean?

| X | 0 | 1 | 2 | 3 | 4 |
|---|---|---|---|---|---|
| P(X) | 0.26 | 0.28 | 0.22 | 0.17 | 0.07 |

3   A biased coin is twice as likely to show a head as a tail. If it is tossed three times, draw a probability distribution, letting $X$ be the number of heads, and find the mean.

4*  The mean of this probability distribution is 3.1. Find $a$ and $b$.

| X | 1 | 2 | 3 | 4 | 5 |
|---|---|---|---|---|---|
| P(X) | 0.11 | 0.24 | $a$ | $b$ | 0.18 |

Answers ➲ p. 181

## 4 Variance and standard deviation

→  Variance and standard deviation are **measures of spread**.

→  The **variance**, Var($X$), is given by $E(X^2) - [E(X)]^2$.

→  The **standard deviation**, $\sigma$, is the square root of the variance ($\sigma \geq 0$). So **Var($X$) = $\sigma^2$**.

### EXAMPLE 1

Consider this probability distribution.

| X | 1 | 2 | 3 | 4 | 5 |
|---|---|---|---|---|---|
| P(X) | 0.05 | 0.15 | 0.45 | 0.25 | 0.1 |

Find:

a   $E(X)$

b   Var($X$)

c   $\sigma$, giving the answer to two decimal places

a   $E(X) = 1 \times 0.05 + 2 \times 0.15 + 3 \times 0.45$
$\qquad\qquad + 4 \times 0.25 + 5 \times 0.1$
$= 3.2$

b  $E(X^2) = 1^2 \times 0.05 + 2^2 \times 0.15 + 3^2 \times 0.45$
$$+ 4^2 \times 0.25 + 5^2 \times 0.1$$

$\quad = 11.2$

*$E(X^2)$ is found by multiplying $X^2$ by $P(X)$ for each value of $X$ and adding those products.*

$Var(X) = E(X^2) - [(E(X)]^2$

$\quad = 11.2 - (3.2)^2$

$\quad = 0.96$

c  $\sigma = \sqrt{0.96}$

$\quad = 0.979\,795\,897\ldots$

$\quad = 0.98 \quad (2 \text{ d.p.})$

*A calculator can also be used to find the mean and standard deviation, using the statistics mode.*

## EXAMPLE 2

Three dice are rolled simultaneously. Let $X$ be the number of sixes that are uppermost. The probability distribution is shown in the table. Find the mean and standard deviation.

| X | 0 | 1 | 2 | 3 |
|---|---|---|---|---|
| P(X) | $\dfrac{125}{216}$ | $\dfrac{75}{216}$ | $\dfrac{15}{216}$ | $\dfrac{1}{216}$ |

$E(X) = 0 \times \dfrac{125}{216} + 1 \times \dfrac{75}{216} + 2 \times \dfrac{15}{216} + 3 \times \dfrac{1}{216}$

$\quad = \dfrac{1}{2}$

$E(X^2) = 0^2 \times \dfrac{125}{216} + 1^2 \times \dfrac{75}{216} + 2^2 \times \dfrac{15}{216} + 3^2 \times \dfrac{1}{216}$

$\quad = \dfrac{2}{3}$

$Var(X) = \dfrac{2}{3} - \left(\dfrac{1}{2}\right)^2$

$\quad = \dfrac{5}{12}$

$\sigma = \sqrt{\dfrac{5}{12}}$

$\quad = 0.645\,497\,224\ldots$

$\quad = 0.65 \quad (2 \text{ d.p.})$

*The measure of spread tells us whether the values are close to the mean or spread far apart.*

The mean is 0.5 and the standard deviation is 0.65, to two decimal places.

## → PRACTICE

1  Consider this probability distribution.

| X | 1 | 2 | 3 | 4 | 5 |
|---|---|---|---|---|---|
| P(X) | 0.17 | 0.29 | 0.35 | 0.13 | 0.06 |

Find:

a  $E(X)$

b  $Var(X)$

c  $\sigma$, giving the answer to two decimal places

2  Four dice are rolled simultaneously. Let $X$ be the number of times that the uppermost face is greater than 4. The probability distribution is shown in the table. Find the mean and standard deviation.

| X | 0 | 1 | 2 | 3 | 4 |
|---|---|---|---|---|---|
| P(X) | $\dfrac{16}{81}$ | $\dfrac{32}{81}$ | $\dfrac{24}{81}$ | $\dfrac{8}{81}$ | $\dfrac{1}{81}$ |

3*  It is known that 12% of patients develop significant side effects to a particular prescription medication. Three people are prescribed the medication. Draw a probability distribution table, letting $X$ be the number of people who develop side effects, and find the mean, variance and standard deviation.

Answers ⊃ pp. 181–182

## 5 Samples of the population

→ If a sample is taken from the whole population then the **sample mean**, $\bar{x}$, is an estimate of the population mean $\mu$.

→ The **sample standard deviation**, $s$, is an estimate of the population standard deviation, $\sigma$.

→ As the **sample size increases**, the estimates improve.

## EXAMPLE 1

a  Two coins are tossed together. Let $X$ be the number of heads. Draw a probability distribution table and find the mean and standard deviation.

b  Harold completed three trials of tossing two coins together 10 times each trial and recorded the result.

| | Trial 1 | | | Trial 2 | | | Trial 3 | | |
|---|---|---|---|---|---|---|---|---|---|
| Number of heads | 0 | 1 | 2 | 0 | 1 | 2 | 0 | 1 | 2 |
| Frequency | 5 | 4 | 1 | 2 | 6 | 2 | 2 | 5 | 3 |

Draw a probability distribution table for each trial, using the relative frequency. Find the mean and standard deviation for each.

c  Comment on the results and compare with the answer to part a.

a

| $X$ | 0 | 1 | 2 |
|---|---|---|---|
| $P(X)$ | $\frac{1}{4}$ | $\frac{1}{2}$ | $\frac{1}{4}$ |

$E(X) = 0 \times \frac{1}{4} + 1 \times \frac{1}{2} + 2 \times \frac{1}{4}$

$= 1$

$E(X^2) = 0 \times \frac{1}{4} + 1 \times \frac{1}{2} + 4 \times \frac{1}{4}$

$= 1\frac{1}{2}$

$\text{Var}(X) = 1\frac{1}{2} - 1^2$

$= \frac{1}{2}$

$\sigma = \sqrt{\frac{1}{2}}$

$= 0.707\,106\,781\ldots$

$= 0.707 \quad (3 \text{ d.p.})$

b  Trial 1:

| $X$ | 0 | 1 | 2 |
|---|---|---|---|
| $P(X)$ | 0.5 | 0.4 | 0.1 |

$\bar{x} = 0 \times 0.5 + 1 \times 0.4 + 2 \times 0.1$

$= 0.6$

Now $0 \times 0.5 + 1 \times 0.4 + 2^2 \times 0.1 = 0.8$

$\text{Var} = 0.8 - 0.6^2$

$= 0.44$

$s = \sqrt{0.44}$

$= 0.663\,324\,958\ldots$

$= 0.663 \quad (3 \text{ d.p.})$

Trial 2:

| $X$ | 0 | 1 | 2 |
|---|---|---|---|
| $P(X)$ | 0.2 | 0.6 | 0.2 |

$\bar{x} = 0 \times 0.2 + 1 \times 0.6 + 2 \times 0.2$

$= 1$

Now $0 \times 0.2 + 1 \times 0.6 + 2^2 \times 0.2 = 1.4$

$\text{Var} = 1.4 - 1^2$

$= 0.4$

$s = \sqrt{0.4}$

$= 0.632\,455\,53\ldots$

$= 0.632 \quad (3 \text{ d.p.})$

Trial 3:

| $X$ | 0 | 1 | 2 |
|---|---|---|---|
| $P(X)$ | 0.2 | 0.5 | 0.3 |

$\bar{x} = 0 \times 0.2 + 1 \times 0.5 + 2 \times 0.3$

$= 1.1$

Now $0 \times 0.2 + 1 \times 0.5 + 2^2 \times 0.3 = 1.7$

$\text{Var} = 1.7 - 1.1^2$

$= 0.49$

$s = \sqrt{0.49}$

$= 0.7$

c  Each of the trials is very small but all produce results that are not greatly different to the population results. Combining the information from all the trials would probably result in better estimates.

The answers for the mean and standard deviation could themselves be averaged to give a better result.

## EXAMPLE 2

A survey was conducted among adult female shoppers at a particular shopping centre. Each woman was asked how many children she had given birth to. A probability distribution table was drawn from the results, with $X$ being the number of children.

| $X$ | 0 | 1 | 2 | 3 | 4 | 5 | 6 | 7 |
|---|---|---|---|---|---|---|---|---|
| $P(X)$ | 0.24 | 0.23 | 0.31 | 0.15 | 0.05 | 0.01 | 0 | 0.01 |

a  Find the mean number of children per woman.

b  Given that the actual fertility rate for the population was 1.8 children per woman, comment on the results of the survey.

a  $\bar{x} = 1 \times 0.23 + 2 \times 0.31 + 3 \times 0.15$
$\qquad + 4 \times 0.05 + 5 \times 0.01 + 7 \times 0.01$

$= 1.62$

b  The sample mean is less than the population mean but not massively different. There is no information about the size of the survey so the estimated mean might improve if the sample size was larger. The survey was only conducted at a single shopping centre so might not be representative of the general population.

There can be many things that affect the result of the survey: the time of day it was taken, the day of the week, the area in which it was taken, and so on.

→ PRACTICE

1  a  Three coins are tossed together. Let *X* be the number of heads. Draw a probability distribution table and find the mean and standard deviation.

   b  Harriet completed two trials of tossing three coins together 10 times each trial and recorded the result.

|  | Trial 1 | | | | Trial 2 | | | |
|---|---|---|---|---|---|---|---|---|
| Number of heads | 0 | 1 | 2 | 3 | 0 | 1 | 2 | 3 |
| Frequency | 0 | 3 | 5 | 2 | 2 | 4 | 3 | 1 |

Draw a probability distribution table for each trial, using the relative frequency. Find the mean and standard deviation for each.

   c  Comment on the results and compare with the answer to part a.

..........................................................

2  A survey was conducted at a one-day cricket match. The number of runs scored each ball was recorded for some of the overs of the match. A probability distribution table was drawn from the results, with *X* being the number of runs scored per ball.

| X | 0 | 1 | 2 | 3 | 4 | 5 | 6 |
|---|---|---|---|---|---|---|---|
| P(X) | 0.28 | 0.35 | 0.16 | 0.11 | 0.07 | 0 | 0.03 |

   a  Find the mean number of runs per ball.

   b  Given that the actual rate for the entire match was 1.15 runs per ball, comment on the results of the survey.

3*  The probability distribution for a population is:

| X | 0 | 1 | 2 | 3 |
|---|---|---|---|---|
| P(X) | 0.59 | 0.21 | 0.15 | 0.05 |

The probability distributions for four different samples from the population are:

| X | 0 | 1 | 2 | 3 |
|---|---|---|---|---|
| P(X) | 0.45 | 0.25 | 0.2 | 0.1 |

| X | 0 | 1 | 2 | 3 |
|---|---|---|---|---|
| P(X) | 0.7 | 0.15 | 0.1 | 0.05 |

| X | 0 | 1 | 2 | 3 |
|---|---|---|---|---|
| P(X) | 0.61 | 0.22 | 0.14 | 0.03 |

| X | 0 | 1 | 2 | 3 |
|---|---|---|---|---|
| P(X) | 0.63 | 0.18 | 0.15 | 0.04 |

Show that the mean of the sample means is the population mean.

Answers ⊃ pp. 182–183

# YEAR 11 EXAM-TYPE QUESTIONS

**Total marks: 50**

## PART A

(Suggested time: 15 minutes)

(1 mark each)

1 Anna, Bill, Col, Dennis and Erin line up in a queue. What is the probability that Bill and Dennis, in that order, are the first two in the queue? (Assume each is equally likely to be in any position.)

A $\dfrac{1}{20}$    B $\dfrac{1}{10}$    C $\dfrac{1}{5}$    D $\dfrac{2}{5}$

2 If $P = \{1, 2, 3, 4, 5, 6\}$ and $Q = \{2, 4, 6, 8, 10\}$ how many elements are in $P \cup Q$?

A 3    B 8    C 9    D 11

3 Jimmy is one of six musicians in a band. Two musicians from the band are randomly chosen to do a publicity stunt. What is the probability that Jimmy is chosen?

A $\dfrac{1}{15}$    B $\dfrac{2}{15}$    C $\dfrac{1}{30}$    D $\dfrac{1}{3}$

4 Stacey drew up the tree diagram to show the possible outcomes when two golf tees are chosen, one after the other without replacement, from a bag holding one red, one white and one blue tee. What is the probability that one tee is red and the other is blue?

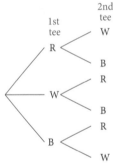

A $\dfrac{1}{3}$    B $\dfrac{1}{6}$

C $\dfrac{1}{9}$    D $\dfrac{5}{6}$

5 If $P(X) = 0.36$, $P(Y) = 0.4$, $P(X \cup Y) = 0.6$ and $P(X \cap Y) = 0.16$, what is $P(X|Y)$?

A $\dfrac{2}{5}$    B $\dfrac{4}{15}$    C $\dfrac{1}{9}$    D $\dfrac{4}{9}$

6 Four black and five white counters are in a bag. Two counters are drawn randomly, one after the other without replacement. If the first counter was black, what is the probability that the second counter is also black?

A $\dfrac{4}{9}$    B $\dfrac{1}{6}$    C $\dfrac{3}{8}$    D $\dfrac{1}{3}$

7 In a group of 70 language students, 42 study Japanese, 49 study Indonesian, and 28 study both. What is the probability that a student, chosen randomly from the group, studies neither Japanese nor Indonesian?

A $\dfrac{1}{5}$    B $\dfrac{1}{10}$    C $\dfrac{1}{7}$    D $\dfrac{7}{10}$

8 If two coins are tossed together what is the probability of at least one head?

A $\dfrac{1}{4}$    B $\dfrac{1}{3}$    C $\dfrac{2}{3}$    D $\dfrac{3}{4}$

9 Considering this probability distribution, what is $P(X = 1)$?

| $X$ | 0 | 1 | 2 | 3 |
|---|---|---|---|---|
| $P(X)$ | $\dfrac{1}{8}$ | | $\dfrac{5}{12}$ | $\dfrac{1}{4}$ |

A $\dfrac{1}{3}$    B $\dfrac{5}{12}$    C $\dfrac{3}{8}$    D $\dfrac{5}{24}$

10 A group of gardeners were surveyed and it was found that the probability of growing peas is 0.52, the probability of growing beans is 0.3 and the probability of growing both is 0.17. What is the probability of growing peas or beans?

A 0.22    B 0.48    C 0.65    D 0.82

11 There are three charged batteries and one flat battery in a box. If two are taken at random, what is the probability that both are charged?

A $\dfrac{9}{16}$    B $\dfrac{1}{2}$    C $\dfrac{1}{3}$    D $\dfrac{1}{4}$

12 Three cards are identical except for the numbers 1, 2 and 3 written on them, one digit on each card. Two of the cards are randomly placed to form a two-digit number. What is the probability that the number is odd?

A $\dfrac{1}{2}$    B $\dfrac{1}{3}$    C $\dfrac{2}{3}$    D $\dfrac{5}{9}$

**PART B** (Suggested time: 45 minutes)

Show all working.

13 'As we will either have a storm tomorrow or not have a storm, the probability of a storm tomorrow is $\frac{1}{2}$.' Briefly explain why this statement is false. (1 mark)

14 A dice is rolled a number of times with these results:

| Score | 1 | 2 | 3 | 4 | 5 | 6 |
|---|---|---|---|---|---|---|
| Frequency | 7 | 5 | 9 | 5 | 8 | 6 |

a What is the relative frequency of a score of 5? (1 mark)

b How many times would you expect to get a 5 in 12 rolls of the dice? (1 mark)

15 Pia is a chef working at a local restaurant. She knows that the probability of a customer ordering chicken for their main course is 0.4 and the probability that they will order both chicken for main and pavlova for dessert is 0.24. What is the probability that a customer will order pavlova given that they have chicken for main? (1 mark)

16 Guy buys 25 tickets in a raffle in which 200 tickets are sold and there are two prizes. What is the probability that Guy wins:

a first prize? (1 mark)

b both prizes? (1 mark)

c no prize? (1 mark)

d at least one prize? (1 mark)

e second prize? (1 mark)

17 This Venn diagram was drawn to show the results of a survey of the number of people who had sighted a kookaburra, a magpie and/or a wren one morning.

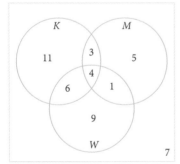

a What is the probability that a person from the group, chosen at random:

i saw all three birds? (1 mark)

ii did not see any of the birds? (1 mark)

iii saw both a kookaburra and a magpie, but not a wren? (1 mark)

iv saw exactly two birds? (1 mark)

b Of those who saw a wren what is the probability they also saw a magpie? (1 mark)

18 There is a 40% chance of catching disease $A$ and a 20% chance of catching disease $B$ in the first five years of life. What is the probability that a child will catch:

a both diseases? (1 mark)

b disease $A$ but not disease $B$? (1 mark)

c neither disease? (1 mark)

d exactly one of the diseases? (2 marks)

e at least one of the diseases? (1 mark)

19 All of the 40 participants at a conference attend at least one of the taxation or marketing lectures. 32 participants attend the taxation lecture and 28 attend the marketing lecture. What is the probability that:

a a participant chosen randomly attends the taxation lecture? (1 mark)

b two participants chosen at random both attend the marketing lectures? (1 mark)

c a randomly chosen participant attends both lectures? (2 marks)

d a participant who attends the taxation lecture also attends the marketing lecture? (1 mark)

20 Assume that the answers to multiple-choice questions are equally likely to be either A, B, C or D. Let $X$ be the number of times the answer C appears in four questions.

| $X$ | 0 | 1 | 2 | 3 | 4 |
|---|---|---|---|---|---|
| $P(X)$ | $\frac{81}{256}$ | $\frac{27}{64}$ | $\frac{27}{128}$ | $\frac{3}{64}$ | $\frac{1}{256}$ |

a What is the probability of exactly two answers of C? (1 mark)

b What is the probability of at least one C? (1 mark)

c What is the probability of more than two Cs? (1 mark)

d What is the mean? Is this what you would expect? Comment. (2 marks)

e What is the standard deviation? (Give the answer to two decimal places.) (2 marks)

21 A particular type of light globe has a 10% chance of being defective. Three of these globes are randomly selected.

a Draw a tree diagram showing whether each globe is good (G) or defective (D), write out the sample space and give the probability for each outcome. (3 marks)

b Let $X$ be the number of defective globes. Draw up a probability distribution table. (2 marks)

c How many of the globes would you expect to be defective? (1 mark)

# ANSWERS

**PRACTICE**

**PROBABILITY AND VENN DIAGRAMS**

## 1 The probability of an event ⊃ p. 156

1 a $P(2) = \dfrac{1}{6}$

b $P(\text{odd}) = \dfrac{3}{6}$

$= \dfrac{1}{2}$

c $P(>4) = \dfrac{2}{6}$

$= \dfrac{1}{3}$

2 $P(\text{winning}) = \dfrac{15}{750} \times 100\%$

$= 2\%$

3 **The statement is false because the events raining or not raining are not equally likely.**

4 a Total marbles $= 5 + 4 + 3$

$= 12$

$P(\text{red}) = \dfrac{5}{12}$

b $P(\text{yellow}) = \mathbf{0}$

c $P(\text{red, green or blue}) = \mathbf{1}$

d $P(\text{red or blue}) = \dfrac{8}{12}$

$= \dfrac{2}{3}$

## 2 Relative frequency ⊃ pp. 157–158

1 a Total frequency $= 3 + 5 + 4 + 6 + 4 + 2$

$= 24$

| 1 | 2 | 3 | 4 | 5 | 6 |
|---|---|---|---|---|---|
| 3 | 5 | 4 | 6 | 4 | 2 |

Relative frequency of $5 = \dfrac{4}{24}$

$= \dfrac{1}{6}$

b Relative frequency of $4 = \dfrac{6}{24}$

$= \dfrac{1}{4}$

Expected number in 30 rolls $= \dfrac{1}{4} \times 30$

$= 7.5$

2 a Number of tails $= \dfrac{7}{15} \times 30$

$= 14$

Number of heads $= 30 - 14$

$= 16$

b Second trial:

Number of tails $= \dfrac{14}{25} \times 50$

$= 28$

Number of heads $= 50 - 28$

$= 22$

Whole experiment:

Total heads $= 16 + 22$

$= 38$

Total tosses $= 30 + 50$

$= 80$

Relative frequency of heads $= \dfrac{38}{80}$

$= \mathbf{0.475}$

3 a Relative frequency of 'don't know' $= 1 - \left(\dfrac{2}{9} + \dfrac{1}{3}\right)$

$= \dfrac{4}{9}$

b Number answering 'no' $= \dfrac{1}{3} \times 72$

$= \mathbf{24}$

## 3 Multi-stage events ⊃ p. 159

1 Number of arrangements $= 8 \times 7 \times 6 \times 5 \times 4 \times 3 \times 2 \times 1$

$= 40\,320$

**The acts could be arranged in 40 320 different ways.**

2 $P(\text{FOOD}) = P(\text{F}) \times P(\text{O}) \times P(\text{O}) \times P(\text{D})$

$= \dfrac{1}{4} \times \dfrac{2}{3} \times \dfrac{1}{2} \times 1$

$= \dfrac{1}{12}$

**The probability that the cards spell FOOD is $\dfrac{1}{12}$.**

3 $P(\text{win both prizes}) = P(\text{first}) \times P(\text{second})$

$= \dfrac{5}{200} \times \dfrac{4}{199}$

$= \dfrac{1}{1990}$

∴ **the probability that Sara wins both prizes is $\dfrac{1}{1990}$.**

4 a $P(\text{tails}) = \dfrac{3}{4}$

b **Hh   Ht   Th   Tt**

c $P(\text{Tt}) = \dfrac{3}{4} \times \dfrac{1}{2}$

$= \dfrac{3}{8}$

5 a $P(\text{first prize}) = \dfrac{6}{50}$

$= \dfrac{3}{25}$

b $P(\text{all prizes}) = \dfrac{6}{50} \times \dfrac{5}{49} \times \dfrac{4}{48}$

$= \dfrac{1}{980}$

c $P(\text{not winning a prize}) = \dfrac{44}{50} \times \dfrac{43}{49} \times \dfrac{42}{48}$

$= \dfrac{473}{700}$

## 4 Tree diagrams ⊃ pp. 160–161

1

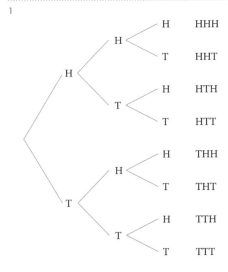

a $P(\text{HHH}) = \dfrac{1}{8}$

b $P(\text{2H, 1T}) = \dfrac{3}{8}$

c $P(\text{at least 2 tails}) = \dfrac{1}{2}$

d $P(\text{first and last the same}) = \dfrac{1}{2}$

2 a

2nd ticket — Sample space

1st ticket $\frac{5}{7}$ G — GG

$\frac{5}{7}$ G

$\frac{2}{7}$ Y — GY

$\frac{5}{7}$ G — YG

$\frac{2}{7}$ Y

$\frac{2}{7}$ Y — YY

b i $P(\text{GG}) = \dfrac{5}{7} \times \dfrac{5}{7}$

$= \dfrac{25}{49}$

ii $P(\text{YY}) = \dfrac{2}{7} \times \dfrac{2}{7}$

$= \dfrac{4}{49}$

iii $P(\text{1 green, 1 yellow}) = P(\text{GY}) + P(\text{YG})$

$= \dfrac{5}{7} \times \dfrac{2}{7} + \dfrac{2}{7} \times \dfrac{5}{7}$

$= \dfrac{20}{49}$

3

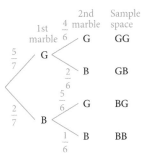

$P(\text{same colour}) = P(\text{GG}) + P(\text{BB})$

$= \dfrac{5}{7} \times \dfrac{4}{6} + \dfrac{2}{7} \times \dfrac{1}{6}$

$= \dfrac{11}{21}$

4

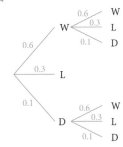

$P(\text{loses at least 1 game})$

$= 0.6 \times 0.3 + 0.3 + 0.1 \times 0.3$

$= 0.51$

5 a

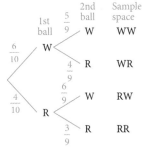

b $P(\text{different colours}) = P(\text{WR}) + P(\text{RW})$

$= \dfrac{6}{10} \times \dfrac{4}{9} + \dfrac{4}{10} \times \dfrac{6}{9}$

$= \dfrac{8}{15}$

$= 53\dfrac{1}{3}\%$

**So Ted is correct.**

## 5 Venn diagrams ⊃ p. 178

**1** **a** Number winning gold medals
$$= 7 + 3 + 2 + 5$$
$$= \mathbf{17}$$

**b** Number winning both silver and bronze but not gold = **6**

**c** Total in the group
$$= 17 + 11 + 6 + 14 + 9$$
$$= 57$$
Number winning silver
$$= 3 + 2 + 6 + 11$$
$$= 22$$
$P(\text{silver}) = \dfrac{\mathbf{22}}{\mathbf{57}}$

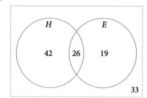

**d** Number winning at least 2 medals $= 3 + 2 + 5 + 6$
$$= 16$$
$P(\text{at least 2 medals}) = \dfrac{\mathbf{16}}{\mathbf{57}}$

**2** **a**

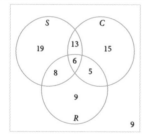

**b** $P(\text{study neither}) = \dfrac{33}{120}$
$$= \dfrac{\mathbf{11}}{\mathbf{40}}$$

**3** Number who responded $= 84 - 9$
$$= 75$$
Now $46 + 39 + 28 = 113$
Difference $= 113 - 75$
$$= 38$$
Number mentioning at least 2 legs
$$= 19 + 11 + 14$$
$$= 44$$

Number mentioning all 3 legs $= 44 - 38$
$$= 6$$
$P(\text{mentions all 3 legs}) = \dfrac{6}{84}$
$$= \dfrac{\mathbf{1}}{\mathbf{14}}$$

**4** **a** $19 + x + 7 + y = 41$
$$\therefore x + y = 15 \quad \text{(i)}$$
$$x + 13 + 7 + z = 38$$
$$\therefore x + z = 18 \quad \text{(ii)}$$
$$y + 7 + z + 22 = 42$$
$$\therefore y + z = 13 \quad \text{(iii)}$$
(ii) − (i): $\quad z - y = 3 \quad \text{(iv)}$
(iii) + (iv): $\quad 2z = 16$
$$z = 8$$
Substitute in (iii): $y + 8 = 13$
$$\therefore y = 5$$

Substitute in (i): $x + 5 = 15$
$$\therefore x = 10$$
**So $x = 10$, $y = 5$ and $z = 8$.**

**b** Total $= 41 + 13 + 8 + 22 + 11$
$$= 95$$
$P(\text{apple and banana but not orange})$
$$= \dfrac{10}{95}$$
$$= \dfrac{\mathbf{2}}{\mathbf{19}}$$

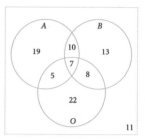

## 6 Set notation ⊃ pp. 163–164

**1** $A = \{1, 3, 5, 7, 9, 11, 13, 15, 17, 19\}$
$B = \{3, 6, 9, 12, 15, 18\}$

**a** $\bar{A} = \mathbf{\{2, 4, 6, 8, 10, 12, 14, 16, 18\}}$
**b** $A \cup B = \mathbf{\{1, 3, 5, 6, 7, 9, 11, 12, 13, 15, 17, 18, 19\}}$
**c** $A \cap B = \mathbf{\{3, 9, 15\}}$
**d** $\bar{A} \cup B = \mathbf{\{2, 3, 4, 6, 8, 9, 10, 12, 14, 15, 16, 18\}}$
**e** $\bar{B} = \{1, 2, 4, 5, 7, 8, 10, 11, 13, 14, 16, 17, 19\}$
$A \cap \bar{B} = \mathbf{\{1, 5, 7, 11, 13, 17, 19\}}$

**2** **a** Total $= 17 + 11 + 20 + 23$
$$= 71$$
$P(C \cap D) = \dfrac{\mathbf{11}}{\mathbf{71}}$

**b** $17 + 11 + 20 = 48$
$$P(C \cup D) = \dfrac{\mathbf{48}}{\mathbf{71}}$$

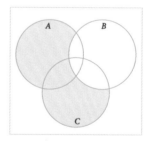

**c** $P(C \cap \bar{D}) = \dfrac{\mathbf{17}}{\mathbf{71}}$

**3** $(A \cup C) \cap \bar{B}$

**4** $A = \{5, 10, 15, 20\}$
$B = \{4, 8, 12, 16, 20, 24\}$
$C = \{3, 6, 9, 12, 15, 18, 21, 24\}$
**a** $B \cap C = \{12, 24\}$
$A \cup (B \cap C) = \mathbf{\{5, 10, 12, 15, 20, 24\}}$
**b** $B \cup C = \{3, 4, 6, 8, 9, 12, 15, 16, 18, 20, 21, 24\}$
$A \cap (B \cup C) = \mathbf{\{15, 20\}}$
**c** $A \cup B = \{4, 5, 8, 10, 12, 15, 16, 20, 24\}$
$(A \cup B) \cap C = \mathbf{\{12, 15, 24\}}$
**d** $A \cap B = \{20\}$
$(A \cap B) \cup C = \mathbf{\{3, 6, 9, 12, 15, 18, 20, 21, 24\}}$

## 7 Further rules with probability ⊃ p. 165

1.   $P(\text{girl wins a game}) = \dfrac{4}{6}$

                        $= \dfrac{2}{3}$

  $P(\text{girls win all 3 games}) = \dfrac{2}{3} \times \dfrac{2}{3} \times \dfrac{2}{3}$

                            $= \dfrac{8}{27}$

  $P(\text{at least one is won by a boy}) = 1 - \dfrac{8}{27}$

                                     $= \dfrac{19}{27}$

2.   $P(\text{not read } A) = 1 - 0.3$

                     $= 0.7$

   $P(\text{not read } B) = 1 - 0.25$

                     $= 0.75$

   $P(\text{read neither}) = 0.7 \times 0.75$

                     $= \mathbf{0.525}$

3.   $P(B \cup W) = \dfrac{2}{9} + \dfrac{1}{4}$

              $= \dfrac{17}{36}$

  $P(Y) = 1 - P(B \cup W)$

        $= 1 - \dfrac{17}{36}$

        $= \dfrac{19}{36}$

**The probability of a yellow ball is $\dfrac{19}{36}$.**

4.   $P(P \cup G) = P(P) + P(G) - P(P \cap G)$

            $= \dfrac{35}{50} + \dfrac{17}{50} - \dfrac{9}{50}$

            $= \dfrac{43}{50}$

**The probability that a block of units has a pool or a gym is $\dfrac{43}{50}$.**

5.   $P(L \cup C) = P(L) + P(C) - P(L \cap C)$

           $= 68\% + 42\% - 26\%$

           $= 84\%$

**There is an 84% chance that a person is a member of the library or club.**

6.   $P(A \cup M) = P(A) + P(M) - P(A \cap M)$

  But $P(A \cup M) = 1$

  $\therefore P(A \cap M) = P(A) + P(M) - 1$

              $= 0.65 + 0.55 - 1$

              $= 0.2$

**The probability that a student studies both art and music is 0.2.**

## 8 Conditional probability ⊃ p. 166

| | Crows | Eagles | Total |
|---|---|---|---|
| Male | 28 | 32 | 60 |
| Female | 33 | 17 | 50 |
| Total | 61 | 49 | 110 |

1.   a   $P(\text{a female supports the Crows}) = \dfrac{33}{50}$

   b   $P(\text{a Crows supporter is female}) = \dfrac{33}{61}$

2.   a   $P(A|B) = \dfrac{P(A \cap B)}{P(B)}$

             $= \dfrac{\frac{3}{14}}{\frac{9}{14}}$

             $= \dfrac{1}{3}$

   b   $P(B|A) = \dfrac{P(A \cap B)}{P(A)}$

             $= \dfrac{\frac{3}{14}}{\frac{4}{7}}$

             $= \dfrac{3}{8}$

3.   Let $A$ be the event that a construction will be on time and let $B$ be the event that there will be no rain delays.

   $P(A|B) = \dfrac{P(A \cap B)}{P(B)}$

          $= \dfrac{0.56}{0.72}$

          $= \dfrac{7}{9}$

**So there is a $77.\dot{7}$% chance that a construction will be on time given that there are no rain delays.**

4.   Let $F$ be the event that there is a large fire over summer and let $D$ be the event that there is major damage.

   $P(D|F) = \dfrac{P(D \cap F)}{P(F)}$

          $= \dfrac{0.08}{0.2}$

          $= 0.4$

∴ the probability that, given that there is a large fire, it will cause major damage is 0.4.

**So the probability that, given that there is a large fire, it will not cause major damage is 0.6.**

## 9 Independent events ⊃ p. 167

1.   $P(\text{heads}) = \dfrac{1}{2}$

2 a $P(\text{both red}) = \frac{12}{21} \times \frac{15}{27}$

$= \frac{20}{63}$

b $P(\text{both green}) = \frac{9}{21} \times \frac{12}{27}$

$= \frac{4}{21}$

c $P(\text{different}) = 1 - \left(\frac{20}{63} + \frac{4}{21}\right)$

$= \frac{31}{63}$

3 $P(\text{previous visit}) = 0.8 \times 90\% + 0.2 \times 30\%$

$= \textbf{78\%}$

4 a $P(\text{4th is female}) = \frac{1}{2}$

b $P(\text{female}) = P(\text{1 of first 3}) + P(\text{1 of the last 5 and female})$

$= \frac{3}{8} + \frac{5}{8} \times \frac{1}{2}$

$= \frac{11}{16}$

DISCRETE PROBABILITY DISTRIBUTIONS

1 Definitions ⊃ p. 168

1 **No, it is not a random sample because every shopper does not have an equal chance of being selected. Those who are just coming in for a quick purchase, for example, are unlikely to visit the food court.**

2 a **continuous**

b **discrete**

c **continuous**

d **discrete**

3 **No, Izzy is not correct. The random variable is the number of days so, being a number, it is discrete.**

2 Probability distributions ⊃ p. 169

1 Sum of given probabilities $= \frac{625}{1296} + \frac{125}{324} + \frac{5}{324} + \frac{1}{1296}$

$= \frac{191}{216}$

Missing probability $= 1 - \frac{191}{216}$

$= \frac{25}{216}$

2 a i $P(\text{4 tails}) = \frac{5}{32}$

ii $P(\text{at least 4 tails}) = P(\text{4 tails}) + P(\text{5 tails})$

$= \frac{5}{32} + \frac{1}{32}$

$= \frac{3}{16}$

b The distribution in part **a** can be used to model the number of female kittens in a litter of five.

$P(\text{at least 2 females}) = \frac{5}{16} + \frac{5}{16} + \frac{3}{16}$

$= \frac{13}{16}$

So the probability of getting at least two female kittens would also be $\frac{13}{16}$.

3 a

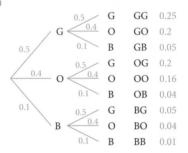

b $P(\text{no orange}) = P(GG) + P(GB) + P(BG) + P(BB)$

$= 0.25 + 0.05 + 0.05 + 0.01$

$= 0.36$

$P(\text{1 orange}) = P(GO) + P(OG) + P(OB) + P(BO)$

$= 0.2 + 0.2 + 0.04 + 0.04$

$= 0.48$

Let $X$ be the number of orange balls.

| $X$ | 0 | 1 | 2 |
|---|---|---|---|
| $P(X)$ | 0.36 | 0.48 | 0.16 |

4

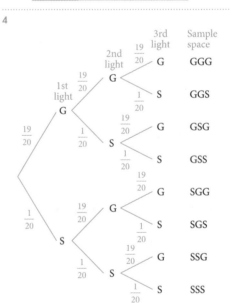

$P(\text{stop 3 times}) = \left(\frac{1}{20}\right)^3$

$= \frac{1}{8000}$

$$P(\text{stop twice}) = 3 \times \left(\frac{1}{20}\right)^2 \times \frac{19}{20}$$

$$= \frac{57}{8000}$$

$$P(\text{stop once}) = 3 \times \frac{1}{20} \times \left(\frac{19}{20}\right)^2$$

$$= \frac{1083}{8000}$$

$$P(\text{no stop}) = \left(\frac{19}{20}\right)^3$$

$$= \frac{6859}{8000}$$

Let $X$ be the number of times that Sam has to stop.

| X | 0 | 1 | 2 | 3 |
|---|---|---|---|---|
| P(X) | $\frac{6859}{8000}$ | $\frac{1083}{8000}$ | $\frac{57}{8000}$ | $\frac{1}{8000}$ |

## 3 Mean or expected value ⊃ p. 170

1  $E(X) = 0 \times \frac{1000}{2197} + 1 \times \frac{900}{2197} + 2 \times \frac{270}{2197} + 3 \times \frac{27}{2197}$

$$= \frac{9}{13}$$

2  $\mu = 0 \times 0.26 + 1 \times 0.28 + 2 \times 0.22 + 3 \times 0.17 + 4 \times 0.07$

$$= 1.51$$

**The mean is 1.51.**

3  $P(\text{heads}) = \frac{2}{3}$ and $P(\text{tails}) = \frac{1}{3}$.

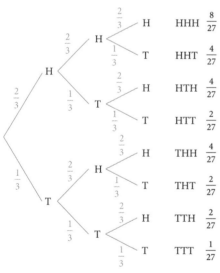

Let $X$ be the number of heads obtained.

| X | 0 | 1 | 2 | 3 |
|---|---|---|---|---|
| P(X) | $\frac{1}{27}$ | $\frac{2}{9}$ | $\frac{4}{9}$ | $\frac{8}{27}$ |

$E(X) = 0 \times \frac{1}{27} + 1 \times \frac{2}{9} + 2 \times \frac{4}{9} + 3 \times \frac{8}{27}$
$= 2$

**The mean is 2.**

4  The sum of the probabilities must be 1.

$0.11 + 0.24 + a + b + 0.18 = 1$

$\qquad\qquad\qquad a + b = 0.47 \quad$ (i)

| X | 1 | 2 | 3 | 4 | 5 |
|---|---|---|---|---|---|
| P(X) | 0.11 | 0.24 | a | b | 0.18 |

Now $E(X) = 3.1$

So $3.1 = 1 \times 0.11 + 2 \times 0.24 + 3 \times a + 4 \times b + 5 \times 0.18$

$\quad 3.1 = 3a + 4b + 1.49$

$\quad 1.61 = 3a + 4b \quad$ (ii)

(i) $\times$ 4:  $4a + 4b = 1.88 \quad$ (iii)

(iii) – (ii):  $\qquad a = 0.27$

Substitute into (i):

$0.27 + b = 0.47$

$\qquad b = 0.2$

∴ ***a* = 0.27 and *b* = 0.2**

## 4 Variance and standard deviation ⊃ p. 171

1  a  $E(X) = 1 \times 0.17 + 2 \times 0.29 + 3 \times 0.35 + 4 \times 0.13 + 5 \times 0.06$

$\qquad = \textbf{2.62}$

 b  $E(X^2) = 1^2 \times 0.17 + 2^2 \times 0.29 + 3^2 \times 0.35 + 4^2 \times 0.13 + 5^2 \times 0.06$

$\qquad = 8.06$

$\quad \text{Var}(X) = E(X^2) - [(E(X)]^2$

$\qquad\qquad = 8.06 - (2.62)^2$

$\qquad\qquad = \textbf{1.1956}$

 c  $\sigma = \sqrt{1.1956}$

$\qquad = 1.093\,434\,95\ldots$

$\qquad = \textbf{1.09} \quad$ (2 d.p.)

2  $E(X) = 0 \times \frac{16}{81} + 1 \times \frac{32}{81} + 2 \times \frac{24}{81} + 3 \times \frac{8}{81} + 4 \times \frac{1}{81}$

$\qquad = 1\frac{1}{3}$

$E(X^2) = 0 \times \frac{16}{81} + 1^2 \times \frac{32}{81} + 2^2 \times \frac{24}{81} + 3^2 \times \frac{8}{81} + 4^2 \times \frac{1}{81}$

$\qquad = 2\frac{2}{3}$

$\text{Var}(X) = 2\frac{2}{3} - \left(1\frac{1}{3}\right)^2$

$\qquad = \frac{8}{9}$

$\sigma = \sqrt{\frac{8}{9}}$

$\quad = 0.942\,809\,041\ldots$

$\quad = 0.94 \quad$ (2 d.p.)

**The mean is $1\frac{1}{3}$ and the standard deviation is 0.94 to two decimal**

**places**.

**3** Let $S$ be the event that there are side effects and $N$ be the event that there are no side effects.

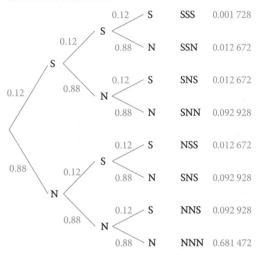

| outcome | probability |
|---|---|
| SSS | 0.001 728 |
| SSN | 0.012 672 |
| SNS | 0.012 672 |
| SNN | 0.092 928 |
| NSS | 0.012 672 |
| SNS | 0.092 928 |
| NNS | 0.092 928 |
| NNN | 0.681 472 |

Let $X$ be the number of people who develop side effects.

| X | 0 | 1 | 2 | 3 |
|---|---|---|---|---|
| P(X) | 0.681 472 | 0.278 784 | 0.038 016 | 0.001 728 |

$E(X) = 0 \times 0.681\,472 + 1 \times 0.278\,784 + 2 \times 0.038\,016$
$\qquad + 3 \times 0.001\,728$
$\qquad = 0.36$

$E(X^2) = 1^2 \times 0.278\,784 + 2^2 \times 0.038\,016 + 3^2 \times 0.001\,728$
$\qquad = \mathbf{0.4464}$

$\mathrm{Var}(X) = 0.4464 - (0.36)^2$
$\qquad = \mathbf{0.3168}$

$\sigma = \sqrt{0.3168}$
$\quad = 0.562\,849\,891\ldots$
$\quad = \mathbf{0.56} \quad \text{(2 d.p.)}$

## 5 Samples of the population ⊃ p. 173

**1 a**

| X | 0 | 1 | 2 | 3 |
|---|---|---|---|---|
| P(X) | $\dfrac{1}{8}$ | $\dfrac{3}{8}$ | $\dfrac{3}{8}$ | $\dfrac{1}{8}$ |

$E(X) = 0 \times \dfrac{1}{8} + 1 \times \dfrac{3}{8} + 2 \times \dfrac{3}{8} + 3 \times \dfrac{1}{8}$

$\qquad = 1\dfrac{1}{2}$

$E(X^2) = 0 \times \dfrac{1}{8} + 1^2 \times \dfrac{3}{8} + 2^2 \times \dfrac{3}{8} + 3^2 \times \dfrac{1}{8}$

$\qquad = 3$

$\mathrm{Var}(X) = 3 - \left(1\dfrac{1}{2}\right)^2$

$\qquad = \dfrac{3}{4}$

$\sigma = \sqrt{\dfrac{3}{4}}$

$\quad = 0.866\,025\,403\ldots$
$\quad = \mathbf{0.87} \quad \text{(2 d.p.)}$

**b** Trial 1:

| X | 0 | 1 | 2 | 3 |
|---|---|---|---|---|
| P(X) | 0 | 0.3 | 0.5 | 0.2 |

$\bar{x} = 0 \times 0 + 1 \times 0.3 + 2 \times 0.5 + 3 \times 0.2$
$\quad = 1.9$
Now $0 \times 0 + 1^2 \times 0.3 + 2^2 \times 0.5 + 3^2 \times 0.2 = 4.1$
$\quad \mathrm{Var} = 4.1 - 1.9^2$
$\qquad = 0.49$
$s = \sqrt{0.49}$
$\quad = \mathbf{0.7}$

Trial 2:

| X | 0 | 1 | 2 | 3 |
|---|---|---|---|---|
| P(X) | 0.2 | 0.4 | 0.3 | 0.1 |

$\bar{x} = 0 \times 0.2 + 1 \times 0.4 + 2 \times 0.3 + 3 \times 0.1$
$\quad = 1.3$
Now $0 \times 0.2 + 1^2 \times 0.4 + 2^2 \times 0.3 + 3^2 \times 0.1 = 2.5$
$\quad \mathrm{Var} = 2.5 - 1.3^2$
$\qquad = 0.81$
$s = \sqrt{0.81}$
$\quad = \mathbf{0.9}$

**c** Each of the trials is very small. The results from trial 1 are less than for the population while the results for trial 2 are greater than for the population so combining the information from both trials would probably result in better estimates.

**2 a** $\bar{x} = 1 \times 0.35 + 2 \times 0.16 + 3 \times 0.11 + 4 \times 0.07 + 6 \times 0.03$
$\qquad = \mathbf{1.46}$

**b** The sample mean is greater than the population mean. There is no information about the size of the survey or whether the overs were chosen randomly over the whole match or were just from the overs of only one of the teams. The time of the innings and the number of wickets would also affect the results.

**3** $\mu = 0 \times 0.59 + 1 \times 0.21 + 2 \times 0.15 + 3 \times 0.05$
$\quad = 0.66$

| X | 0 | 1 | 2 | 3 |
|---|---|---|---|---|
| P(X) | 0.59 | 0.21 | 0.15 | 0.05 |

Sample 1 mean $= 0 \times 0.45 + 1 \times 0.25 + 2 \times 0.2 + 3 \times 0.1$
$\qquad\qquad\quad = 0.95$

| X | 0 | 1 | 2 | 3 |
|---|---|---|---|---|
| P(X) | 0.45 | 0.25 | 0.2 | 0.1 |

Sample 2 mean $= 0 \times 0.7 + 1 \times 0.15 + 2 \times 0.1 + 3 \times 0.05$
$\qquad\qquad\quad = 0.5$

| X | 0 | 1 | 2 | 3 |
|---|---|---|---|---|
| P(X) | 0.7 | 0.15 | 0.1 | 0.05 |

Sample 3 mean $= 0 \times 0.61 + 1 \times 0.22 + 2 \times 0.14 + 3 \times 0.03$
$\qquad\qquad\quad = 0.59$

| X | 0 | 1 | 2 | 3 |
|---|---|---|---|---|
| P(X) | 0.61 | 0.22 | 0.14 | 0.03 |

Sample 4 mean $= 0 \times 0.65 + 1 \times 0.18 + 2 \times 0.15 + 3 \times 0.04$
$= 0.6$

| $X$ | 0 | 1 | 2 | 3 |
|---|---|---|---|---|
| $P(X)$ | 0.63 | 0.18 | 0.15 | 0.04 |

Mean of the sample means $= \dfrac{0.95 + 0.5 + 0.59 + 0.6}{4}$
$= 0.66$

∴ **the mean of the sample means is equal to the population mean.**

## YEAR 11 EXAM-TYPE QUESTIONS

### Part A

**1  A**  $P(\text{Bill, Dennis}) = \dfrac{1}{5} \times \dfrac{1}{4}$
$= \dfrac{1}{20}$

**2  B**  $P = \{1, 2, 3, 4, 5, 6\}, \quad Q = \{2, 4, 6, 8, 10\}$
$P \cup Q = \{1, 2, 3, 4, 5, 6, 8, 10\}$
There are eight elements.

**3  D**  $P(\text{Jimmy chosen}) = \dfrac{2}{6}$
$= \dfrac{1}{3}$

**4  A**  $P(\text{1 red, 1 blue}) = \dfrac{2}{6}$
$= \dfrac{1}{3}$

**5  A**  If $P(X) = 0.36$, $P(Y) = 0.4$, $P(X \cup Y) = 0.6$ and $P(X \cap Y) = 0.16$,
$P(X|Y) = \dfrac{P(X \cap Y)}{P(Y)}$
$= \dfrac{0.16}{0.4}$
$= \dfrac{2}{5}$

**6  C**  If the first counter was black, three black and five white remain.
$P(\text{second is black}) = \dfrac{3}{8}$

**7  B**  Number studying Japanese but not Indonesian
$= 42 - 28$
$= 14$
Total studying either $= 14 + 49$
$= 63$
Total studying neither $= 70 - 63$
$= 7$
$P(\text{studying neither}) = \dfrac{7}{70}$
$= \dfrac{1}{10}$

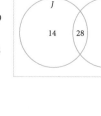

**8  D**  $P(\text{no heads}) = \dfrac{1}{4}$
$P(\text{at least 1 head}) = 1 - \dfrac{1}{4}$
$= \dfrac{3}{4}$

**9  D**  $P(X = 1) = 1 - \left(\dfrac{1}{8} + \dfrac{5}{12} + \dfrac{1}{4}\right)$
$= \dfrac{5}{24}$

**10  C**  $P(P \cup B) = P(P) + P(B) - P(P \cap B)$
$= 0.52 + 0.3 - 0.17$
$= 0.65$

**11  B**  $P(\text{both charged}) = \dfrac{3}{4} \times \dfrac{2}{3}$
$= \dfrac{1}{2}$

**12  C**  $P(\text{odd}) = P(\text{ends in 1 or 3})$
$= \dfrac{2}{3}$

### Part B

**13**  **The statement is false because the outcomes are not equally likely.**  ✓

**14  a**  Total frequency $= 7 + 5 + 9 + 5 + 8 + 6$
$= 40$
Relative frequency of 5 $= \dfrac{8}{40}$
$= \dfrac{1}{5}$  ✓

**b**  Expected number $= \dfrac{1}{5} \times 12$
$= \textbf{2.4 times}$  ✓

**15**  $P(P|C) = \dfrac{P(P \cap C)}{P(C)}$
$= \dfrac{0.24}{0.4}$
$= \textbf{0.6}$  ✓

**16  a**  $P(\text{Guy wins 1st prize}) = \dfrac{25}{200}$
$= \dfrac{1}{8}$  ✓

**b**  $P(\text{both prizes}) = \dfrac{25}{200} \times \dfrac{24}{199}$
$= \dfrac{3}{199}$  ✓

**c**  $P(\text{no prize}) = \dfrac{175}{200} \times \dfrac{174}{199}$
$= \dfrac{609}{796}$  ✓

**d**  $P(\text{at least 1 prize}) = 1 - P(\text{no prize})$
$= 1 - \dfrac{609}{796}$
$= \dfrac{187}{796}$  ✓

**e**  $P(\text{second prize}) = \dfrac{25}{200}$
$= \dfrac{1}{8}$  ✓

**17** Total surveyed

$= 11 + 3 + 4 + 6 + 5 + 1 + 9 + 7$

$= 46$

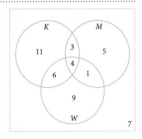

**a** **i** $P(\text{saw all 3 birds}) = \dfrac{4}{46}$

$= \dfrac{2}{23}$ ✓

**ii** $P(\text{saw none}) = \dfrac{7}{46}$ ✓

**iii** $P(\text{kookaburra and magpie but no wren}) = \dfrac{3}{46}$ ✓

**iv** $P(\text{exactly 2 birds}) = \dfrac{10}{46}$

$= \dfrac{5}{23}$ ✓

**b** Number who saw wren $= 6 + 4 + 1 + 9$

$= 20$

$P(\text{of those who saw wren also saw magpie}) = \dfrac{5}{20}$

$= \dfrac{1}{4}$ ✓

**18 a** $P(\text{both diseases}) = 0.4 \times 0.2$

$= 0.08$

$= \mathbf{8\%}$ ✓

**b** $P(\text{disease A but not disease B}) = 0.4 \times 0.8$

$= 0.32$

$= \mathbf{32\%}$ ✓

**c** $P(\text{neither disease}) = 0.6 \times 0.8$

$= 0.48$

$= \mathbf{48\%}$ ✓

**d** $P(\text{exactly one disease}) = 0.4 \times 0.8 + 0.6 \times 0.2$ ✓

$= 0.44$

$= \mathbf{44\%}$ ✓

**e** $P(\text{at least one disease}) = 1 - P(\text{no disease})$

$= 1 - 0.48$

$= 0.52$

$= \mathbf{52\%}$ ✓

**19 a** $P(\text{attends tax lecture}) = \dfrac{32}{40}$

$= \dfrac{4}{5}$ ✓

**b** $P(\text{both marketing}) = \dfrac{28}{40} \times \dfrac{27}{39}$

$= \dfrac{63}{130}$ ✓

**c** Number attending both $= (32 + 28) - 40$

$= 20$ ✓

$P(\text{attends both}) = \dfrac{20}{40}$

$= \dfrac{1}{2}$ ✓

**d** $P(\text{tax attendee also attends marketing}) = \dfrac{20}{32}$

$= \dfrac{5}{8}$ ✓

**20 a** $P(\text{exactly 2 answers C}) = \dfrac{27}{128}$ ✓

**b** $P(\text{at least 1 C}) = 1 - P(\text{no C})$

$= 1 - \dfrac{81}{256}$

$= \dfrac{175}{256}$ ✓

**c** $P(\text{more than 2 C's}) = \dfrac{3}{64} + \dfrac{1}{256}$

$= \dfrac{13}{256}$ ✓

**d** $E(X) = 0 \times \dfrac{81}{256} + 1 \times \dfrac{27}{64} + 2 \times \dfrac{27}{128} + 3 \times \dfrac{3}{64} + 4 \times \dfrac{1}{256}$

$= 1$

The mean is **1**. ✓

**This is exactly what you would expect if there are four options in multiple-choice questions. The option C should appear once in four questions.** ✓

**e** $E(X^2) = 0 \times \dfrac{81}{256} + 1^2 \times \dfrac{27}{64} + 2^2 \times \dfrac{27}{128} + 3^2 \times \dfrac{3}{64} + 4^2 \times \dfrac{1}{256}$

$= 1\dfrac{3}{4}$

$\text{Var}(X) = 1\dfrac{3}{4} - 1^2$

$= \dfrac{3}{4}$ ✓

$\sigma = \sqrt{\dfrac{3}{4}}$

$= 0.866\,025\,403\ldots$

$= \mathbf{0.87}$ (2 d.p.) ✓

**21 a**

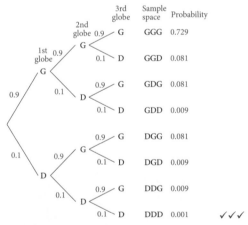

**b** Let $X$ be the number of defective globes.

| X | 0 | 1 | 2 | 3 |
|---|---|---|---|---|
| P(X) | 0.729 | 0.243 | 0.027 | 0.001 |

✓✓

**c** $E(X) = 0 \times 0.729 + 1 \times 0.243 + 2 \times 0.027 + 3 \times 0.001$

$= 0.3$

**You would expect 0.3 globes to be defective.** ✓

# SAMPLE YEAR 11 EXAMINATION 1

**General instructions**
- Reading time: 5 minutes
- Working time: 2 hours
- Write using black pen.
- Calculators approved by NESA may be used.
- Attempt all questions.

**Total marks: 100**
Section I: 10 marks
Section II: 90 marks

## Section I: 10 Marks

Allow about 15 minutes for this section.

### Objective-response questions     (1 mark each)

Choose the letter A, B, C or D that corresponds to the best answer.

**1** What is $|-6| - 2|-5|$ equal to?

   **A** $-4$    **B** $4$    **C** $9$    **D** $16$

**2** A box holds five cards which are identical except for the letters written on them. One card has E, one card has I, one has L, one M and one shows S. If the cards are drawn at random, one after the other, and laid out on a table in the order that they are drawn, what is the probability that they spell SMILE?

   **A** $\dfrac{1}{5}$    **B** $\dfrac{1}{15}$    **C** $\dfrac{1}{120}$    **D** $\dfrac{1}{3125}$

**3** What is the value of $e^2$ to four decimal places?

   **A** $0.6931$    **B** $1.8842$    **C** $5.4366$    **D** $7.3891$

**4** If $f(x) = \begin{cases} 3x^2 + 1 \text{ if } x \geq -2 \\ 12 - 5x \text{ if } x < -2 \end{cases}$ what is $f(-2)$?

   **A** $-11$             **B** $13$

   **C** $22$              **D** $37$

**5** What is the value of $\theta$ to the nearest degree?

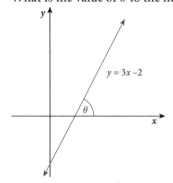

   **A** $34°$    **B** $56°$
   **C** $63°$    **D** $72°$

**6** What is the value of $\operatorname{cosec} \dfrac{3\pi}{8}$ to four decimal places?

   **A** $0.9239$
   **B** $1.0824$
   **C** $2.6131$
   **D** $48.6376$

**7** In a group of 30 students, 16 study geography, 15 study history and 7 study both. If a student is selected at random from the group, what is the probability that they study neither history nor geography?

   **A** $0$             **B** $\dfrac{4}{15}$

   **C** $\dfrac{1}{5}$            **D** $\dfrac{1}{6}$

**8** Which is correct about the roots of the quadratic equation $5x^2 - 2x + 3 = 0$?

   **A** not real
   **B** real but not rational
   **C** real, rational but not equal
   **D** real, rational and equal

**9** What is $\dfrac{d}{dx}(3x-2)^4$?

   **A** $4(3x-2)^3$
   **B** $12(3x-2)^3$
   **C** $3(3x-2)^3$
   **D** $(3x-2)^3$

**10** Which is equivalent to $1 + \log_a x$?

   **A** $\log_a x$
   **B** $\log_a(x+1)$
   **C** $\log_a ax$
   **D** $\log_{a+1} x$

**Allow about 1 hour and 45 minutes for this section.**

11 Simplify $\dfrac{\left(2m^3\right)^3 \div \left(8m^2\right)^0}{4m^{-2} \times 2m^{-3}}$. (1 mark)

12 Express $75°$ in radians in terms of $\pi$. (1 mark)

13 Evaluate $\log_4 6 + \log_4 2 - \log_4 3$. (1 mark)

14 Find the exact value of $\cos \dfrac{5\pi}{4}$. (1 mark)

15 Simplify $\dfrac{m^2 - 25}{m^2 - 7m + 10} \div \dfrac{m^2 + 9m + 20}{m^2 + m - 6}$. (2 marks)

16 If $f(x) = 3x - 2$ and $g(x) = x^2 + 2$ find:

  a $f(0)$ (1 mark)

  b $g(-3)$ (1 mark)

  c $f(g(x))$ (1 mark)

  d $g(f(x))$ (1 mark)

17 Find the equation of the line through $(-2, -13)$ and $(4, 5)$. (2 marks)

18 Find $\log_3 15$ correct to two decimal places. (2 marks)

19 Solve $3x^2 = 4x + 1$ giving the answers in simplest surd form. (2 marks)

20 Simplify
$\sin\theta \sin(180° - \theta) - \sin(90° - \theta)\cos(180° - \theta)$ (2 marks)

21 Differentiate:

  a $7e^{2x}$ (1 mark)

  b $y = x^4(9x - 1)^5$ (2 marks)

  c $y = \dfrac{2}{(7-x)^4}$ (2 marks)

  d $y = \sqrt{2x - 5}$ (2 marks)

  e $y = \dfrac{3x + 2}{6x - 2}$ (2 marks)

22 Box A holds 12 red apples and nine green apples. Box B holds eight red and seven green apples. Ken chooses a box at random and then takes two apples from the box. By drawing a tree diagram, or otherwise, find the probability that the apples are the same colour. (3 marks)

23 $P$, $Q$ and $R$ are the corners of a triangular paddock which has recently been surveyed. $Q$ is 273.5 m from $P$ on a bearing of $068°$. The bearing of $Q$ from $R$ is $317°$, and of $R$ from $P$ is $105°$.

  a Show this information on a diagram. (1 mark)

  b What is the size of $\angle PRQ$? (1 mark)

  c Find the length of the side $QR$. (2 marks)

  d Find the area of the paddock in hectares, correct to two decimal places. (2 marks)

24 On the same set of axes sketch $y = 5^x$ and $y = \log_5 x$. (2 marks)

25 Consider $y = x^2 - 2x - 15$.

  a What is the $y$-intercept? (1 mark)

  b Find the $x$-intercepts. (2 marks)

  c What is the domain and range? (2 marks)

26 From first principles, find the derivative of the function $f(x) = 2x^2 - 3x$. (3 marks)

27 The length of an arc of a sector is $6\pi$ cm and it subtends an angle of $\dfrac{2\pi}{5}$ radians.

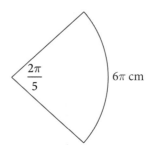

  a Find the radius of the sector. (2 marks)

  b Find the exact area of the sector. (1 mark)

28 a Show that $f(x) = x^3 - 3x$ is an odd function. (1 mark)

  b Show that $f'(x)$ is an even function. (2 marks)

29 Find the mean, variance and standard deviation for this probability distribution. (3 marks)

| $X$ | 0 | 1 | 2 | 3 |
|---|---|---|---|---|
| $P(X)$ | 0.008 | 0.096 | 0.384 | 0.512 |

30 Solve $2\ln x = \ln(5x + 14)$. (3 marks)

31 Solve, for $0 \le x \le 2\pi$, $2\sin x = \sqrt{3}$. (2 marks)

32 Find the equation of the normal to the curve $y = -x^2 + 6x - 2$ at $(2, 6)$. (3 marks)

33 The formula $R = \frac{2}{3}\log_{10}k - 0.9$ is used to find the Richter scale magnitude, $R$, of an earthquake that releases $k$ kilojoules of energy.

   a  What is the magnitude of an earthquake that produces $6.5 \times 10^7$ kJ of energy?   (1 mark)

   b  How much energy is released by an earthquake measuring 6.8 on the Richter scale?   (2 marks)

34  a  Sketch $y = \cos x$ and $y = \frac{1}{2}$ on the same set of axes for $-2\pi \le x \le 2\pi$.   (2 marks)

   b  Write down all solutions, $-2\pi \le x \le 2\pi$, for which $\cos x = \frac{1}{2}$.   (1 mark)

35 A particle is moving along the $x$-axis. At time $t$ seconds, the displacement from the origin, $x$ metres, of the particle is given by $x = 7 + 20t - 2t^2$.

   a  When and where is the particle at rest?   (3 marks)

   b  Find an expression for the acceleration. Comment briefly on the significance of the answer.   (2 marks)

36 In $\triangle ABC$, $AC = 12$ cm and $BC = 17$ cm. If $\angle ABC = 38°$, find the size of $\angle BAC$ to the nearest degree.   (3 marks)

37 Write as a single logarithm: $\log_3 2 + \log_9 16$.   (2 marks)

38 The numbers 6, 7, 8, 9 and 10 appear on a wheel which, when spun, is equally likely to stop on any of the numbers. The wheel is spun twice and the numbers added. What is the probability that:

   a  the sum is greater than 15?   (2 marks)

   b  if at least one of the numbers is 7, the sum is greater than 15?   (1 mark)

39 $AB$ represents a tower of height 32 m. From $C$, which is due east of $B$ on level ground, the angle of elevation of $A$ is $24°$. From $D$, which is on a bearing of $215°$ from $B$ on level ground, the angle of elevation of $A$ is $17°$. Find the distance from $C$ to $D$.   (3 marks)

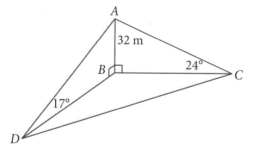

40 There are three red, one blue and two yellow pegs in a bag. One peg is selected at random, its colour noted and the peg replaced. A second peg is then drawn.

   a  Draw a tree diagram and show the sample space and the probability for each element of the sample space.   (2 marks)

   b  Let $X$ be the random variable of the number of yellow pegs drawn. Draw a probability distribution.   (2 marks)

   c  What is the expected number of yellow pegs?   (1 mark)

## Section I: 10 Marks

Allow about 15 minutes for this section.

### Objective-response questions    (1 mark each)

Choose the letter A, B, C or D that corresponds to the best answer.

1  What is the exact value of $\sec \dfrac{\pi}{6}$?

  A  $\dfrac{\sqrt{3}}{2}$    B  $\dfrac{2}{\sqrt{3}}$    C  $\dfrac{1}{\sqrt{3}}$    D  $\sqrt{2}$

2  If $\log_a b = 0.36$ what is the value of $\log_a \sqrt{b}$?

  A  0.06    B  0.18    C  0.6    D  0.72

3  The equation of the tangent to the curve $y = x^2 - 4x$ at $P$ is $y = 2x - 9$. What is the gradient of the normal to $y = x^2 - 4x$ at $P$?

  A  $\dfrac{1}{9}$    B  $\dfrac{1}{2}$    C  $-\dfrac{1}{9}$    D  $-\dfrac{1}{2}$

4  In simplest form, $\sqrt{12} + \sqrt{48} =$?

  A  $\sqrt{60}$    B  $2\sqrt{15}$    C  $6\sqrt{2}$    D  $6\sqrt{3}$

5  What is the vertex of $y = x^2 - 8x + 12$?

  A  $(-4, -4)$    B  $(4, -4)$
  C  $(4, 4)$    D  $(-4, 4)$

6  A partially completed probability distribution is shown. $X$ is the number of heads when a biased coin is tossed three times.

| $X$ | 0 | 1 | 2 | 3 |
|---|---|---|---|---|
| $P(X)$ | $\dfrac{1}{64}$ | $\dfrac{9}{64}$ | | $\dfrac{27}{64}$ |

What is the probability of at least two heads?

  A  $\dfrac{27}{32}$    B  $\dfrac{27}{64}$

  C  $\dfrac{37}{64}$    D  $\dfrac{5}{32}$

7  What is the true bearing equivalent to the compass bearing S 35° E?

  A  145°    B  215°
  C  135°    D  225°

8  If $f(x) = 9 - 2e^{-5x}$, what is $f'(x)$?

  A  $10e^{-5x}$    B  $-10e^{-5x}$
  C  $-2e^{-5x}$    D  $-e^{-5x}$

9  If the probability that a project will be both started on time and finished on time is 0.24 and the probability that it will be started on time is 0.32, what is the probability that it will be finished on time given that it is started on time?

  A  0.08    B  0.56
  C  0.75    D  0.8

10  Which is correct about $y = f(x)$ at the point $P$?

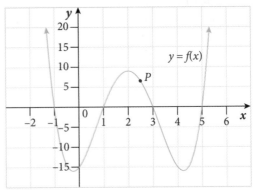

  A  increasing at an increasing rate
  B  increasing at a decreasing rate
  C  decreasing at an increasing rate
  D  decreasing at a decreasing rate

11 Find the exact value of $\tan 300°$. (1 mark)

12 Express $\dfrac{2}{x^2+2x} - \dfrac{3}{x^2+3x}$ as a single fraction in simplest form. (2 marks)

13 a If $f(x) = p + qx - rx^2$, find $f(x) + f(-x)$. (2 marks)

  b Is $f(x) + f(-x)$ an even or odd function? (1 mark)

14 Solve $|15x - 27| = 18$. (2 marks)

15 Express $\dfrac{8^{2x} \times 4^{3x}}{16^{x+2} \div 2^x}$ in simplest index form. (2 marks)

16 Show that $\tan \theta - \sin^2\theta \tan \theta = \sin \theta \cos \theta$. (2 marks)

17 Solve $5x^2 - 8x + 2 = 0$ giving each answer correct to three decimal places. (2 marks)

18 If $\log_5(x + y) = 0$ and $\log_5(x - y) = 1$, find the values of $x$ and $y$. (2 marks)

19 If $f(x) = 9 - x^2$ and $g(x) = 2x - 3$ find $f(g(x))$. (2 marks)

20 Find:

  a $P(X \cap Y)$ (1 mark)

  b $P(Y \cup Z)$ (1 mark)

  c $P(X|Z)$ (1 mark)

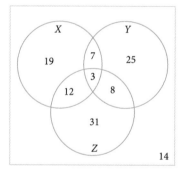

21 Differentiate:

  a $y = 4x^3 - 7x^2 + 2x - 9$ (1 mark)

  b $y = x^5(6x - 5)^3$ (2 marks)

  c $y = \sqrt[3]{3x-8}$ (2 marks)

  d $y = \dfrac{2x+5}{3x-2}$ (2 marks)

22 If $\tan \theta = -1$ and $0° \le \theta \le 180°$, find $\theta$. (2 marks)

23 Find the coordinates of the centre and the length of the radius of the circle $x^2 + y^2 = 4x - 6y - 12$. (2 marks)

24 Water is flowing into a one-litre container. At time $t$ minutes the volume of water, $V$ millilitres, in the container is given by $V = 3t^2 + 5t + 250$.

  a Find the amount of water in the container when the water begins to flow. (1 mark)

  b Find the rate at which the water is flowing when $t = 5$. (2 marks)

25 In a particular class at a school five of the females are 18 years old and eight are 17. Of the males, six are 18 and five are 17 years old. One male and one female student are chosen at random. What is the probability that:

  a both are 17 years old? (1 mark)

  b one is 17 and one is 18? (1 mark)

26 The diagram shows a sector of a circle, centre $O$. The region $ABCD$ represents an area to be concreted to form a path.

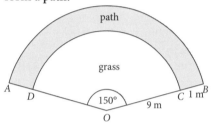

  a Find how many cubic metres of concrete will be needed for the path if it is to be 12 cm thick. (2 marks)

  b While doing the concreting a woman working at point $B$ needs a trowel which she left at point $A$. How much longer is it for her to walk around the arc from $B$ to $A$, than from $B$ to $C$ straight across the grass to $D$ and then to $A$? (3 marks)

27 Find the gradient of the secant $AB$ to the curve $y = 3x^2 - 5$, if at $A$, $x = 1$ and at $B$, $x = 3$. (2 marks)

28 $ABCD$ is a parallelogram. $AB = 5$ m, $BC = 3$ m and $\angle ABC = 60°$.

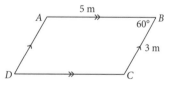

  a Find the length of the diagonal $BD$. (2 marks)

  b Find the exact area of the parallelogram. (2 marks)

29 For what range of values of $m$ does the equation $P(x) = 0$ have real roots given that $P(x) = (m - 2)x^2 + (m + 1)x + 3$? (2 marks)

30 Solve, for $0 \le x \le 2\pi$, $\tan x - 2 \sin x = 0$. (2 marks)

**31 a** On the same set of axes graph
$y = \sqrt{25 - x^2}$ and $y = 2x - 2$. (2 marks)

**b** Hence write down any solutions
of the equation $2x - 2 = \sqrt{25 - x^2}$. (1 mark)

**32** Find, from first principles, the gradient
function of the curve $y = 3x^2 + 4x - 5$. (3 marks)

**33** If $2 \ln x = \ln(3x + 4)$, find, correct to three decimal
places, the value of $\ln 2x$. (3 marks)

**34** A section of a model railway contains three sets of
lights each of which may show either red or green. If the
light is red the train will stop, but if the light is green it
will pass straight through. The lights are twice as likely
to show green as red. A train completes one circuit of
the track.

**a** Draw a tree diagram to show the possible
sequence of lights and the
probability of each. (3 marks)

**b** What is the probability that the train
had to stop exactly once? (1 mark)

**c** What is the probability that the train had to stop at
least once? (1 mark)

**35** $A$ and $B$ are two points 800 m apart
on a straight road. A monument, $M$,
is located to one side of the road so
that $\angle MAB = 64°$ and $\angle MBA = 71°$
as shown in the diagram.

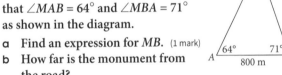

**a** Find an expression for $MB$. (1 mark)
**b** How far is the monument from
the road?
Give the answer to the nearest 10 m. (2 marks)

**36 a** On the same diagram graph
$y = -\sin x$ and $y = \cos\dfrac{x}{2}$, for $0 \le x \le 2\pi$. (3 marks)

**b** Write down the value(s) of $x$, $0 \le x \le 2\pi$,
for which $\cos\dfrac{x}{2} + \sin x = 0$. (1 mark)

**37** For what value(s) of $x$ does $e^{2x} = e^x$? (2 marks)

**38** $D$ is 250 m due south of $B$ on level ground. The angle of
elevation of $A$ from $D$ is $18°$.

**a** Find the height of $AB$ in metres to the
nearest metre. (1 mark)
**b** Find the distance of $C$ from $B$ given that
the angle of elevation of $A$ from $C$ is $23°$. (1 mark)
**c** $C$ is due east of $B$. Find the distance
from $C$ to $D$ to the nearest metre. (1 mark)

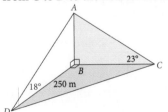

**39** This spinner is equally likely to land
on any of the sectors. It is spun
twice.

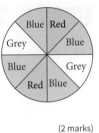

**a** Draw a tree diagram showing
the possible colours for each
spin and give the probability
for each element in the sample
space. (2 marks)

**b** Let $X$ be the number of times the spinner
landed on red. Complete a probability
distribution. (2 marks)

**c** What is the mean, variance and standard
deviation (to two decimal places)? (3 marks)

**40 a** $OABC$ is a sector of a circle of radius 264 m. The
shaded area in this diagram is bounded by the arc
$ABC$ of the sector and the chord $AC$. Show that the
shaded area is given by $5808(2\pi - 3\sqrt{3})$ m². (2 marks)

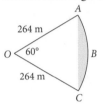

**b** $PAQC$ is a sector of a circle of radius 510 m. The
shaded area is bounded by the arc $AQC$ and the
chord $AC$. Find a similar expression for the shaded
area. (2 marks)

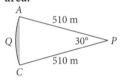

**c** The area between two intersecting circles is shaded
in the diagram below. Find the area in square metres
to one decimal place. (1 mark)

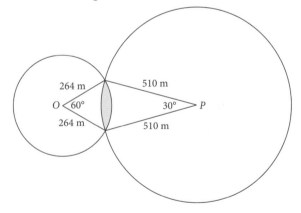

# ANSWERS

## SAMPLE HSC EXAMINATION 1

### Section I

**1  A**  $|-6| - 2|-5| = 6 - 2 \times 5$
$= -4$

**2  C**  $P(\text{SMILE}) = \dfrac{1}{5} \times \dfrac{1}{4} \times \dfrac{1}{3} \times \dfrac{1}{2} \times 1$
$= \dfrac{1}{120}$

**3  D**  $e^2 = 7.389\,056\,09\ldots$
$= 7.3891$    (4 d.p.)

**4  B**  $f(x) = \begin{cases} 3x^2 + 1 & \text{if } x \geq -2 \\ 12 - 5x & \text{if } x < -2 \end{cases}$
$f(-2) = 3 \times (-2)^2 + 1$
$= 13$

**5  D**  The line has gradient $m = 3$.
Now $m = \tan \theta$
$\therefore \theta = \tan^{-1}(3)$
$= 71.565\,0511\ldots^\circ$
$= 72^\circ$    (nearest degree)

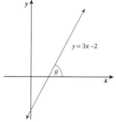

**6  B**  $\operatorname{cosec} \dfrac{3\pi}{8} = \dfrac{1}{\sin\left(\dfrac{3\pi}{8}\right)}$
$= 1.082\,392\ldots$
$= 1.0824$    (4 d.p.)

**7  C**  $P(\text{studies neither}) = \dfrac{6}{30}$
$= \dfrac{1}{5}$

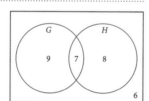

**8  A**  $5x^2 - 2x + 3 = 0$
Now $\Delta = b^2 - 4ac$
$= (-2)^2 - 4 \times 5 \times 3$
$= -56$
As $\Delta < 0$ the roots are not real.

**9  B**  $\dfrac{d}{dx}(3x-2)^4 = 4(3x-2)^3 \times 3$
$= 12(3x-2)^3$

**10  C**  $1 + \log_a x = \log_a a + \log_a x$
$= \log_a ax$

### Section II

**11**  $\dfrac{\left(2m^3\right)^3 \div \left(8m^2\right)^0}{4m^{-2} \times 2m^{-3}} = \dfrac{8m^9 \div 1}{8m^{-5}}$
$= m^{14}$  ✓

**12**  $75^\circ = \dfrac{75\pi}{180}$
$= \dfrac{5\pi}{12}$  ✓

**13**  $\log_4 6 + \log_4 2 - \log_4 3 = \log_4\left(\dfrac{6 \times 2}{3}\right)$
$= \log_4 4$
$= 1$  ✓

**14**  $\cos \dfrac{5\pi}{4} = \cos\left(\pi + \dfrac{\pi}{4}\right)$
$= -\cos \dfrac{\pi}{4}$
$= -\dfrac{1}{\sqrt{2}}$  ✓

**15**  $\dfrac{m^2 - 25}{m^2 - 7m + 10} \div \dfrac{m^2 + 9m + 20}{m^2 + m - 6}$
$= \dfrac{m^2 - 25}{m^2 - 7m + 10} \times \dfrac{m^2 + m - 6}{m^2 + 9m + 20}$
$= \dfrac{(m+5)(m-5)}{(m-2)(m-5)} \times \dfrac{(m+3)(m-2)}{(m+5)(m+4)}$  ✓
$= \dfrac{m+3}{m+4}$  ✓

**16**  $f(x) = 3x - 2$    $g(x) = x^2 + 2$
  **a**  $f(0) = 3 \times 0 - 2$
     $= -2$  ✓
  **b**  $g(-3) = (-3)^2 + 2$
     $= 11$  ✓
  **c**  $f(g(x)) = 3(x^2 + 2) - 2$
     $= 3x^2 + 4$  ✓
  **d**  $g(f(x)) = (3x - 2)^2 + 2$
     $= 9x^2 - 12x + 4 + 2$
     $= 9x^2 - 12x + 6$  ✓

**17**  $(-2, -13)$,    $(4, 5)$
$m = \dfrac{y_2 - y_1}{x_2 - x_1}$
$= \dfrac{5 - (-13)}{4 - (-2)}$
$= 3$  ✓
$y - y_1 = m(x - x_1)$
$y - (-13) = 3(x - (-2))$
$y + 13 = 3x + 6$
$y = 3x - 7$  ✓

**18**  $\log_3 15 = \dfrac{\log_{10} 15}{\log_{10} 3}$    $\left(\text{or } \dfrac{\ln 15}{\ln 3}\right)$  ✓
$= 2.464\,973\,52\ldots$
$= 2.46$    (2 d.p.)  ✓

**19**
$$3x^2 = 4x + 1$$
$$3x^2 - 4x - 1 = 0$$
$$x = \frac{-b \pm \sqrt{b^2 - 4ac}}{2a}$$
$$= \frac{-(-4) \pm \sqrt{(-4)^2 - 4 \times 3 \times -1}}{2 \times 3}$$
$$= \frac{4 \pm \sqrt{28}}{6} \quad \checkmark$$
$$= \frac{4 \pm 2\sqrt{7}}{6}$$
$$= \frac{2 \pm \sqrt{7}}{3} \quad \checkmark$$

**20** $\sin \theta \sin (180° - \theta) - \sin (90° - \theta) \cos (180° - \theta)$
$$= \sin \theta \sin \theta - \cos \theta (-\cos \theta) \quad \checkmark$$
$$= \sin^2\theta + \cos^2\theta$$
$$= 1 \quad \checkmark$$

**21 a** $y = 7e^{2x}$
$$\frac{dy}{dx} = 14e^{2x} \quad \checkmark$$

**b** $y = x^4(9x - 1)^5$
$$\frac{dy}{dx} = x^4 \times 5(9x - 1)^4 \times 9 + (9x - 1)^5 \times 4x^3 \quad \checkmark$$
$$= 45x^4(9x - 1)^4 + 4x^3(9x - 1)^5$$
$$= x^3(9x - 1)^4(45x + 4(9x - 1))$$
$$= x^3(9x - 1)^4(81x - 4) \quad \checkmark$$

**c** $y = \dfrac{2}{(7-x)^4}$
$$= 2(7 - x)^{-4}$$
$$\frac{dy}{dx} = -8(7 - x)^{-5} \times -1 \quad \checkmark$$
$$= 8(7 - x)^{-5}$$
$$= \frac{8}{(7-x)^5} \quad \checkmark$$

**d** $y = \sqrt{2x - 5}$
$$= (2x - 5)^{\frac{1}{2}}$$
$$\frac{dy}{dx} = \frac{1}{2}(2x - 5)^{-\frac{1}{2}} \times 2 \quad \checkmark$$
$$= \frac{1}{\sqrt{2x-5}} \quad \checkmark$$

**e** $y = \dfrac{3x + 2}{6x - 2}$
$$\frac{dy}{dx} = \frac{(6x - 2) \times 3 - (3x + 2) \times 6}{(6x - 2)^2} \quad \checkmark$$
$$= \frac{18x - 6 - 18x - 12}{(6x - 2)^2}$$
$$= \frac{-18}{(6x - 2)^2} \quad \checkmark$$

**22**

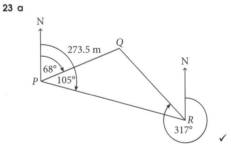

$P(\text{both red}) = P(2 \text{ red from box A}) + P(2 \text{ red from box B})$
$$= \frac{1}{2} \times \frac{12}{21} \times \frac{11}{20} + \frac{1}{2} \times \frac{8}{15} \times \frac{7}{14}$$
$$= \frac{61}{210} \quad \checkmark$$
$P(\text{both green}) = \dfrac{1}{2} \times \dfrac{9}{21} \times \dfrac{8}{20} + \dfrac{1}{2} \times \dfrac{7}{15} \times \dfrac{6}{14}$
$$= \frac{13}{70} \quad \checkmark$$
$P(\text{same colour}) = P(\text{both red}) + P(\text{both green})$
$$= \frac{61}{210} + \frac{13}{70}$$
$$= \frac{10}{21} \quad \checkmark$$

**23 a**

N
*273.5 m*   Q
N
*68°*
P   *105°*
R
*317°*   ✓

**b** Let $X$ be a point due north of $R$.
$$\angle XRQ = 360° - 317°$$
$$= 43°$$
$$\angle XRP + 105° = 180° \quad \text{(co-interior angles)}$$
$$\therefore \angle XRP = 75°$$
$$\angle PRQ = 75° - 43°$$
$$= 32° \quad \checkmark$$

**c** $\angle QPR = 105° - 68°$

$\quad = 37°$

$$\frac{p}{\sin P} = \frac{r}{\sin R}$$

$$\frac{p}{\sin 37°} = \frac{273.5}{\sin 32°} \quad \checkmark$$

$$p = \frac{273.5 \sin 37°}{\sin 32°}$$

$\quad = 310.606\,577\ldots$

$\quad = 310.6 \quad$ (1 d.p.)

**The length of side $QR$ is 310.6 m to one decimal place.** $\checkmark$

**d** $\angle PQR = 180° - (32 + 37)°$

$\quad = 111°$

$$A = \frac{1}{2} pr \sin Q$$

$$= \frac{1}{2} \times 310.606\,577\ldots \times 273.5 \times \sin 111° \quad \checkmark$$

$= 39\,654.2481\ldots$ m²

$= 3.965\,424\,81\ldots$ ha

$= 3.97$ ha $\quad$ (2 d.p.)

**The area of the paddock is 3.97 ha to two decimal places.** $\checkmark$

**24**

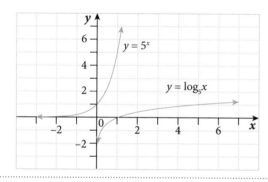

$\checkmark\checkmark$

**25 a** $y = x^2 - 2x - 15$

$\quad$ **$y$-intercept $= -15$** $\checkmark$

**b** The curve cuts the $x$-axis when $y = 0$,

$\quad$ i.e. $x^2 - 2x - 15 = 0$

$\quad (x + 3)(x - 5) = 0 \quad \checkmark$

$\quad\quad\quad x = -3 \quad$ or $\quad x = 5$

$\quad$ **The $x$-intercepts are $-3$ and $5$.** $\checkmark$

**c** Domain: **all real $x$** $\checkmark$

$\quad$ Axis: $x = \dfrac{-3 + 5}{2}$

$\quad\quad\quad x = 1$

$\quad$ When $x = 1$, $y = 1^2 - 2 \times 1 - 15$

$\quad\quad\quad\quad\quad = -16$

$\quad$ So the vertex is $(1, -16)$ and the curve is concave up.

$\quad$ **Range is $y \geq -16$** $\checkmark$

---

**26** $f(x) = 2x^2 - 3x$

$$f'(x) = \lim_{h \to 0} \frac{f(x + h) - f(x)}{h}$$

$$= \lim_{h \to 0} \frac{2(x + h)^2 - 3(x + h) - (2x^2 - 3x)}{h} \quad \checkmark$$

$$= \lim_{h \to 0} \frac{2x^2 + 4xh + 2h^2 - 3x - 3h - 2x^2 + 3x}{h}$$

$$= \lim_{h \to 0} \frac{4xh + 2h^2 - 3h}{h} \quad \checkmark$$

$$= \lim_{h \to 0} \frac{h(4x + 2h - 3)}{h}$$

$$= \lim_{h \to 0} (4x + 2h - 3)$$

$$= 4x - 3 \quad \checkmark$$

**27 a** $l = r\theta$

$\quad 6\pi = r \times \dfrac{2\pi}{5} \quad \checkmark$

$\quad r = 6\pi \div \dfrac{2\pi}{5}$

$\quad\quad = 6\pi \times \dfrac{5}{2\pi}$

$\quad\quad = 15$

$\quad$ **The radius of the sector is 15 cm.** $\checkmark$

**b** $A = \dfrac{1}{2} r^2 \theta$

$\quad\quad = \dfrac{1}{2} \times 15^2 \times \dfrac{2\pi}{5}$

$\quad\quad = 45\pi$

$\quad$ **The exact area is $45\pi$ cm².** $\checkmark$

---

**28 a** $f(x) = x^3 - 3x$

$\quad f(-x) = (-x)^3 - 3 \times (-x)$

$\quad\quad\quad = -x^3 + 3x$

$\quad\quad\quad = -(x^3 - 3x)$

$\quad\quad\quad = -f(x)$

$\quad$ **$\therefore f(x)$ is an odd function.** $\checkmark$

**b** $f'(x) = 3x^2 - 3 \quad \checkmark$

$\quad f'(-x) = 3(-x)^2 - 3$

$\quad\quad\quad = 3x^2 - 3$

$\quad\quad\quad = f'(x)$

$\quad$ **$\therefore f'(x)$ is an even function.** $\checkmark$

---

**29** $\quad \mu = 0 \times 0.008 + 1 \times 0.096 + 2 \times 0.384 + 3 \times 0.512$

$\quad\quad = 2.4 \quad \checkmark$

$\quad E(X^2) = 0 \times 0.008 + 1^2 \times 0.096 + 2^2 \times 0.384 + 3^2 \times 0.512$

$\quad\quad = 6.24$

$\quad \text{Var}(X) = 6.24 - 2.4^2$

$\quad\quad = 0.48 \quad \checkmark$

$\quad \sigma = \sqrt{0.48}$

$\quad\quad = 0.692\,820\,32\ldots$

$\quad\quad = 0.69 \quad$ (2 d.p.) $\checkmark$

| $X$ | 0 | 1 | 2 | 3 |
|---|---|---|---|---|
| $P(X)$ | 0.008 | 0.096 | 0.384 | 0.512 |

**30**
$$2 \ln x = \ln (5x + 14)$$
$$\ln x^2 = \ln (5x + 14)$$
$$\therefore x^2 = 5x + 14$$
$$x^2 - 5x - 14 = 0 \quad \checkmark$$
$$(x + 2)(x - 7) = 0$$
So $x = -2$ or $x = 7$.   $\checkmark$
But $\ln x$ is only defined for $x > 0$,
$$\therefore \boldsymbol{x = 7} \quad \checkmark$$

**31**   $2 \sin x = \sqrt{3}$
$$\sin x = \frac{\sqrt{3}}{2}$$
Now $\sin \dfrac{\pi}{3} = \dfrac{\sqrt{3}}{2}$

$\sin$ is positive in the first and second quadrants.
$$\therefore x = \frac{\pi}{3} \quad \text{or} \quad x = \pi - \frac{\pi}{3}$$
$$\boldsymbol{x = \frac{\pi}{3} \ \text{or} \ \frac{2\pi}{3}} \quad \checkmark\checkmark$$

**32**   $y = -x^2 + 6x - 2$
$$\frac{dy}{dx} = -2x + 6$$
When $x = 2$,
$$\frac{dy}{dx} = -2 \times 2 + 6$$
$$= 2$$
$\therefore$ the gradient of the tangent at $(2, 6)$ is 2.   $\checkmark$

The gradient of the normal at $(2, 6)$ is $-\dfrac{1}{2}$.   $\checkmark$
$$m = -\frac{1}{2}, \quad (2, 6)$$
$$y - y_1 = m(x - x_1)$$
$$y - 6 = -\frac{1}{2}(x - 2)$$
$$= -\frac{1}{2}x + 1$$
$$\boldsymbol{y = -\frac{1}{2}x + 7} \quad \checkmark$$

**33 a**   $R = \dfrac{2}{3}\log_{10} k - 0.9$
When $k = 6.5 \times 10^7$,
$$R = \frac{2}{3}\log_{10}(6.5 \times 10^7) - 0.9$$
$$= 4.308\,608\,90\ldots$$
$$= 4.3 \quad (1 \text{ d.p.})$$
**The earthquake would have a magnitude of 4.3.**   $\checkmark$

**b**   $R = \dfrac{2}{3}\log_{10} k - 0.9$
When $R = 6.8$,
$$\frac{2}{3}\log_{10} k - 0.9 = 6.8$$
$$\frac{2}{3}\log_{10} k = 7.7$$
$$\log_{10} k = 11.55 \quad \checkmark$$
$$k = 10^{11.55}$$
$$= 3.548\,133\,89\ldots \times 10^{11}$$
**The energy released is approximately $3.5 \times 10^{11}$ kJ.**   $\checkmark$

**34 a**

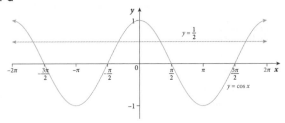

**b**   $\cos x = \dfrac{1}{2}$ when $x = -\dfrac{5\pi}{3}, -\dfrac{\pi}{3}, \dfrac{\pi}{3}$ and $\dfrac{5\pi}{3}$.   $\checkmark$

**35 a**   $x = 7 + 20t - 2t^2$
$$\frac{dx}{dt} = 20 - 4t \quad \checkmark$$
The particle is at rest when the velocity is zero,
i.e. $20 - 4t = 0$
$$4t = 20$$
$$t = 5 \quad \checkmark$$
When $\quad t = 5$,
$$x = 7 + 20 \times 5 - 2 \times 5^2$$
$$= 57$$
**The particle is at rest after 5 seconds at a position 57 m to the right of the origin.**   $\checkmark$

**b**   $v = \dfrac{dx}{dt}$
$$= 20 - 4t$$
$$a = \frac{dv}{dt}$$
$$= -4 \quad \checkmark$$
**The acceleration is constant at $-4$ ms$^2$.**   $\checkmark$

**36**   $\dfrac{\sin A}{a} = \dfrac{\sin B}{b}$
$$\frac{\sin A}{17} = \frac{\sin 38°}{12}$$
$$\sin A = \frac{17 \sin 38°}{12} \quad \checkmark$$
$$A = \sin^{-1}\left(\frac{17 \sin 38°}{12}\right)$$
$$= 60.713\,7967\ldots°$$
$$= 61° \quad \text{(nearest degree)} \quad \checkmark$$
$\angle BAC = 61°$ or $180° - 61°$
$$\therefore \boldsymbol{\angle BAC = 61° \ \text{or} \ 119°} \quad \checkmark$$

**37**   $\log_3 2 + \log_9 16 = \log_3 2 + \dfrac{\log_3 16}{\log_3 9}$
$$= \log_3 2 + \frac{1}{2}\log_3 16 \quad \checkmark$$
$$= \log_3 2 + \log_3 16^{\frac{1}{2}}$$
$$= \log_3 2 + \log_3 4$$
$$= \boldsymbol{\log_3 8} \quad \checkmark$$

**38 a**

| + | 6 | 7 | 8 | 9 | 10 |
|---|---|---|---|---|---|
| **6** | 12 | 13 | 14 | 15 | 16 |
| **7** | 13 | 14 | 15 | 16 | 17 |
| **8** | 14 | 15 | 16 | 17 | 18 |
| **9** | 15 | 16 | 17 | 18 | 19 |
| **10** | 16 | 17 | 18 | 19 | 20 |

✓

$$P(\text{sum} > 15) = \frac{15}{25}$$

$$= \frac{3}{5} \quad ✓$$

**b** If one number is 7, $P(\text{sum} > 15) = \dfrac{4}{9}$ ✓

**39** In $\triangle ABC$,

$$\tan 24° = \frac{32}{BC}$$

$$\therefore BC = \frac{32}{\tan 24°}$$

In $\triangle ABD$,

$$\tan 17° = \frac{32}{BD}$$

$$\therefore BD = \frac{32}{\tan 17°} \quad ✓$$

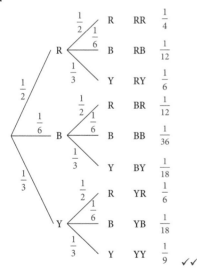

Now $C$ is due east of $B$ so the bearing of $C$ from $B$ is 90°.

$$\angle CBD = 215° - 90°$$

$$= 125°$$

In $\triangle CBD$,

$$CD^2 = \left(\frac{32}{\tan 24°}\right)^2 + \left(\frac{32}{\tan 17°}\right)^2 - 2 \times \frac{32}{\tan 24°} \times \frac{32}{\tan 17°} \cos 125° \quad ✓$$

$$= 24\,750.7612\ldots$$

$$CD = 157.323\,746\ldots$$

$$= \textbf{157 m} \quad \text{(nearest metre)} \quad ✓$$

**40 a**

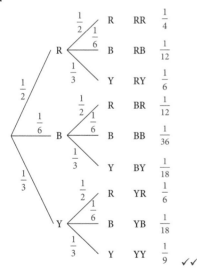

✓✓

---

**b** Let $X$ be the number of yellow pegs.

| $X$ | 0 | 1 | 2 |
|---|---|---|---|
| $P(X)$ | $\dfrac{4}{9}$ | $\dfrac{4}{9}$ | $\dfrac{1}{9}$ |

✓✓

**c** $E(X) = 0 \times \dfrac{4}{9} + 1 \times \dfrac{4}{9} + 2 \times \dfrac{1}{9}$

$$= \frac{2}{3}$$

The expected number of yellow pegs is $\dfrac{2}{3}$. ✓

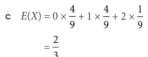

**Section I**

**1 B** $\sec\dfrac{\pi}{6} = \dfrac{1}{\cos\dfrac{\pi}{6}}$

$$= \frac{1}{\dfrac{\sqrt{3}}{2}}$$

$$= \frac{2}{\sqrt{3}}$$

**2 B** $\log_a b = 0.36$

$$\log_a \sqrt{b} = \log_a b^{\frac{1}{2}}$$

$$= \frac{1}{2}\log_a b$$

$$= \frac{1}{2} \times 0.36$$

$$= 0.18$$

**3 D** The equation of the tangent is $y = 2x - 9$.

So the gradient of the tangent is 2.

The gradient of the normal is $-\dfrac{1}{2}$.

**4 D** $\sqrt{12} + \sqrt{48} = \sqrt{4} \times \sqrt{3} + \sqrt{16} \times \sqrt{3}$

$$= 2\sqrt{3} + 4\sqrt{3}$$

$$= 6\sqrt{3}$$

**5 B** $y = x^2 - 8x + 12$

When $y = 0$,

$$x^2 - 8x + 12 = 0$$

$$(x - 2)(x - 6) = 0$$

$$x = 2 \quad \text{or} \quad x = 6$$

Axis: $x = \dfrac{2+6}{2}$

$$x = 4$$

When $x = 4$,

$$y = 4^2 - 8 \times 4 + 12$$

$$= -4$$

So the vertex is $(4, -4)$.

**6 A** $P(\text{at least 2 heads}) = 1 - P(\text{less than 2 heads})$

$$= 1 - \left(\frac{1}{64} + \frac{9}{64}\right)$$

$$= \frac{27}{32}$$

**7 A** True bearing $= 180° - 35°$

$\qquad = 145°$

**8 A** $f(x) = 9 - 2e^{-5x}$

$\qquad f'(x) = -2e^{-5x} \times -5$

$\qquad\quad = 10e^{-5x}$

**9 C** $P(F|S) = \dfrac{P(F \cap S)}{P(S)}$

$\qquad\quad = \dfrac{0.24}{0.32}$

$\qquad\quad = 0.75$

**10 C** The gradient of the tangent is negative at $P$ so the function is decreasing. It is decreasing at an increasing rate.

## Section II

**11** $\tan 300° = \tan (360 - 60)°$

$\qquad\qquad = -\tan 60°$

$\qquad\qquad = -\sqrt{3}$ ✓

**12** $\dfrac{2}{x^2+2x} - \dfrac{3}{x^2+3x}$

$= \dfrac{2}{x(x+2)} - \dfrac{3}{x(x+3)}$

$= \dfrac{2(x+3)-3(x+2)}{x(x+2)(x+3)}$ ✓

$= \dfrac{2x+6-3x-6}{x(x+2)(x+3)}$

$= \dfrac{-x}{x(x+2)(x+3)}$

$= \dfrac{-1}{(x+2)(x+3)} \qquad \left(or\ \dfrac{-1}{x^2+5x+6}\right)$ ✓

**13 a** $\qquad f(x) = p + qx - rx^2$

$f(x) + f(-x) = p + qx - rx^2 + p + q(-x) - r(-x)^2$

$\qquad\qquad = p + qx - rx^2 + p - qx - rx^2$ ✓

$\qquad\qquad = 2p - 2rx^2$ ✓

**b** $f(x) + f(-x)$ is even. ✓

**14** $|15x - 27| = 18$

$\quad 15x - 27 = 18 \quad$ or $\quad 15x - 27 = -18$

$\qquad 15x = 45 \quad$ or $\qquad 15x = 9$

$\qquad\quad x = 3 \quad$ or $\qquad\quad x = 0.6$ ✓✓

**15** $\dfrac{8^{2x} \times 4^{3x}}{16^{x+2} \div 2^x} = \dfrac{\left(2^3\right)^{2x} \times \left(2^2\right)^{3x}}{\left(2^4\right)^{x+2} \div 2^x}$

$= \dfrac{2^{6x} \times 2^{6x}}{2^{4x+8} \div 2^x}$ ✓

$= \dfrac{2^{12x}}{2^{3x+8}}$

$= 2^{9x-8}$ ✓

**16** $\tan\theta - \sin^2\theta \tan\theta = \tan\theta\,(1 - \sin^2\theta)$

$\qquad\qquad = \tan\theta \cos^2\theta$ ✓

$\qquad\qquad = \dfrac{\sin\theta}{\cos\theta} \times \cos^2\theta$

$\qquad\qquad = \sin\theta \cos\theta$ ✓

**17** $5x^2 - 8x + 2 = 0$

$\quad a = 5, \quad b = -8, \quad c = 2$

$x = \dfrac{-b \pm \sqrt{b^2 - 4ac}}{2a}$

$\quad = \dfrac{-(-8) \pm \sqrt{(-8)^2 - 4 \times 5 \times 2}}{2 \times 5}$

$\quad = \dfrac{8 \pm \sqrt{24}}{10}$ ✓

$x = 1.289\,897\,94\ldots$ or $x = 0.310\,102\,051\ldots$

$x = \mathbf{1.290} \quad$ or $\quad x = \mathbf{0.310} \quad$ (3 d.p.) ✓

**18** $\log_5(x + y) = 0$

$\quad \therefore x + y = 1 \quad$ (i)

$\quad \log_5(x - y) = 1$

$\quad \therefore x - y = 5 \quad$ (ii) ✓

(i) + (ii): $\ 2x = 6$

$\qquad\qquad x = 3$

Substitute into (i): $\ 3 + y = 1$

$\qquad\qquad\qquad y = -2$

**So $x = 3$ and $y = -2$.** ✓

**19** $f(x) = 9 - x^2 \quad g(x) = 2x - 3$

$f(g(x)) = 9 - (2x - 3)^2$ ✓

$\qquad = 9 - (4x^2 - 12x + 9)$

$\qquad = 9 - 4x^2 + 12x - 9$

$\qquad = -4x^2 + 12x$ ✓

**20 a** $\qquad$ Total $= 19 + 7 + 25 + 12 + 3 + 8 + 31 + 14$

$\qquad\qquad = 119$

$\quad P(X \cap Y) = \dfrac{10}{119}$ ✓

**b** $\ P(Y \cup Z) = \dfrac{86}{119}$ ✓

**c** $\qquad P(X|Z) = \dfrac{P(X \cap Z)}{P(Z)}$

$\qquad\qquad = \dfrac{\frac{15}{119}}{\frac{54}{119}}$

$\qquad\qquad = \dfrac{5}{18}$ ✓

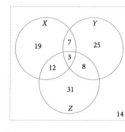

**21 a** $\ y = 4x^3 - 7x^2 + 2x - 9$

$\quad \dfrac{dy}{dx} = 12x^2 - 14x + 2$ ✓

**b** $\ y = x^5(6x - 5)^3$

$\quad \dfrac{dy}{dx} = x^5 \times 3(6x - 5)^2 \times 6 + (6x - 5)^3 \times 5x^4$ ✓

$\qquad = 18x^5(6x - 5)^2 + 5x^4(6x - 5)^3$

$\qquad = x^4(6x - 5)^2[18x + 5(6x - 5)]$

$\qquad = x^4(6x - 5)^2(48x - 25)$ ✓

**c** $\ y = \sqrt[3]{3x - 8}$

$\qquad = (3x - 8)^{\frac{1}{3}}$

$\quad \dfrac{dy}{dx} = \dfrac{1}{3}(3x - 8)^{-\frac{2}{3}} \times 3$ ✓

$\qquad = (3x - 8)^{-\frac{2}{3}}$

$\qquad = \dfrac{1}{\left(\sqrt[3]{3x - 8}\right)^2}$ ✓

**d** $y = \dfrac{2x+5}{3x-2}$

$\dfrac{dy}{dx} = \dfrac{(3x-2)\times 2 - (2x+5)\times 3}{(3x-2)^2}$ ✓

$= \dfrac{6x - 4 - 6x - 15}{(3x-2)^2}$

$= \dfrac{-19}{(3x-2)^2}$ ✓

**22** $\tan\theta = -1$

Now $\tan^{-1}(1) = 45°$

tan is negative in the second quadrant. ✓

$\therefore \theta = 180° - 45°$

$= 135°$ ✓

**23**
$$x^2 + y^2 = 4x - 6y - 12$$
$$x^2 - 4x + y^2 + 6y = -12$$
$$x^2 - 4x + 4 + y^2 + 6y + 9 = -12 + 4 + 9$$
$$(x - 2)^2 + (y + 3)^2 = 1 \;✓$$

**The centre is at (2, –3) and the length of the radius is 1 unit.** ✓

**24 a** $V = 3t^2 + 5t + 250$

When $t = 0$,

$V = 3 \times 0^2 + 5 \times 0 + 250$

$= 250$

**There is 250 mL in the container when the water begins to flow.** ✓

**b** $V = 3t^2 + 5t + 250$

$\dfrac{dV}{dt} = 6t + 5$ ✓

When $t = 5$,

$\dfrac{dV}{dt} = 6 \times 5 + 5$

$= 35$

**The water is flowing at the rate of 35 mL per minute.** ✓

**25 a** $P(\text{both } 17) = P(\text{girl is } 17) \times P(\text{boy is } 17)$

$= \dfrac{8}{13} \times \dfrac{5}{11}$

$= \dfrac{40}{143}$ ✓

**b** $P(\text{one is } 17 \text{ and one is } 18)$

$= P(\text{girl } 17, \text{boy } 18) + P(\text{girl } 18, \text{boy } 17)$

$= \dfrac{8}{13} \times \dfrac{6}{11} + \dfrac{5}{13} \times \dfrac{5}{11}$

$= \dfrac{73}{143}$ ✓

**26 a** $A = \dfrac{\theta}{2}(R^2 - r^2)$

$= \dfrac{1}{2} \times 150° \times \dfrac{\pi}{180°} \times (10^2 - 9^2)$

$= 24.870\,9418\ldots \text{ m}^2$ ✓

$V = 24.870\,9418\ldots \times 0.12 \text{ m}^3$

$= 2.984\,513\,02\ldots \text{ m}^3$

**So approximately 3 cubic metres of concrete will be needed.** ✓

**b** Arc: $l = r\theta$

$= 10 \times 150° \times \dfrac{\pi}{180°}$

$= 26.179\,9387\ldots$

$= 26.18 \text{ m} \quad (2 \text{ d.p.})$ ✓

In $\triangle OCD$,

$CD^2 = 9^2 + 9^2 - 2 \times 9 \times 9 \times \cos 150°$

$= 302.296\,115\ldots$

$\therefore CD = 17.386\,6648\ldots$

$= 17.39 \text{ m} \quad (2 \text{ d.p.})$ ✓

Distance from $B$ to $A$ is $(17.39 + 2)$ m $= 19.39$ m

Difference $= (26.18 - 19.39)$ m

$= 6.79$ m

**It is about 6.8 m further around the arc.** ✓

**27** $y = 3x^2 - 5, \quad x_1 = 1, \quad x_2 = 3$

$m = \dfrac{f(x_2) - f(x_1)}{x_2 - x_1}$

$= \dfrac{3 \times 3^2 - 5 - (3 \times 1^2 - 5)}{3 - 1}$ ✓

$= 12$

$\therefore$ **the gradient of the secant $AB$ is 12.** ✓

**28 a** $DC = AB = 5$ m

$\angle BCD = 180° - 60° \quad$ (co-interior angles, parallel lines)

$= 120°$

In $\triangle BCD$,

$c^2 = b^2 + d^2 - 2bd \cos C$

$= 5^2 + 3^2 - 2 \times 5 \times 3 \times \cos 120°$ ✓

$= 49$

$c = 7 \quad (c > 0)$

**The length of diagonal $BD$ is 7 m.** ✓

**b** $A = 2 \times \dfrac{1}{2}ac \sin B$

$= 3 \times 5 \times \sin 60°$ ✓

$= 15 \times \dfrac{\sqrt{3}}{2}$

$= \dfrac{15\sqrt{3}}{2} \text{ m}^2$ ✓

**29** $P(x) = (m-2)x^2 + (m+1)x + 3$

$\Delta = b^2 - 4ac$

$= (m+1)^2 - 4(m-2) \times 3$

$= m^2 + 2m + 1 - 12m + 24$

$= m^2 - 10m + 25$ ✓

$= (m - 5)^2$

Now $(m-5)^2 \geq 0$ for all values of $m$.

$\therefore$ **$P(x)$ has real roots for all values of $m$.** ✓

**30** $\tan x - 2 \sin x = 0$

$\dfrac{\sin x}{\cos x} - 2 \sin x = 0$

$\sin x\left(\dfrac{1}{\cos x} - 2\right) = 0$

$\sin x = 0 \quad \text{or} \quad \dfrac{1}{\cos x} = 2$ ✓

$\sin x = 0 \quad \text{or} \quad \cos x = \dfrac{1}{2}$

$x = 0, \pi \text{ or } 2\pi \quad \text{or} \quad x = \dfrac{\pi}{3} \text{ or } 2\pi - \dfrac{\pi}{3}$

**So $x = 0, \dfrac{\pi}{3}, \pi, \dfrac{5\pi}{3} \text{ or } 2\pi$.** ✓

**31 a**

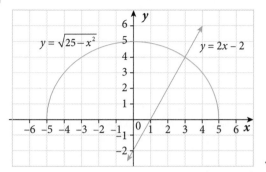

**b** $2x - 2 = \sqrt{25 - x^2}$ when $x = 3$. ✓

**32** $f(x) = 3x^2 + 4x - 5$

$$f'(x) = \lim_{h \to 0} \frac{f(x+h) - f(x)}{h}$$

$$= \lim_{h \to 0} \frac{3(x+h)^2 + 4(x+h) - 5 - (3x^2 + 4x - 5)}{h} \quad ✓$$

$$= \lim_{h \to 0} \frac{3x^2 + 6xh + 3h^2 + 4x + 4h - 5 - 3x^2 - 4x + 5}{h}$$

$$= \lim_{h \to 0} \frac{6xh + 3h^2 + 4h}{h} \quad ✓$$

$$= \lim_{h \to 0} \frac{h(6x + 3h + 4)}{h}$$

$$= \lim_{h \to 0} (6x + 3h + 4)$$

$$= \mathbf{6x + 4} \quad ✓$$

**33** $\quad 2\ln x = \ln(3x + 4)$

$\quad\quad \ln x^2 = \ln(3x + 4)$

$\quad\quad \therefore x^2 = 3x + 4$ ✓

$\quad x^2 - 3x - 4 = 0$

$\quad (x + 1)(x - 4) = 0$

$\quad x = -1$ or $x = 4$

But $x > 0$,

$\quad\quad\quad \therefore x = 4$ ✓

$\ln 2x = \ln 8$

$\quad = 2.079\,441\,54...$

$\quad = \mathbf{2.079}$ (3 d.p.) ✓

**34 a**

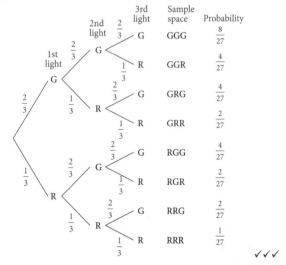

**b** $P(\text{stop once}) = P(GGR) + P(GRG) + P(RGG)$

$$= 3 \times \frac{4}{27}$$

$$= \frac{12}{27} \quad ✓$$

**c** $P(\text{stop at least once}) = 1 - P(GGG)$

$$= 1 - \frac{8}{27}$$

$$= \frac{19}{27} \quad ✓$$

**35 a** $\angle AMB = 180° - (64 + 71)° \quad (\angle \text{ sum } \Delta)$

$$= 45°$$

$$\frac{a}{\sin A} = \frac{m}{\sin M}$$

$$\frac{MB}{\sin 64°} = \frac{800}{\sin 45°}$$

$$MB = \frac{800 \sin 64°}{\sin 45°} \quad ✓$$

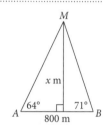

**b** Let the distance from the monument to the road be $x$ m.

$$\sin 71° = \frac{x}{MB}$$

$$x = MB \sin 71°$$

$$= \frac{800 \sin 64° \sin 71°}{\sin 45°} \quad ✓$$

$$= 961.468\,891...$$

**The distance of the monument from the road is 960 m to the nearest 10 m.** ✓

**36 a** $\quad\quad y = \cos\dfrac{x}{2}$

$$\text{Period} = \frac{2\pi}{\frac{1}{2}}$$

$$= 4\pi$$

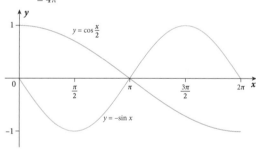

**b** $\cos\dfrac{x}{2} + \sin x = 0$

$$\cos\frac{x}{2} = -\sin x$$

**From the graph this occurs when $x = \pi$.** ✓

**37** $\quad\quad e^{2x} = e^x$

$\quad\quad e^{2x} - e^x = 0$

$\quad e^x(e^x - 1) = 0$

$\quad\quad e^x = 0 \quad$ or $\quad e^x = 1$ ✓

No solution or $\quad x = 0$

**The only solution of $e^{2x} = e^x$ is $x = 0$.** ✓

**38 a** In $\triangle ABD$,

$$\tan 18° = \frac{AB}{250}$$

$$\therefore AB = 250 \tan 18°$$

$$= 81.229\,9240\ldots$$

**So the height of $AB$ is 81 m to the nearest metre.** ✓

**b** In $\triangle ABC$,

$$\tan 23° = \frac{AB}{BC}$$

$$\therefore BC = \frac{AB}{\tan 23°}$$

$$= 191.365\,708\ldots$$

**So the distance from $C$ to $B$ is 191 m to the nearest metre.** ✓

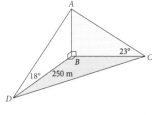

**c** In $\triangle BCD$,

$$CD^2 = 250^2 + (191.365\,708\ldots)^2$$

$$= 99\,120.8344\ldots$$

$$CD = 314.834\,614\ldots$$

**So the distance from $C$ to $D$ is 315 m to the nearest metre.** ✓

**39 a**

|  | 2nd spin | Sample space | Probability |
|---|---|---|---|
| 1st spin $\frac{1}{4}$ R $\frac{1}{4}$ | R | RR | $\frac{1}{16}$ |
|  $\frac{1}{2}$ | B | RB | $\frac{1}{8}$ |
|  $\frac{1}{4}$ | G | RG | $\frac{1}{16}$ |
| $\frac{1}{2}$ B $\frac{1}{4}$ | R | BR | $\frac{1}{8}$ |
|  $\frac{1}{2}$ | B | BB | $\frac{1}{4}$ |
|  $\frac{1}{4}$ | G | BG | $\frac{1}{8}$ |
| $\frac{1}{4}$ G $\frac{1}{4}$ | R | GR | $\frac{1}{16}$ |
|  $\frac{1}{2}$ | B | GB | $\frac{1}{8}$ |
|  $\frac{1}{4}$ | G | GG | $\frac{1}{16}$ |

✓✓

**b** Let $X$ be the number of times the spinner landed on red.

| $X$ | 0 | 1 | 2 |
|---|---|---|---|
| $P(X)$ | $\frac{9}{16}$ | $\frac{3}{8}$ | $\frac{1}{16}$ |

✓✓

**c** $E(X) = 0 \times \dfrac{9}{16} + 1 \times \dfrac{3}{8} + 2 \times \dfrac{1}{16}$

$$= \frac{1}{2}$$

**The mean is $\dfrac{1}{2}$.** ✓

$$E(X^2) = 0 \times \frac{9}{16} + 1^2 \times \frac{3}{8} + 2^2 \times \frac{1}{16}$$

$$= \frac{5}{8}$$

$$\text{Var}(X) = \frac{5}{8} - \left(\frac{1}{2}\right)^2$$

$$= \mathbf{\frac{3}{8}} \quad ✓$$

$$\sigma = \sqrt{\frac{3}{8}}$$

$$= 0.612\,372\,435\ldots$$

$$= \mathbf{0.61} \quad \text{(2 d.p.)} \quad ✓$$

**40 a** $A = \dfrac{1}{2}r^2(\theta - \sin\theta)$

$$= \frac{1}{2} \times 264^2 \times \left(\frac{\pi}{3} - \sin\frac{\pi}{3}\right) \quad ✓$$

$$= 34\,848\left(\frac{\pi}{3} - \frac{\sqrt{3}}{2}\right)$$

$$= 34\,848\left(\frac{2\pi - 3\sqrt{3}}{6}\right)$$

$$= \mathbf{5808(2\pi - 3\sqrt{3})\ m^2} \quad ✓$$

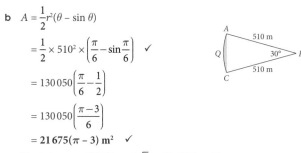

**b** $A = \dfrac{1}{2}r^2(\theta - \sin\theta)$

$$= \frac{1}{2} \times 510^2 \times \left(\frac{\pi}{6} - \sin\frac{\pi}{6}\right) \quad ✓$$

$$= 130\,050\left(\frac{\pi}{6} - \frac{1}{2}\right)$$

$$= 130\,050\left(\frac{\pi - 3}{6}\right)$$

$$= \mathbf{21\,675(\pi - 3)\ m^2} \quad ✓$$

**c** Shaded area $= 5808(2\pi - 3\sqrt{3}) + 21\,675(\pi - 3)$

$$= 9382.5077\ldots$$

$$= \mathbf{9382.5\ m^2} \quad \text{(1 d.p.)} \quad ✓$$

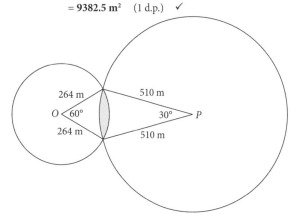

ISBN 978 1 74125 679 6

Pascal Press
PO Box 250
Glebe NSW 2037
(02) 8585 4044
www.pascalpress.com.au

Publisher: Vivienne Joannou
Project editor: Rosemary Peers
Edited by Rosemary Peers
Answers checked by Peter Little
Cover and page design by Sonia Woo
Typesetting by Julianne Billington (lj Design)
Printed by Vivar Printing/Green Giant Press

**Students**
All care has been taken in the preparation of this study guide, but please check with your teacher
or the NSW Education Standards Authority about the exact requirements of the course you are
studying as these can change from year to year.

The validity and appropriateness of the internet addresses (URLs) in this book were checked at
the time of publication. Due to the dynamic nature of the internet, the publisher cannot accept
responsibility for the continued validity or content of these web addresses.